Algrove Publishing Limited
1090 Morrison Drive
Ottawa, Ontario
Canada  K2H 1C2

**Canadian Cataloguing in Publication Data**

Main entry under title:

    Popular mechanics shop notes for ...

(Classic reprint series)
Includes indexes.
Originally published: Chicago : Popular Mechanics Co., 1905-
"Compiled from the "Shop notes" department of Popular mechanics
    magazine, and "Written so you can understand it;" tells easy
    ways to do hard things" --Added t.p., v. 1.
Contents: v. 1. 1905 - v. 2. 1906 - v. 3. 1907 - v. 4. 1908 - v. 5. 1909 - v. 6. 1910 - v. 7. 1911 -
    v. 8. 1912 - v. 9. 1913 - v. 10. 1914 - v. 11. 1915 - v. 12. 1916 - v. 13. 1917 - v. 14. 1918 -
    v. 15. 1919 - v. 16. 1920 - v. 17. 1921 - v. 18. 1922 - v. 19. 1923.
ISBN 0-921335-87-3 (v. 11) - ISBN 0-921335-91-1 (v. 12) - ISBN 0-921335-94-6 (v. 13) -
ISBN 0-921335-96-2 (v. 14) - ISBN 0-921335-98-9 (v. 15) - ISBN 0-921335-93-8 (v. 16) -
ISBN 0-921335-95-4 (v. 17) - ISBN 0-921335-97-0 (v. 18) - ISBN 0-921335-99-7 (v. 19) -


    1. Do-it-yourself work.  2. Industrial arts.  I. Title: Shop notes for ...  II. Series: Classic reprint series (Ottawa, Ont.)

TJ1160.P66 2000                600                C99-900763-7

Printed in Canada
#10900

# *Publisher's Note*

Virtually every woodworking magazine in the English-speaking world has a shop notes section and has published an accumulation of them in book form. This was all started in 1905 with the first annual issue of *Popular Mechanics Shop Notes*, a compilation of advice on jigs, fixtures, methods of work, processes and projects. The earlier issues focussed primarily on metalworking, but with tips for a variety of other trades liberally sprinkled throughout. As years went by, the contents shifted more and more to woodworking and handyman projects. Each book is profusely illustrated. The line drawings of the earlier issues were supplanted by superb engravings until photographs started to creep in during the 1920s. Each year has its charm but all issues share the attribute of being clear, concise and widely informative.

Leonard G. Lee, Publisher
Ottawa
September, 1999

# WARNING

This is a reprint of a book compiled in the early 1900s. The book describes what was recommended to be done in accordance with the knowledge of the day.

It would be advisable to treat all corrosive, explosive and toxic materials with much greater caution than is indicated here, particularly any materials that come in contact with the body.

Similarly, some of the recommended projects were dangerous then and remain so now. All of this material should be regarded with a judicious eye and necessary precautions taken.

# POPULAR MECHANICS

# SHOP NOTES

FOR

## 1919

——

## EASY WAYS TO DO HARD THINGS

——

## OF DAILY USE
## TO EVERY MECHANIC

——

*Vol. XV—Table of Contents, Pages 3095-3110*

——

POPULAR MECHANICS, CHICAGO

COPYRIGHT, 1919 BY H. H. WINDSOR

# Building A Fast Nineteen-Foot Runabout

By B. FRANCIS DASHIELL

SEAWORTHINESS in rough water, simplicity and strength of construction, and fair speed with comparatively low power, are features of the small runabout motorboat, shown in the illustrations and detailed in the working drawings. It is of the V-bottom type, and the high, flaring bow enables it to cut the water with slight pounding or spray. A light-weight motor of 4 hp. is satisfactory, and for greater speed one of not over 8 hp. may be installed with a proper margin of safety, and freedom from excessive vibration. The deck plan is shown in Fig. 7 of the page plate; the structural framework in Fig. 6 in plan, and in a vertical section from bow to stern, in Fig. 8.

Before beginning the work of construction Figs. 6, 7, and 8 should be understood, and then full-size paper patterns are made for the frames A to I, as shown in Fig. 1. The diagram for the transom frame A is shown complete, those for the other frames being given in half section only. Make the frames, other than the transom, of 1 by 3-in. straight-grained oak. The two parts of each side section are bolted

together with a 1-in. piece, 5 in. wide, called a knee, and the two side sections are joined at the keel by means of bolts and a heel, 1½ in. thick, as shown in Figs. 3 and 5. The fastenings are made with ⅜-in. bolts, fitted with washers and nuts. Inspect the frames to make certain that they are not twisted, and mark them A, B, etc., as indicated.

The stern frame, or transom, shown in Fig. 2, as viewed in section at J-K, Figs. 7 and 8, is made of oak, cypress, or pine, preferably in one piece, and 1½ in. thick. Two boards for it may be doweled, as shown in Fig. 1. Paint the pins and joined edges with marine glue, and clamp the pieces together to dry. Then shape the transom as shown, and fasten 1 by 2-in. oak battens across it, fastening them with screws, as shown in Fig. 2. Fasten 1 by 2-in. oak battens around and ½ in. in from the edges, to provide a suitable nailing strip for the planking.

The keel is a straight-grained piece of oak, or yellow pine, 3 by 4 in. by 18 ft., as shown in Figs. 6 and 8. Lay it out on a suitable level area for the fitting and assembling of the frames. They are notched over it, as shown in

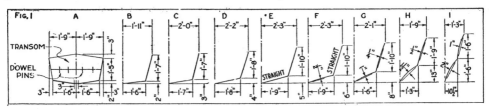

Sectional Diagrams of the Transom and Frames: To be Laid Out Full Size on Paper Patterns, to Which the Pieces are Fitted Accurately

detail in Fig. 5, and bolted into place through the heel. Countersink the bolt heads. Line the frames up perfectly or trouble will be experienced in producing the desired contour and balance in the craft. Where the propeller shaft extends through or near the keel, it is necessary to fix the frames with two bolts straddling the shaft, as detailed in Fig. 3.

The shape and construction of the stem post, the stem and stern knees, and the method of fastening them into place are shown in Fig. 8, and in detail in Figs. 2 and 9. These parts may often be supplied to the best advantage by dealers in boat stock, in the natural crook, which is most desirable. They may also be built up as shown. To prevent the water from working into the seams of these parts at the joints of the stem and knee, stopwaters are used, as indicated in Fig. 8, and detailed in Fig. 9. They are plugs or dowels of white pine, dipped in marine glue. The stem and knees are bolted to the keel with $\frac{1}{2}$-in. bolts, after painting the joints with glue.

Cut a rabbet, or planking groove, into the stem and stem knee, to provide a suitable nailing support for the planking, as indicated by the dotted line in Fig. 8, and in the stem detail, Fig. 9. Make the rabbet $\frac{1}{2}$ in. deep, to bring the surface of the rabbeted parts flush with that of the planking. The upper corners of the keel are beveled to fit against the garboard, or lower plank, as shown in Fig. 5.

Brace the assembled frame temporarily, and strongly enough to withstand twisting strains. Turn the frame over so that the keel is uppermost, and level it carefully, for the nailing of the planking. The system of planking used is shown in Figs. 2 to 5, and in detail in Fig. 9. The best size for the planks is in lengths of 20 ft. 6 in., so as to give a minimum of end joints. Where short lengths are used, the joints should be supported on blocks on the inside, and the planks butted together. The planking, dressed on both sides, is $\frac{1}{2}$ by $2\frac{1}{2}$ in., though the width may vary slightly, preferably less than this width. Put on the garboard, next to the keel, first, and fit it to the bevel on the keel, as shown in Figs. 4 and 5. Fit the ends of each plank to the transom and into the rabbet at the stem post. The planks are fitted alternately on opposite sides of the hull. Their edges are beveled slightly to form a close fit on the inside, and to provide a space for calking the seams. Nail the garboards into place against the keel by means of wire finishing nails, sunk edgewise through the plank, as shown in Figs. 5 and 9. Fasten the planks to the transom and the stem post with nails or screws, galvanized, or of brass. Fit the planks carefully to the frame. At the chine strake, as indicated in Fig. 4, it may be necessary to trim the sharp corner slightly to produce a good fit for the planks, as shown in the chine detail in Fig. 9. After all of the planks have been put on, plane the top plank, or sheer strake, flush with the upper ends of the frames. Then turn the hull over on its keel, supporting it with braces. The woodwork of the upper portion may now be installed in part.

Notch the frames to receive a 1 by 3-in. filler piece of oak or pine behind the coaming, as shown in Fig. 3 and in the coaming detail, Fig. 9. Make the coaming of $\frac{1}{2}$ by 6-in. oak, fitting the pieces for it into place only temporarily at first. The position of the coaming at the ends of the cockpit is shown in Fig. 8. The side decking is of $\frac{1}{2}$-in. oak, or cypress, fastened with brass screws. Fill in the corners with quarter-round molding, as shown in Fig. 9. The forward and rear decks are of the same material, and are supported on deck beams fixed across the hull, as shown in Fig. 8.

The shaft log and engine bed should then be located. The position of the engine is about 7 ft. aft of the bow. Its exact location will vary with different types and sizes of engines, and should be determined carefully to give the proper stability. The engine is mounted on bed timbers bolted to the frame and keel. The engine shaft is carried in a wooden shaft log, fixed on the inside

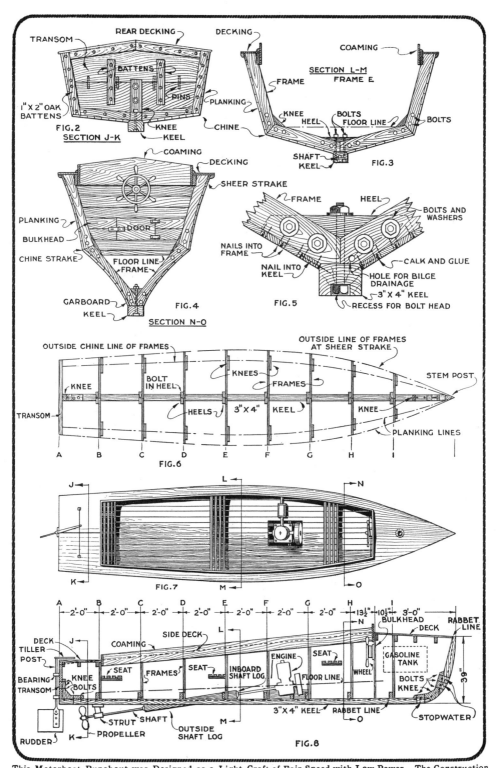

TRANSOM — REAR DECKING — DECKING

COAMING

SECTION L-M
FRAME E

FRAME

BATTENS

PINS

1" X 2" OAK BATTENS

FIG.2
SECTION J-K

KNEE
KEEL

PLANKING

CHINE

KNEE
HEEL

BOLTS
FLOOR LINE

BOLTS

SHAFT
KEEL

FIG.3

COAMING — DECKING

SHEER STRAKE

FRAME

HEEL

BOLTS AND WASHERS

PLANKING

BULKHEAD

CHINE STRAKE

FLOOR LINE
FRAME

NAILS INTO FRAME

NAIL INTO KEEL

CALK AND GLUE

HOLE FOR BILGE DRAINAGE

3" X 4" KEEL

GARBOARD

KEEL

FIG.4

SECTION N-O

FIG.5

RECESS FOR BOLT HEAD

OUTSIDE CHINE LINE OF FRAMES

OUTSIDE LINE OF FRAMES
AT SHEER STRAKE

KNEE

BOLT IN HEEL

KNEES

FRAMES

STEM POST

TRANSOM

HEELS

3" X 4" KEEL

KNEE

PLANKING LINES

A      B      C      D      E      F      G      H      I

FIG.6

J

L

N

FIG.7

K

M

O

A    2'-0"    B    2'-0"    C    2'-0"    D    2'-0"    E    2'-0"    F    2'-0"    G    2'-0"    H    13½"    10½"    3'-0"    RABBET LINE

N

BULKHEAD    DECK

DECK

TILLER
POST

J

COAMING

SIDE DECK

L

ENGINE

SEAT

GASOLINE
TANK

BEARING
TRANSOM

KNEE
BOLTS

SEAT

FRAMES

SEAT

INBOARD
SHAFT LOG

FLOOR LINE

WHEEL

39"

BOLTS
KNEE

STRUT    SHAFT

3" X 4" KEEL

RABBET LINE

RUDDER    K    PROPELLER

OUTSIDE
SHAFT LOG

M

O

STOPWATER

FIG.8

This Motorboat Runabout was Designed as a Light Craft of Fair Speed with Low Power. The Construction of the Framework and Other Details Is Comparatively Simple, and Feasible for the Home Mechanic. The General Arrangement of the Framework and Main Working Parts is Shown in Figs. 6 and 8, and the Deck Plan in Fig. 7

and the outside of the keel, as shown in Fig. 8. If desired, the hole through the shaft log may be bored at a mill which may have furnished the keel and other special wooden parts. Metal stuffing boxes are fitted to the ends of

STOPWATER DETAIL

BOLTS

PLUG

TIMBERS

PLANKING DETAIL

FRAME

WIRE FINISHING NAILS

COAMING $\frac{1}{2}$" X 6"

$\frac{1}{2}$" DIA. ROUND

DECK $\frac{1}{2}$" X 6"

1" X 3" FILLER PIECE

$\frac{1}{4}$" PLANK

FRAME

COAMING DETAIL

FRAME

CALKING MARINE GLUE

PLANK

RABBET

CALKING DETAIL

STEM

KNEE

CALK AND GLUE

PLANK

STEM DETAIL

BOLTS

CALK AND GLUE

PLANK

FRAMING AT CHINE

FIG. 9

ROD

COTTER PIN

WASHER

$\frac{3}{4}$"

RUDDER SUPPORT

PIN

CALK AND GLUE

RUDDER

RIVETS

$\frac{3}{32}$" PLATE

12"

27"

12"

2"

$\frac{3}{4}$"

RUDDER DETAILS

Details for the Rudder, Coaming, Stopwater Plug, and Other Constructional Features

the shaft log, and the joint of the shaft log and keel is made water-tight with marine glue or white lead, and bolted, as shown in Fig. 3.

The cockpit is finished with flooring and siding, and bulkheads are built at the stern and the bow. The stern bulkhead is made by paneling the frame B, and the forward bulkhead, by building in a partition, as shown in Fig. 8, and in detail in Fig. 4. The siding for the cockpit is nailed to the frames, and the flooring to 1 by 3-in. floor beams. The seams of the decking are calked with marine glue.

The calking of the hull must be done thoroughly to insure that the craft will be seaworthy. Twisted calking cotton is tamped into the seams, as shown in the calking detail, Fig. 9, by means of a calking iron. The calking is covered with a $\frac{1}{8}$-in. layer of black marine glue. Soften the glue by heating it in a water-jacket container, and force it well into the seams, overfilling them

slightly. The glue does not become very hard, and when set, the hull should be scraped, removing excess glue. The outside should be given two coats of oil primer, and two of finishing paint. Paint the interior parts also, creosote or asphaltum paint being preferable for this purpose. The cockpit should be painted first with an oil primer and then with a finishing coat. The coaming and decks may be finished with paint or several coats of spar varnish.

The general arrangement of the fittings is shown in Figs. 7 and 8. The metal fittings may best be purchased, but some of them may be made if desired. The location of the gasoline tank in the bow, the seats of wooden strips, the steering wheel, propeller and connections, and the method of fixing the rudder into place, are shown in Fig. 8. A detail of the rudder and its supports is shown in Fig. 9. The rudder is controlled from the wheel by means of wire-reinforced rope extending from a cross arm at the top of the rudder shaft, around the coaming, and through pulleys to the wheel drum.

## Making Cupped Leather Piston Washers

Leather washers, cupped to fit the piston of a pump, were required to

make a repair, and were made quickly as follows: The pump barrel was $1\frac{1}{2}$ in. in diameter, and the disks were cut $\frac{3}{4}$ in. larger in diameter. A spool of a diameter two thicknesses of the leather less than $1\frac{1}{2}$ in. was used to form the washers, as shown in the sketch. The washer is moistened and tied over the spool, centered with a pencil in putting on the strings, and then placed on the same or another spool with a metal ring or strong cord to hold it, as shown at the right, and permitted to dry into shape.—Herbert Consterdine, Hammond, La.

## Ridding a Garage of Automobile Exhaust Gas

The exhaust gas from an automobile proved offensive in a closed garage and the difficulty was remedied by installing a pipe with a hose connection to the exhaust pipe of the car, and connecting it to the chimney. This method can be applied to garages having no chimney by the installation of a suitable flue, or outlet.—J. M. Straughan, Sprague, Wash.

## Sink for Washing Blueprints

The blueprint sink detailed in the sketch is simple in construction and practical in use.

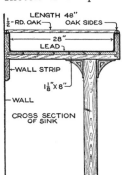

Four pieces, preferably oak, are made for the sides and ends. A groove is planed near the lower edge so that the tongue-and-groove bottom will fit in all the way around. This groove supports the bottom, and provides for shrinkage and expansion, avoiding buckling of the lead lining. Two cross strips are screwed to the under side, and a leg is fastened to each by means of brackets. The lead lining is fitted, and the upper edges turned over, and tacked down. Half-round strips are nailed over the lead, and the woodwork finished as desired.

¶ A spool cut at the middle provides two useful knobs.

## Headlight as Emergency Lamp for Operating Room

A surgeon found it necessary to perform an operation after dark, in a

An Emergency Surgical Operation was Performed by the Aid of an Automobile Light

town where commercial electric light current was unavailable. As an open light should not be used in a room where an anesthetic is administered, the electric headlight of an automobile was made to serve. The car was run up to the window of the room; the reflector and bulb from one of the headlights were removed, and after hanging the reflector over the operating table, the wires were run through the window and connections made. To assure proper results, the system was tested carefully, and it was made certain that the storage battery was fully charged. An extra bulb was provided, in case the one in use should burn out. The light proved quite satisfactory, the reflector shading the eyes of the operators, and concentrating the light on a small area, as desired.—Harry M. Kennard, Charles City, Ia.

## Raising Level of Gasoline in a Blowtorch

When the gasoline level is low in a blowtorch the pressure causes an excess of air in the burner supply pipe, blowing out the flame. In an emergency, a little water poured into the gasoline will cause the latter to float to a high enough level to operate the torch satisfactorily.

## Handling Long Pipes in a Small Shop

Pipes, long rods, and similar pieces, are difficult to handle in a small shop.

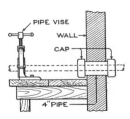

A 4-in. pipe, fitted through the wall of a small plumber's shop, made it possible to thread pipes of considerable length without bringing them into the shop. The pipes were drawn through the opening in the wall and clamped at one end, as shown. To thread the opposite end it was necessary only to reverse the pipe. When the opening was not in use, its ends were covered with pipe caps.—W. P. Langreich, New York, N. Y.

## Holder for Slip Stones

Slip stones of good quality are fairly expensive, and easily broken if left to

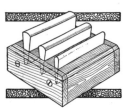

lie about the bench or machine. They may be kept safely and conveniently in a block like that shown. The grooves of several sizes are chiseled into the block, which is as long as the longest stone to be fitted into it. The ends are guarded with strips of wood.—Henry Wedde, Chicago, Ill.

## Cutting Porcelain Insulators

Considerable difficulty was experienced in cutting round porcelain in-

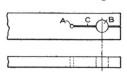

sulators used in electrical work. The job was satisfactorily accomplished as follows: A piece of flat, cold-rolled steel, twice as wide as the diameter of the insulators and of the same thickness as the smaller insulators desired, was procured. A small hole, A, was drilled through it, and a slot C cut from the end to the hole, with a hacksaw. The hole B was drilled the same size as the insulators. The latter were then clamped in the hole B, in a vise. With a blow of a hammer on a cold chisel, set on the upper surface of the steel strip, the insulators were cut neatly, and to the proper height, the same as the thickness of the strip. In half an hour, 500 insulators were cut, with only eight damaged ones. Carrying on this method of cutting under water, produced better edges on the insulators.—George N. Garrison, East Orange, N. J.

## Device for Cutting Tire Fabric on Bias

A wet knife instead of shears is used in cutting tire fabric on the bias in a

large plant. A straightedge of hard wood, to which two 45° guide blocks are fastened, reaches across the table, as shown, and is used as a guide in cutting. The straightedge is held at the proper angle by keeping the guide blocks against the edges of the table.

## Painter's Brush Preserver and Carrier

A wood finisher and painter constructed the receptacle shown in the

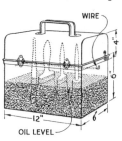

sketch to keep his paintbrushes in good condition, and also for use in carrying them to and from his work. The container is 12 by 6 by 6 in. in size. It is fitted with a raised cover, 4 in. deep, hinged to one side. The cover is built to fit inside the container somewhat like the cover of a dinner pail. Two hooks hold it in place, when being carried by means of a handle. A small hole is bored in the middle of each end, about 1 in. from the top edge. A stiff wire is passed through the two holes, leaving a little to spare at each end. Holes are bored through the handles of the brushes and the latter strung upon the wire. Sufficient oil or turpentine is poured in to immerse the bristles completely.—L. B. Robbins, Harwich, Mass.

## General-Utility Sawhorse

A sawhorse which will serve the purposes that two ordinary sawhorses serve in many instances is shown in the sketch. It may be built quickly of stock timber, and of a size suited to particular needs, the dimensions indicated being suitable for work of average size in carpentry. If desired, the construction may be made more permanent by fastening the pieces together with screws, making housed joints where the legs are fixed to the main piece, and bracing them securely below. A convenient height for the sawhorse is 22 in., and a length of about 8 ft. is satisfactory. The work is supported on this device at three points when ripping, making the frequent shifting of the board to get a solid backing unnecessary. The center board is made shorter than the end pieces, so that it will not interfere in ripping, yet

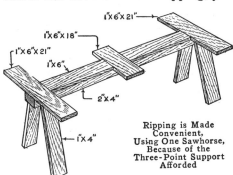

Ripping is Made Convenient, Using One Sawhorse, Because of the Three-Point Support Afforded

give a support at the middle. This is especially handy in ripping long narrow strips.—Harry Simon, Laguna Beach, Calif.

❡ Oiling of bearings by an occasional flood of oil is wasteful and inefficient.

## Trolley Tool Rack for Shop or Laboratory

A trolley tool rack made up of a tray suspended from a two-wheeled

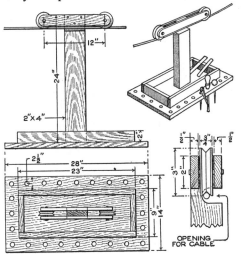

The Tool Rack and Tray is Moved to the Point Where the Tools are Needed by Shifting It on the Cable

hanger on a rod or stiff wire is convenient in bringing tools to the point where the work in hand is being done. The device may be placed above a long bench or adjacent to a row of machines, and has other uses even in such work as electrical installations. The rack proper consists of a board, 7/8 by 14 by 28 in., around the edge of which holes of various sizes are bored for the tools. A frame, 2 in. high, provides a tray. A piece of 2 by 4-in. stuff supports the tray from the hanger.—R. E. Edward, Seattle, Wash.

## Preventing Breaking of Plaster by Door Knobs

A 6-in. square of sheet cork, or composition, of the same thickness as the plaster, may be used, at the point of contact, to prevent the breaking of plastered walls by door knobs when no stops are provided at the floor. This method was used with success in a repair job and the patches of composition board were painted over the same color as the wall.—E. L. Thomas, Pittsburgh, Pa.

## An Adhesion and Impulse Engine

The rotary-fan type of power mechanism shown in the illustration was

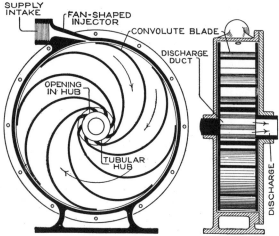

Steam is Forced from the Injector at High Pressure, and, by Adhesion as Well as Impulse on the Convolute Blades, Relatively High Power is Developed

designed and built to apply a moving jet of steam economically to a set of blades, making use of the impulsive force as well as the adhesion of the gas in contact with the peculiarly shaped blades. A jet of steam is forced at high pressure into the chamber from the fan-shaped injector connected to the supply intake. The steam comes into contact with the convolute blades and is carried toward the center of the chamber where the blades converge, passing out into the discharge tube. The curve of the blades is such that the maximum rotary propulsive force is obtained from the steam pressing against them. The device develops a relatively high power on the shaft, the openings through which the steam escapes being designed so that the gas is held in the chamber under sufficient pressure to produce the maximum power, without retaining it long enough to permit condensation.

The chamber is built up of a metal shell, having a circular plate riveted to its open side, and bearings cast as part of the shell and cover, as shown in the sectional view at the right. The injector is fitted in the top of the chamber and is fan-shaped, the width of the chamber. The revolving wheel, housed in the chamber, is of sheet metal and fitted with a solid shaft on the left side, as shown in the sectional view, and a hollow hub, for the discharge of the steam, on the right. Eight convolute blades are fitted between the side plates of the wheel, and openings are provided between them to permit the steam to escape into the hub discharge tube.

The steam enters the chamber under pressure and is forced against the outer edge of the convolute blades, reacting against the curve and being carried toward the hub. I have obtained very high speeds with the device, and this seeming disadvantage was readily overcome by increasing the proportionate size of the wheel. It has given satisfactory results as a water motor, and when the wheel is well under way, and the chamber is filled with water in revolution, the power derived has been found to be large in proportion to the water pressure. This is caused by the centrifugal action of the water, the resulting power being applied largely upon the curved blades rather than upon the inner surface of the chamber.—J. S. Zerbe.

## Soapsuds Reduces Carbon Deposit in Compressor

Trouble was experienced with an air compressor, due to the accumulation of carbon in the cylinders, and after several methods for removing it had been tried unsuccessfully the feeding of soapsuds into the cylinders from an oil cup was suggested. While it did not prevent completely the formation of the carbon, the compressor could be run much longer without cleaning, and when it was shut down the deposit was found to be soft and easily removed. The soapsuds were introduced into the cylinder for about one-half hour once a day, and the feed from the oil cups was increased at this time.—T. S. Burns, Elmira, N. Y.

## A Homemade Concrete-Tile Machine

I built this tile machine for a farmer who made concrete drain tile in his spare time. The machine may be of various sizes, this one being for tile of 6-in. diameter, 1-in. wall, and 12 in. long. Heavy galvanized sheet iron, 12 by 26 in., was bent to a circular shape, and an internal diameter of 6 in., for the form A. The ends, at J, overlap 2 in. Make two straps, B, 1/8 by 1 by 8 in., and bend eyes for the rod D, of 3/8-in. iron. Make two 4-in. pieces, E, similarly, and rivet both sets to the form A, as shown. Bend the 3/8-in. iron rod D into shape and fasten it to the bands B and E. Make a hopper for the top, completing the outer form A.

Sheet metal, 14 by 12 in., is used for the inner form F, which is 4 in. in outside diameter. Rivet on, as shown, four straps of iron, C, provided with eyes, for the rod H. This rod is arranged so that, when the end H is set as shown, the outside diameter of the core is 4 in., and when released, becomes less. Make a cap, G, used only while filling the mold.

To use the machine, the form A is set on a suitable board, and the core F centered. The latter is then expanded, and the cap and hopper are put on. The concrete mixture is tamped in, the

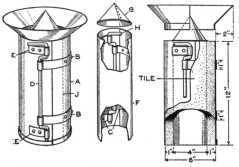

A Farmer Made Concrete Tile for His Land in Spare Time by Means of This Simple Machine

core is released by the handle H, and removed. The form A is taken off by releasing the rod D, leaving the tile on the board to cure.—R. S. Matzen, Fort Collins, Colo.

## Weather Curtain for Converted Sleeping Room

The arrangement shown in the sketch served to convert an ordinary bedchamber into an out-of-door sleep-

The Curtains are Held Taut and Rolled by the Center Cord Fixed to a Sash Weight

ing porch. The windows were removed from their frames to give plenty of fresh air. An awning was necessary to protect the room from the weather and to screen it properly. The awning cloth, pulleys, cord, and bearings for the rod were obtained at an awning store. A curtain pole served to wind the canvas; brass hinge pins, slipped through standard awning sockets and made fast in the ends of the pole, provided excellent bearings for the pole to revolve upon. The problem was to find some means of rerolling the awning automatically and keeping it stretched taut in the wind. To do this, one of the counterweight cords in the window sash was extended, wound around the awning pole in a direction opposite to that of the canvas, and made fast. The awning proved effective and strong.— Jack Bechdolt, Seattle, Wash.

## Repairing a Damaged Universal Chuck

A universal lathe chuck was broken, as at A in the illustration, two of the jaws being ineffective. It was thrown

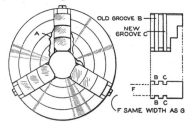

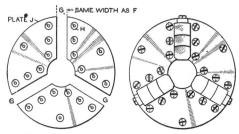

New Grooves were Cut in the Jaws to Fit Plates Fixed to the Face

into the scrap heap, and I repaired it as follows: New grooves, C, were cut on the sides of the jaws of the same size as the old grooves B, the jaws being annealed. A plate of soft steel, to fit groove C, was made of the same diameter as the face of the chuck, and a center hole cut in it. It was drilled, tapped, and counterbored, as at H, at the left, and fastened with screws. Three slots, G, were milled in the plate to correspond with the old guides for the jaws, thus forming the plate J. The jaws were fitted in the grooves G, and the chuck gave good service.— Richard H. Jehlicka, Worcester, Mass.

## Making a Loose Wooden Thread Fit Tightly

A loose handle, which was threaded into a mop, was tightened by driving a row of nails around the worn threads so that the fit was snug. The handle could be removed easily, just as if the threads were their original size. Nails with small or rounded heads are best for this purpose.—Charles L. DeCou, Los Angeles, Calif.

## The Manipulation of Gold Leaf

An old Pittsburgh sign painter told me how he used to sit on the bows of the river boats and gild the figureheads, with much of his gold leaf blowing away. Finally he thought out this method: After removing the first leaf of gold, and thus exposing the next one, he turned over the paper leaf separating the gold, exposing as much of the gold leaf as he required for use, and, running his forefinger nail along the creased paper, cut the gold, after which he lifted it up on the tip. This is the method used generally today by sign painters, and many others who use gold leaf.

In gilding on glass, it is necessary to size the surface with water size, flowing plenty on until it runs off in quite a stream; onto this the expert swings his leaf, and it lands somewhere on the outlines of the lettering—he is not particular just how accurately, so that the letter is covered; and when he has all the letter spaces covered, with perhaps a great deal of space not included within the letters, he permits it to become dry. The leaf settles down flat on the glass.

There are several brands of gold leaf, grading according to amount of pure gold contained and the intended use. One variety is made expressly for gilding on glass, another for gilding on wood. The difference is mainly in the degree of thinness. One layer of leaf makes a good job on wood, while on glass two layers make a better job than one. For exterior gilding the medium shade of gold leaf does best; the pale-colored leaf contains silver, hence tarnishes from gas or smoke.

Water gilding is that in which the leaf is laid on a size composed of isinglass, or glue and water; oil gilding is done on a size composed of oxidized linseed oil. Water size is for gilding on glass, and oil size for gilding on wood. Oil size may also be used on certain textiles, and other surfaces, just as water sizes are sometimes used in decorative work. Water-size gilding is burnished as soon as the size and leaf are dry, by rubbing with a wad of raw cotton; the same with oil-size gilding. One book of gold leaf will gild 1½ sq. ft. of surface.

Varnish impairs the luster and color of gold leaf. If varnish must be applied, first coat it with pale shellac.

Gold leaf is injured by dampness and cold. If gilded work is varnished before it is perfectly dry it will show scratches. To avoid this, apply a thin coat of white shellac, which will soon dry, and upon this the coat of varnish may be laid. To remove gold leaf from any part where not desired, as in letter gilding, or lining, use a dampened chamois skin.

In oil-size gilding, if the size is too fresh it will drown the gilding or injure its luster. Better have the size too dry than too wet. If too dry, breathe upon it, which will give sufficient "tack" to the size to hold the leaf.

Where two pieces of leaf overlap they will often cause a joint to show, and this may be removed by gently stippling it with the tips of a bristle brush. To prevent laps showing on very smooth surfaces, have the size quite tacky. When gilding becomes dull from gases and smoke, its color may be restored by a weak solution of sulphuric acid.

To gild carved wooden letters, dip them into a thin priming paint, made from white lead and raw linseed oil, with a little drying japan. Then hang them up to dry. When dry, sandpaper smooth, using steel wool for getting into the curves. Next apply a coat of paint thinned out with turpentine and containing a little varnish. When dry, sandpaper lightly to smooth the surfaces and apply another coat of flat paint. When this is dry, apply a coat of shellac, to insure a perfect surface. Use a slow oil size. Then gild, when of the right "tack."

To prevent gold leaf from adhering where not wanted, as when letters of gold are to be made on a painted, or other, surface, a raw potato cut in two, and rubbed over the parts that are to resist the leaf, may be used.—A. Ashmun Kelly, Malvern, Pa.

## A Double-Hood Roadster Automobile

A novel automobile which proved very convenient in "trouble shooting" at a garage, and which was also used

This Car was Dubbed "Automobile Janus" by Reason of Its Two "Faces"

for local advertising purposes, was made by rebuilding a car to have two hoods, seats, and steering columns, as shown in the photograph reproduced. The extra fittings were bought at small cost, and this arrangement provided for the gasoline tank under the rear hood and gave plenty of space for tools, etc. The entire body was painted and striped in orange and black. In towing disabled cars one man faces the car being towed, and can readily inform the driver, if need be.—A. P. Swaidmark, Concord, N. H.

## Adjusting Drawer Key to Insure Privacy

Where the locks in a cupboard or similar place are alike, and it is desired  to make one of them private, a simple and efficient device is to saw off a piece of the key, about ¹⁄₁₆ in. long. Force this washerlike ring down tight over the post of the lock in the keyhole, as shown. This key will unlock the lock, but when another is tried it will not go far enough into the lock to turn.—Oliver Higgins, Napoleon, Ohio.

## Improvised Frame for Broken Eyeglasses

In an emergency, when a pair of glasses was broken, and it was found difficult to get along without them, a pair of old lenses, broken at the fastenings only, was fitted into a frame made of cardboard. The frame was made of the proper size so that the lenses were centered over the

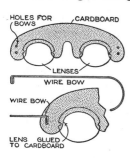

HOLES FOR BOWS — CARDBOARD
LENSES
WIRE BOW
WIRE BOW
LENS GLUED TO CARDBOARD

eyes, and the lenses were glued to it. Bows were made of wire and fastened in holes at the ends of the cardboard. This improvised frame gave reasonable satisfaction, in spite of its peculiar appearance.—A. B. Wegener, Madison, N. J.

## Folding Bracket for a Ladder

Pails, brushes, or other tools and materials used in working from a ladder, may be supported conveniently on folding brackets like those shown in the sketch. They are hooked to adjoining rungs and a board is fastened across them. When not in use they are

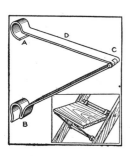

folded out of the way, or removed from the ladder. They are made by forming a hinge joint in two strips of iron, as at C. The upper end A and the lower end B are curved to fit the rung without slipping off easily. The upper strip D is drilled to provide a fastening for the shelf.—James E. Noble, Portsmouth, Canada.

⊄A washer placed around the neck of a bottle containing poison marks it effectively.

## Small Cutters or Dies Kept on Safety Pins

In the tool-dressing department of a machine shop there are usually many small parts, such as dies and cutters, to be ground. In order to keep the sets together, it was found convenient to place them on large safety pins made of spring-brass wire.—J. R. Minter, Washington, Ind.

## Protective Flap for Drawers of Drawing-File Cabinet

Drawings, tracings, etc., are wrinkled when the drawers of the file cabinet become so filled that the contents catch on the bottom of the next drawer above. The sketch shows how to avoid this by attaching a flap of flexible cardboard, or canvas, as indicated. Bind the front

edge with a ½ by ¾-in. strip and provide handholes along it. Metal corner plates prevent the flap corners from lifting when they are tucked in. When selecting a drawing from the drawer, hang the flap on the knob of an upper drawer.

## Stand for Stacking Irregular Castings

A stand which prevents breakage of irregular-shaped castings and economizes space is shown in the sketch. It may be made of a size suitable to the castings to be stacked upon it. The base is a plate of cast iron and into it is threaded an iron

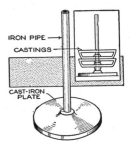

IRON PIPE
CASTINGS
CAST-IRON PLATE

pipe. A number of pipes may also be arranged on one base.—E. A. Binney, St. Louis, Mo.

## Formula for Calculating Automobile Speeds

It is often desired to calculate the speed of an automobile, the engine speed, gear ratio, etc., being known. The formulas ordinarily used are long and involved, with considerable possibility of error. The following formula will make the calculation easier. The abbreviations used are: S, speed of car in miles per hour; s, speed of motor, in revolutions per minute; R, gear ratio; T, diameter of tires on rear wheels, in inches; K, a constant, 336, by which the process is shortened.

Tracing the power from the engine through a known gear ratio, R, the speed of the rear axle will be $R \times s$ revolutions per minute. Each wheel has a circumference of 3.14 multiplied by the diameter, or $3.14 \times T$ in., which is $3.14 \times T \div 12$, if reduced to feet.

The car will be propelled a distance equal to the circumference of the wheels, with each revolution of the rear axle. Thus, to find the distance in feet traveled in a minute, multiply the speed of the rear axle—$R \times s$ revolutions per minute—by the circumference of the wheels—$3.14 \times T \div 12$. To change this rate to miles per hour, before dividing by 12, multiply the result by 60, and also multiply the 12 by 5,280. Reducing this result, it is found that the process may be simplified so that T multiplied by R, multiplied by s, and the result divided by 336, gives the speed in miles per hour. Thus 336 is established as the constant K, for use in shortening the calculation. The formulas, carried through the above process are:

$$S = \frac{60 \times 3.14 \times T \times R \times s}{12 \times 5{,}280} = \frac{T \times R \times s}{336},$$

$$\text{or} = \frac{T \times R \times s}{K},$$

as outlined in the detailed process above. — Claude Schuder, Takoma Park, D. C.

---

¶A bundle of short strings, or cords, bound together can be used as a brush or swab.

## Shop-Order Box Saves Time of Workmen

To facilitate the work in a large railroad roundhouse, the jobs for the

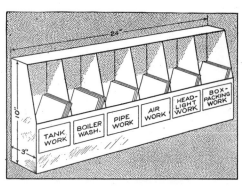

The Workmen Take Their Orders from the Box Instead of Having the Foreman Deliver the Cards to Them

various workmen were assigned by means of a card system. By placing the cards in an order box, subdivided for the various kinds of work, much time was saved, since the workmen removed the cards from their department files when passing the box, which was situated in a convenient place.

---

## Oil Cups Remodeled to Adjustable Feed

A number of plain oil cups were changed to a satisfactory self-feeding type at little expense as follows: The hinged cap of the oil cup was tapped for a $\frac{5}{16}$-in. cone-pointed setscrew, and a locknut applied to prevent the screw from jarring loose. This 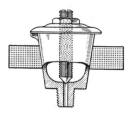 screw acted as a needle valve, seating on the edge of the small hole in the bottom. A hole for filling the cup was drilled through the cover, and the latter was then sweated fast. A feed as slow as one drop in ten minutes was obtained, and when once set for its particular purpose, the valve needed no further attention.—D. A. Hampson, Middletown, N. Y.

## Illuminated Flag Remains Unfurled

On days when there is only a slight wind blowing it is difficult to make a large flag remain unfurled unless it is

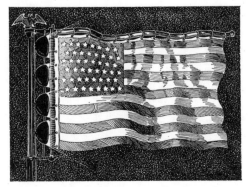

The Flag Remains Unfurled Even in a Light Breeze and is Illuminated at Night

supported. The device shown in the illustration, which is a permanent fixture of the staff, combines this feature with the illumination of the flag. A frame made of a piece of pipe, curved to cause the flag to have the appearance of being blown in a breeze, is supported at the top from the flagstaff. A vertical section is fixed to this and attached to the staff at its lower end by a short piece of pipe. The flag is suspended from the pipe by rings. Shaded lights are arranged along the staff to move with the flag in a change of wind.—L. E. Crane, Hastings, Minn.

## Carrying Storage Battery in Tool Box

Motorists are often cautioned against carrying a storage battery in a tool box

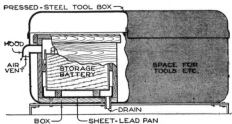

PRESSED-STEEL TOOL BOX
HOOD
AIR VENT
STORAGE BATTERY
SPACE FOR TOOLS ETC.
BOX
DRAIN
SHEET-LEAD PAN

Space was Economized by Incasing the Battery in the Tool Box, without Injury to the Tools

because of its injurious effect on tools, clothes, etc. Sometimes the tool box

is most convenient for housing the starting and lighting battery, and this problem was solved as shown in the illustration. A wooden box was made, to hold the battery, having a tight-fitting cover, and painted inside with asphaltum acid-resisting paint. A sheet-lead pan was made to fit the bottom of the box, and provided with a drain pipe of lead, discharging to the ground. A lead-pipe vent passed through the side of the steel case to allow the gases to escape. The wires passed out through rubber packings in the front of the battery box.—Victor W. Pagé, Bristol, Conn.

## Positive-Grip Hose Coupling

In order to splice, or mend, various kinds of rubber, or fabric, hose I made

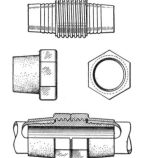

the coupling shown in the illustration. The central section is a brass union having corrugations at the end and a threaded portion at the middle. The ends of the hose to be joined are held in place by two caps having a hexagonal nut at one end, the latter threaded to fit the center portion of the union. The caps are slipped over the ends of the hose, which are fitted snugly on the corrugation. By drawing up the cap, a close joint is secured.—E. E. Burnham, Amite City, La.

## Electric Drier Used in Drafting Room

A portable combination heater and fan, such as is ordinarily used by barbers, was employed successfully for the drying of ink on tracings and drawings, and for drying prints and mounted sheets in a drafting room. This kink saved considerable time in inking drawings, as it was not necessary to wait long for the ink to dry.

## Wax Patterns for Making Plaster Molds

In experimental work, as well as in the making of patterns for ornamental or shaped pieces, the use of wax patterns is economical and practical. Pour the melted beeswax into a rough mold, or box, approximately the size of the pattern. Cool it, and carve it to the desired form, using a knife, or other sharp tool, slightly warm. If a plaster mold is desired for the casting of the pattern in metal, immerse the beeswax pattern in plaster of Paris, pouring it into a suitable container, which may be used when the resulting mold is poured in metal. Provision for the entrance of the metal should be made by cutting gates in the plaster mold, or by making suitable additions to the wax pattern before pouring the plaster around it. The wax is removed from the mold by heating it gradually and then pouring the molten metal, solder or lead, into the mold. The latter is sawed open carefully and can then be used again. The soft metal may be shaped further to form a pattern for molding in sand, if desired.

## Spiked-Roller Garden Harrow

Proper cultivation of perennials in the home garden, beds of which cannot be spaded handily without injury to the plants, was provided by the use of a homemade roller harrow. In the spring, when the asparagus, for example, comes up, the bed is harrowed thoroughly, stirring up the soil, and pulverizing it, without cutting the roots. The piercing of the plants by the spikes does no serious harm. The frame supporting the harrow may be fitted to a plain roller when desired.

The roller harrow was made as follows: A large can was fitted with 6-in. spikes, spaced as shown in the detail sketch. A pipe was set in the center of the can, which was then filled with

The Roller is Run over Beds of Perennials, Cultivating Them with Only Slight Injury to the Roots, Which does Not Hinder Growth

concrete. A rakelike cleaning bar, made of 2 by 2-in. stock, and fitted with spikes, spaced to mesh with those on the roller, was fixed to the handle and the strap-iron braces. The latter were set on a long bolt, inserted in the center pipe, and provided with a cotter for easy removal.—E. B. Smith, Chicago, Ill.

## Garbage-Can Housing of Reinforced Concrete

The unsightliness, and most of the common insanitary features, of the home garbage can were overcome by

The Garbage Can is Concealed in a Container Which Serves Also as a Flower Box

providing a concrete receptacle for it. The upper part was arranged as a flower box. A large lard can was used as the garbage container, its comparatively small size making it necessary to empty it frequently. The can is set on a shelf, bracketed to the door which is hinged on a wooden strip, set into the concrete. A metal latch holds the door shut.

The size of the housing is suited to the can. That shown is 36 in. high. The hollow base is cast separately, without reinforcement. The form for the base consists of one box within another, the intervening space being filled with concrete, the concrete for the top of the base being placed over the top of the inner box, and leveled off on the upper edges of the outer form.

The main section of the housing is built up around a wire-mesh frame. The mesh is cut to form reinforcement for the three longer vertical sides, and

bent into shape. The smaller piece for the front is wired into place. The mesh for the bottom of the flower box is also wired securely. The concrete is applied to the sides of the mesh, a roughing coat being first applied. The surface of this is left rough to afford a good hold for the finishing coat. For the roughing coat a mixture of 1 part Portland cement and 2 parts of clean, fairly fine sand is used; and for the finishing coat, 1 part cement and 1 part fine sand. The surfaces are troweled smooth.—M. Veldman, Grand Rapids, Mich.

## Cableway for Handling Shipbuilding Material

Rigging for the handling of material for the building of ships that offers suggestion for application to other types of large construction was devised for a plant in Seattle, as indicated in the diagram. At each end of the slip, in which the craft lies, are two posts, 110 ft. high, well guyed and anchored. A steel cable, 1½ in. in diameter, extends between the posts and carries a trolley operated by power winches, of the double-drum type. One drum on each winch raises

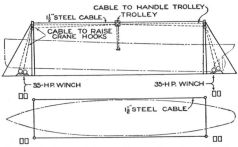

The Cable Suspended from the 110-Foot Posts Carries a Trolley for Handling Material

and lowers the crane hook on the trolley and the other pulls the trolley back and forth.—B. W. Brintnall, Seattle, Washington.

❡A coat of raw linseed oil brightens and preserves old outside paint. Do not permit it to gather in drops on the lower edges of clapboards and similar edges.

## Two Shovels Used as Post-Hole Auger

When only a few holes for posts are to be made, and no auger is at hand, a good substitute may be devised by using two spades or shovels. A strong rope is tied around the handles of the shovels to form a loop, about 8 in. long when extended. Grasp the shovels by the handles, extend them within the rope, and drive them into the ground. The earth is cut loose, and then removed from the hole by spreading the handles, and drawing it up between the shovels.

## Saw-Setting Anvil and Hammer

A set of tools such as are often used by saw setters may be made readily by mechanics. A hammer and anvil with gauges are shown in the sketch. The hammer is tempered and provided with a hickory handle. The anvil is mounted in an oak, or maple, block, or post, to be set on a bench, or on the floor. The latter is preferable, as it makes a more solid base. The anvil is fitted into the block deeply, and pins are driven through the side holes. The anvil, not receiving the blow of the hammer directly, may be left hard. Mild-steel pieces are fixed on each end

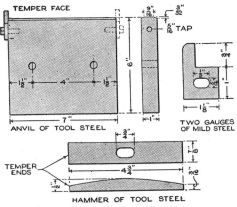

TEMPER FACE

ANVIL OF TOOL STEEL

TWO GAUGES OF MILD STEEL

TEMPER ENDS

HAMMER OF TOOL STEEL

This Outfit Is Practical for Individual Use, or for Saw Setting as a Business

of the anvil, and adjusted for various sizes of saw teeth, which are set over the beveled edge of the anvil.—Donald A. Hampson, Middletown, N. Y.

## A Rack for Washing Vegetables

A simple device for washing vegetables, and by the use of which a truck farmer was able to get better prices for

Better Prices were Procured for Vegetables Washed by the Use of This Arrangement

his product, is shown in the illustration. It is made of gas pipe and connected to the irrigating system of the farm. A 2-in. pipe is connected to a smaller one and a cut-off is placed between them. A 1-in. pipe is connected to the cut-off and reduced to smaller connecting pipes on each branch. The water finally reaches four short lengths of pipe. On the upper side of the lower pipes and on the lower side of the two upper ones, small holes are drilled in a line. The small streams make two vertical sheets of water. The vegetables are placed on a screen, which is set on top of the trough. A cover of sheet iron is fitted over the pipes and the tray. It prevents the water from sprinkling on the person washing the vegetables.—M. Glen Kirkpatrick, Des Moines, Ia.

❮ Local reductions of density in photographic negatives may be effected by rubbing with a bit of old handkerchief dampened with alcohol. The cloth "bites" best when nearly dry, and two folds should be used over the end of a match for working in small areas.

## Garage Roof as a Playhouse

In building a garage in a small city lot, the roof was utilized to make up for the space taken from the play area

The Roof of the Garage was Fitted Out as a Useful Play Area and Recreation Spot

of the children, by building a pergola on it, as shown in the photograph reproduced. A high coping was built around the edge of the wall and an outside stairway provided. The space is very popular as an open-air room for the whole family, a safe play place for the children, and a cool recreational spot for informal little parties. Porch furniture was fitted to the playhouse and increased its usefulness.—Lee Mc-Crea, Claremont, Calif.

## Device for Repairing Water Hose

If breaks in rubber or fabric hose are repaired promptly, the life of the hose can be extended considerably. By

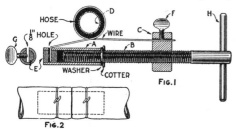

Draw the Wire Up Closely, and Lock It by Twisting the Device

the use of the device shown in the sketch, repairs of this kind may be made quickly and substantially. A short nipple is placed in the ends of

the hose, as shown in Fig. 2, and binding wires fixed around them, by the method shown in Fig. 1. The wire tightener is made as follows: A short piece of ½-in. iron pipe, A, is fitted with a threaded bolt, B, which slides in it. A cotter is set through the bolt, and engages a washer at the end of the pipe A. A metal block, C, is tapped to fit the bolt B, and a hole is drilled in it for the wire, which is clamped by means of the thumbscrew F. The end of the pipe A is plugged, as shown at E, and a ⅛-in. hole drilled for the wire, clamped by the screw G. When the wire is in position around the hose D, the handle H is turned, and the wire drawn up tightly. The device is then twisted so that the wire is held securely around the hose and the nipple.—W. Drynan, Kansas City, Mo.

## Foot-Lever Wire Cutter Made of a Plier

In cutting a large quantity of wire in short lengths, when only a hand cutting plier was available, considerable time was saved by rigging the plier with a foot lever and a gauge, as shown. The plier was mounted on a slotted block by means of two straps of sheet iron, and a 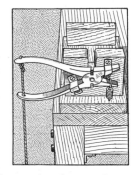 spring was fixed to the lower jaw, and to the base block of the device. A hole was drilled into the lower handle and a cord from the foot lever was passed through it and fixed to the upper handle. The wire was passed through the slot, its end against the gauge block, and cut off by a light stroke on the foot lever.—James P. Lewis, Golden, Colo.

❡A large leather or rubber washer on the handle of a brush, used overhead, prevents the liquid being applied from dripping on the hand.

# A Homemade Refrigerator
## At Small Cost
### by Charles A. King

AIR-PROOF walls, free circulation of cool, dry air, the purity of the ice, and the cleanliness of the ice chamber, are essential factors in the efficiency of a refrigerator. That described in this article, and detailed in the illustrations, was designed with these factors considered, and makes ample provision for the needs of a large family. It was built at a cost of $17.50. If it is kept well iced, the circulation of the air, which is fundamental, will be maintained by the rising of the warmer, and the falling of the colder, air. The interior is of spruce—whitewood or poplar are good—having no odor to affect milk or butter.

The stock bill, lumber listed in lineal feet unless otherwise specified, is as follows:

95 board ft. matched spruce; insides; ⅞ in., 10 and 16 ft. lengths.
85 board ft. matched pine; outsides; ⅞ in., 10 and 16 ft. lengths.
100 ft. strapping; furrings; ⅞ by 2 in.
18 ft. spruce; linings and furrings, corners of front; ⅞ by 2 in.
14 ft. spruce; linings and furrings, header and base of front; ⅞ by 4 in.
4 ft. spruce; linings and furrings under ice door of front; ⅞ by 5 in.
9 ft. spruce; linings and furrings for mullion; ⅞ by 2½ in.
9 ft. pine; corners of front; ⅞ by 3 in.
4 ft. pine; mullion; ⅞ by 2⅝ in.
7 ft. pine; header and base; ⅞ by 4 in.
4 ft. pine; under ice door; ⅞ by 5 in.
3 ft. pine; legs; 1¾ by 5¾ in.
3 ft. pine; legs; 1¾ by 3¾ in.
12 ft. pine; cap; ½ by 3 in.
12 ft. pine; base; ½ by 4 in.
30 ft. spruce; door jambs, milled; 1¼ by 2⅜ in.
30 ft. spruce; door frames, milled; 1¾ by 2½ in.
50 ft. whitewood; shelves; ½ by 1½ in.
140 sq. ft. building paper.
1 sheet galvanized iron, No. 26 gauge; 28 by 96 in.
1 sheet galvanized iron, No. 26 gauge; 21 by 40 in.
1 lb. solder.
1 piece lead pipe, light weight; for waste pipe.
2 lb. sixpenny common nails.
1 lb. 2-in. tinned clinch nails.
2 lb. eightpenny common nails.
1 lb. sixpenny finish nails.
1 lb. eightpenny finish nails.
3 pair galvanized-iron hinges, 4 in.
3 lever door fasteners; galvanized, 4 in.
8 screws; 3½ in., No. 15; to fasten legs.
1 pt. shellac.
1 qt. paint.

First make horizontal frames C and D for the top and bottom, of 2-in. strapping, as shown in Figs. 1 and 3. Square them carefully to give a good support for the structure. Tack building paper for insulation on the inner side, and nail spruce lining boards over it. From the stock for the outside, cut pieces for the outer sides of the top and bottom, to project about 3 in. around the edges of the frames, as indicated at E, Fig. 3. Tack building paper upon the open side of each frame, and nail on a part of the boarding, leaving an opening for packing in the filling. The latter may be dry shavings, sawdust, mineral wool, paper, or other nonconducting material. When the

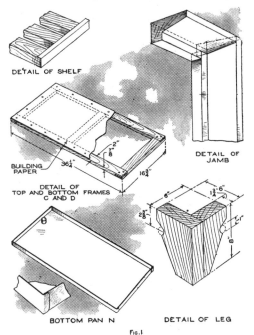

DETAIL OF SHELF

DETAIL OF JAMB

BUILDING PAPER

DETAIL OF TOP AND BOTTOM FRAMES C AND D

BOTTOM PAN N

DETAIL OF LEG

Fig. 1
Details of Several Constructional Features and Fittings

filling is in place, nail on the rest of the boards. Bore a hole for the waste pipe F, centered 1½ in. from the end and 4¼ in. from the back edges of the lower frame.

Cut spruce lining, 4 ft. 4¼ in. long, to make a width of 6 ft., to cover the ments, as detailed in Fig. 3. Care must be taken that the door openings are square.

Cover the furrings of the ends with

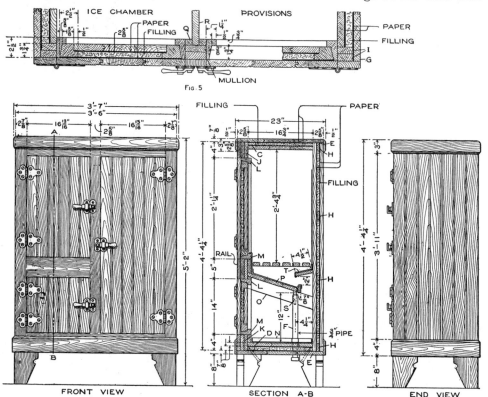

The Working Out of the Parts and Their Assembling Involve Processes Which Are Comparatively Simple, If the Work is Done Systematically as Described

two ends and the back. Remove the grooved edge of one piece and joint it straight; nail it as the first piece of the lining at the front right corner G, Fig. 5. Set the top and bottom frames on end, and nail the lining on with eightpenny common nails. Make certain that the jointed edge is square with the inside surface of each frame. After the lining is in place, cover it with sheathing paper. Nail on the furrings H, clinching the nails in the middle ones on the outside.

Make the corner strips I, Fig. 5, the width shown. The linings J, above, and K, below the doors, are fitted as shown in Fig. 3. The mullion is built up, as detailed in Fig. 5, and the rail between the upper and lower compart-

sheathing paper, and pack the spaces with insulation. Fit and nail the headers L, and thresholds M, of the door jambs, matching the corners as detailed in Fig. 1. The bottom pan N, as shown in Fig. 1, should be ⅜ in. narrower and shorter than the bottom of the inside of the refrigerator. Nail the pan around the top edge with tinned nails. Set the waste pipe F through the bushing of the pan and the hole in the bottom, in nailing the edges of the pan.

The interior of the refrigerator is fitted next. Nail in cleats O, Fig. 3, supporting the ice floor P, of spruce, and cleats similar to those at Q, Fig. 5, on the back, to receive the fence R. The latter is of spruce, fitted horizontally, and extends 6 in. from the top of the interior. A ¾-in. hole is bored in the ice floor to receive the thimble S, fitted into the top of the waste pipe.

The measurements of the metal protection for the ice chamber are next taken. Every part that comes in contact with the ice should be covered. The iron lining on the inside of the door fits between the jambs when the door is closed. After the ice pan, on the floor P, is fitted, the hood T is nailed in, and its iron covering fitted. A trap is fitted on the lower end of the waste pipe F, to prevent the escape of cold air. The making of the metal interior should be left to a tinsmith, unless one is experienced in this work.

The trim on the front is built up in one piece, and fitted into place after the interior is complete. The door frames are fitted to allow for swelling, 1/16 in. on all sides. The doors should be fitted tightly against the rabbet of the jamb, and should not bind on the sides. The fronts of the doors are put on with screws from the back of the rabbets of the door frames. Line and fill the doors as shown in Fig. 5. The cap and the base moldings are mitered and nailed on. The legs, detailed in Fig. 1, are fastened with screws. The trimmings may be of galvanized iron, brass, or bronze. The shelves, detailed in Fig. 1, are made of slats and are bound with iron. Parts of the lining not covered with iron are shellacked two coats, and the outside is suitably finished.

---

## Leather Pattern Fillets Set in Shellac

Thick orange shellac should be used in setting leather fillets in patterns, in preference to glue, as the moisture from the wet sand tends to loosen the leather. Both the fillet and the corner are shellacked with several coats before applying the fillet, which is rubbed in with a round stick of suitable size.

---

⊄In painting or finishing wooden rods, small patterns, etc., it is convenient to hold them by brads driven in the ends.

## Improvised Rigging for Lifting Heavy Machine

In an engine room where there was no crane it was found necessary to remove the armature of a 75-kw. alter-

This Support for Differential Tackle was Devised in an Emergency for Taking Down a Generator

nator and the upper part of its frame. The roof timbers could not be depended upon, and a tripod derrick would lift but not swing aside the armature.

An improvised crane was erected by using two 4 by 8-in. timbers, rigged as shown. One end of the joined timbers was inserted into an adjacent wall, and fastened with a slanting brace. The other end was supported on a strongly braced horse. Two 10-in. diameter pulleys were mounted on a steel bar, the outer ends of which were secured by cotters. A chain was run over the bar to form a short loop, to which the differential block was hooked. The frame was unbolted and the upper part raised 1 ft., and rolled beyond the base, where it was set down. The armature was next lifted and shifted to a truck.—H. S. Rich, Poughkeepsie, N. Y.

## A Barrel Water Filter

A filter, which was constructed for use in a summer camp, and which can be used in various sizes for other situations, is shown in the illustration in a vertical sectional view. A cask of

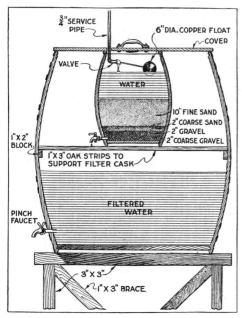

The Water is Filtered through the Layers of Sand and Gravel, and Stored in the Reservoir

about 15-gal. capacity was used as the filter tank, and partly filled with gravel and sand, as indicated. The service pipe was fitted with a check valve operated by a copper float and lever arm. The cask is supported in the larger barrel or reservoir by two oak strips, the water from the filter flowing down into the reservoir, and being drawn from it at the pinch faucet.

The cover of the reservoir is made in two parts, so that it may be removed from around the service pipe. Where water is not available through a pipe line, it can be poured into the filter from pails. The supporting frame is of oak, strongly braced. The reservoir should be painted inside with tar, such as is used in damp-proofing. The sand, particularly the upper portion, should be replaced from time to time.—John E. Cahill, Jr., New York, N. Y.

## Painting Iron to Withstand Wear

Iron should be painted immediately after being cast or fabricated, if the best results in protection by the paint are desired. The paint should be applied in a dry wind or the warm sun, rather than on a damp day or at times of the day when the air is damp. The surfaces to be painted should be free from rust. A first coat of red lead and linseed oil is applied and permitted to dry hard. Two or three additional coats of red or white lead are then applied. If the iron is old, the paint should be burned off, rust and scales removed, and a coating of turpentine applied. Then the process is the same as with new iron.

## Frame for Assembling or Examining Automobile Engine

An automobile engine is hard to handle when being assembled, repaired, or tested, unless a device is provided by which it can be reached at any part. The frame shown in the illustration is useful for the garage or shop, and is made of heavy wood, braced with iron rods and protected at the points of wear with angle iron. The engine is mounted on the frame, which is pivoted at its ends. A locking pin at each end steadies the frame. When it is desired to get at another part of the engine the frame may be turned and locked at the

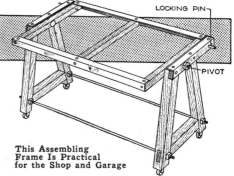

This Assembling Frame Is Practical for the Shop and Garage

desired position. Casters make it convenient to move the frame from place to place.—R. L. Hervey, Washington, District of Columbia.

## A Revolving Feed Mixer

The mixing of feed for poultry, stock, and other animals can be done quickly and thoroughly by means of the

sketches. The iron strips at A and B are formed into a pin at one end, and this is bent and set in the shaft, holding the chamber in place. The door catch is a bolt hinged between two

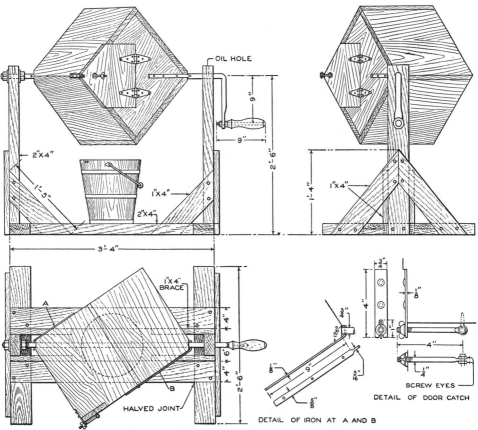

The Front and Side Elevations, Above, and the Plan, Below, Show the General Structure; the Metal Fixtures are Detailed in the Smaller Sketches

homemade mixer shown in the detailed drawings. It consists essentially of a box of ⅞-in. lumber, inclosing a chamber in the form of an 18-in. cube, mounted diagonally on a shaft, and supported by a wooden stand. The detail dimensions may be varied, but the main sizes indicated are such that the device can be handled conveniently. The feed is inserted at the hinged door, and the shaft is turned by means of the crank. The supporting stand is of 2 by 4-in. stuff, strongly braced, and bored to carry the shaft. Metal fittings are provided for the chamber, as shown in the detail

screw eyes, and provided with a wing nut, by means of which the door is clamped at the notched strip of iron at the corner. In any case, the device should be set high enough so that a bucket or feed box may be set under the mixing chamber.—Gus Hansen, Peachland, Canada.

¶Drain tile and similar products are awkward to carry, and a convenient method of handling them with slight breakage is by the use of an iron bar, bent U-shape to form a handle. One end of the bar is inserted in the tile and the other serves as a grip.

## Boat's Wheel Made from Bicycle Sprocket

By mounting an old bicycle sprocket wheel on a wooden ring, cut from a board glued up of several layers, as shown in the sketch, I made a steering wheel for a motor-driven canoe which gave complete satisfaction. The veneered stock was obtained from an old tea-shipping case and was built up to a thickness of 1 in. The wheel is 9 in. in diameter, and the wooden part was varnished, rubbed down with steel wool, and given a high polish. A piece of 3/4-in. pipe was used as the shaft, and the wheel was locked to it with locknuts. —B. E. Dobrée, Battleford, Canada.

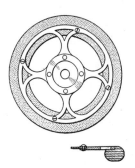

## Jig for Slotting Bushings on Milling Machine

The slotting of three bushings, A, at once, on the milling machine is accomplished by the use of this jig. Part B is bolted to the milling-machine table; part C is also bolted down, at the holes D, but must be loosened and moved back when the work is changed. The bushings are held on the pins E, which are a trifle shorter than the bushings. The bushings should fit snugly on these pins. The adjusting screws F are used to tighten the bushings and take up any slight variation in length. The stop should be set to prevent the saw from going through member C.—C. Anderson, Worcester, Mass.

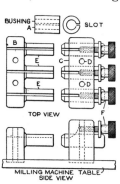

## Garden-Hose Rollers for Graining Woodwork

Short sections of rubber-surface garden hose can be made into satisfactory rollers for use in graining woodwork by cutting rings around the hose carefully, in imitation of the grain of the wood. The hose may be mounted on a wooden roller and fitted with a handle. Used in this way, it is best to make the wood grain fairly straight. The hose may also be cut to give several strips on the surface, extending its length, each strip being notched to produce a grain effect in varying sizes, when drawn over the woodwork.

## Cutting Pliers for Tool Room

A powerful cutter for cutting screws to length without injuring the thread was made in a tool room, as shown in the sketch. The side plates are of wrought iron and the handles and cutters are of tool steel, tempered. Machine screws may be used instead of rivets, and the cutters removed easily for sharpening. The outside cutting edge is not essential but gives the tool a wider range of use.

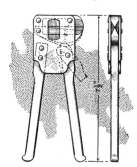

## Preventing Rapid Rusting of Auto Fenders

It is not uncommon to observe automobile fenders through which holes have rusted and which are loose at the fastenings. To prevent this and to give the fenders longer life, wash the mud and dirt from under them frequently. A rust preventive, or any suitable oil, will aid as a preservative, but the most important precaution is to prevent the accumulation of mud, under which the rust soon forms.—C. H. Thomas, Kennett Square, Pa.

## Testing Oils for Lubricating Qualities

The user of lubricating oils should have a knowledge of their merits and this can be gained readily by a series of simple tests, shown in the illustrations. One of the chief characteristics of lubricating oil is its tendency of gumming into a resin by oxidation, rendering it unfit for lubrication purposes.

A simple test can be made by elevating a sheet of glass, 2 by 4 ft., 6 in. at one end, thus forming an inclined plane. A drop of oil from each sample under test is put at the top of the plane. The drops should be placed several inches apart so that they will not spread into each other. A notation is made of the progress of the oil as it flows down the plane, several days being necessary to complete the experiment. It is desirable to make a record of the flow every six hours. The oil flowing the farthest has the best body. The oil under test should be kept free from dust, under cover if possible.

To test the fluidity of oil, heat a piece of $5/8$-in. glass tubing to a red heat, draw out one end to a diameter of $1/16$ in., and cut it to a length of 4 in. Fill it with the oil and note the time required for all of it to drip out at the small end. Repeat this with each sample to learn the relative viscosity.

Oils for gas or oil engines should be selected for their ability to pass suc-

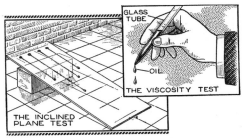

The Inclined Plane Test / The Viscosity Test / Glass Tube / Oil

Ease of Flow Is an Important Factor in Determining the Lubricating Value of Oil

cessfully the "fire test." A metal cup of $1/2$-pt. capacity is filled with oil and heated to a high temperature. A thermometer is held continuously in the

oil so that the temperature at the "flash point" can be determined. As the temperature approaches a high value, pass a lighted taper back and forth across

THERMOMETER / TEST TUBE / OIL / ICE / THE FLASH TEST / THE FREEZING TEST

The Flash and the Freezing Tests Are Both Important in Grading Oils for Lubrication

the top of the cup, $1/2$ in. above the smoking oil. The moment the rising gas "flashes," then goes out, and "flashes" again, note the temperature immediately. This is called the "flash point." Continue to heat the oil until it bursts into flame, and continues in this state. Read the temperature again. This value is known as the "fire point." These two tests are especially valuable in selecting oil for high-speed tool work where the temperature is often high. These tests should be made only in a suitable shop, or a laboratory, and proper precautions against fire taken.

To ascertain the freezing point of an oil, fill a test tube and place it in a vessel of crushed ice. If the oil, which should be continually stirred with a thermometer, does not solidify at this temperature, salt should be mixed with the crushed ice. The moment the oil solidifies, read the temperature, for the "freezing point."—K. M. Coggeshall, Webster Groves, Mo.

---

❡Wax applied to the bottom of cleats, supporting temporary walks over newly finished floors, will prevent the cleats from sticking.

## Reflector for Flood Lighting Construction Work

On a large construction job much of the work was done at night. The problem of providing good illumination

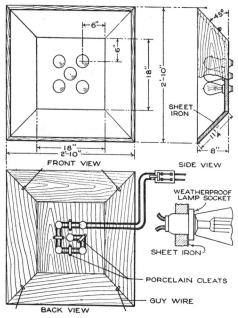

FRONT VIEW

SIDE VIEW

SHEET IRON

WEATHERPROOF LAMP SOCKET

SHEET IRON

PORCELAIN CLEATS

GUY WIRE

BACK VIEW

This Cheaply Constructed Reflector Proved Useful in Illuminating a Large Construction Job

was finally met by the use of the flood-lighting reflector shown, because of the considerable cost of metal fixtures with glass, or porcelain, reflectors. The inside of the reflector was covered with thin sheet iron, and weatherproof lamp sockets were set in place, as shown. The wiring was done on the back. The inside surface was painted with two coats of white enamel and the outside with red lead. The reflectors were fitted with 100-watt nitrogen-filled lamps and suspended on wires, to project the light as desired, and guyed to prevent swinging. Before blasting, it was only necessary to unhook the suspension wires, placing the reflectors flat, planks protecting them from heavy fragments of rock. One of the reflectors was mounted on the boom of each derrick, making the skip, or bucket, plainly visible.—T. S. Burns, Elmira, N. Y.

## Electric Pad Warms Auto Radiator in Garage

In order to prevent the freezing of the water in the radiator of an automobile, stored in an unheated garage, an electric heating pad was used. The pad was flexible, 12 by 15 in. in size, and was connected to the light socket. With the current turned on to "low," ample heat was provided to prevent freezing, at a cost of about six cents a day.—C. E. Drayer, Cleveland, Ohio.

## Device Locates Pounding in Engine or Machinery

Better satisfaction is given by the homemade device shown in the sketch in locating "knocks" in engines and machinery than anything I have yet found. It was made as follows: Two small funnels of metal were fitted into the ends of a 3-ft. length of $\frac{1}{4}$-in. pipe, and a coupling was placed over the joints. Tin disks were soldered into the funnels, as shown, and a cord was drawn tightly through the pipe and tied at the centers of the disks. A ring of rubber packing, with a $1\frac{1}{2}$-in. circular opening in the center, was cemented to the upper edge of each funnel. By placing the packing ring on the engine, or machine, under inspection, a slight pounding in it will be heard distinctly at the other end of the device. Care

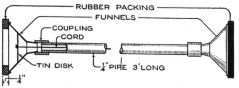

RUBBER PACKING

FUNNELS

COUPLING

CORD

TIN DISK

$\frac{1}{4}$" PIPE 3' LONG

Pounding in Machinery may be Heard Distinctly by the Use of This Telephonelike Device

must be taken that the cord is taut, and does not touch the pipe.—R. S. Matzen, Fort Collins, Colo.

¶A small V-shaped notch cut in one jaw of a vise, $\frac{1}{8}$ in. deep, will be in no way objectionable for other work, and has many uses. It gives a three-point bearing on work held vertical.

## Clip Supports Brush in Pail

Paint brushes are injured by being permitted to stand in the paint pail when temporarily not in use. By fastening a small metal clip to the side of the brush on the wooden part above the bristles, the brush may be hung on the edge of the can or on a wire stretched across it, the bristles hanging straight instead of being curled against the bottom of the pail.

## Danger Sign for Unsafe Grinding Wheel

A workman cannot readily observe whether a grinding wheel is damaged or unsafe, par-
ticularly when the wheel is properly hooded. A safety measure used in a large shop is that suggested in the sketch. When a grinding wheel is
found to be unsafe, a red danger sign usually kept on the side of the machine, is fastened to the front of the grinder.—J. R. Minter, Washington, Indiana.

## Jig for Drilling Holes at Ends of Shafting

Holes like A and B, as shown in the sketch, near the ends of sections of shafting, and at
right angles to each other, were drilled by the use of the jig shown. The body C is of steel with a hole for the shaft D,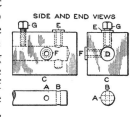
and drill bushings E and F. The setscrew G keeps the shaft in place while the first hole is being drilled. After one hole has been drilled, a pin is inserted, counteracting the tendency to twist the work on the second hole.—L. J. Hansen, Chicago.

## A Sawhorse Tool Kit

For mechanics, carpenters, or for use in odd jobs around the home or shop, the sawhorse tool kit will be found useful. It serves the double purpose of a convenient con-
tainer and carry-
ing case, and a lightweight horse. The trestle is of the common form and the tool kit is built into it by paneling the ends and one side, around a lower shelf.—J. B. Butler, Morganfield, Ky.

## Decimal Dial on Shop Timekeeping Clock

A large structural steel and bridge company has adopted the dial shown, for timekeeping
clocks. Zero is at 7 a. m., the start of the day's work; 5 at 12 a. m. and 1 p. m., the lunch hour; and 10 at 6 p. m., the end of the day's work. A single hand is used, and the
hours are divided decimally, simplifying timekeeping on the various jobs.—Peter W. Seiter, Kansas City, Mo.

## Keeping Dirt Out of Scale Pit

Discarded rubber belting was fastened to the frame around a scale pit, and lapped over
the platform, as shown, to pre-
vent gravel, dirt, and other small particles, from working down into the scale pit.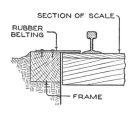
The rubber belt-
ing does not interfere with the scale in weighing.

## Table for Mounting Drawings on Muslin or Backing

A good method of mounting muslin backing on a drawing, or blueprint, is

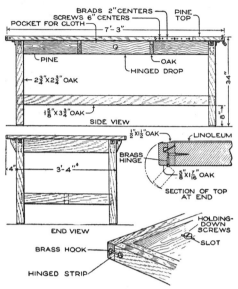

This Large Table, Designed for Mounting Drawings Quickly, Is Also of General Use

as follows: Stretch the muslin on a board, or table, as shown, and tack it around the edges. The stretching should be uniform and should not distort the fabric. Dip the drawing to be mounted in water for about a minute and remove the surplus water between blotters. Place it, face down, on the table and evenly coat the back with paste. Turn it over, put the muslin on, and roll it down flat, working from the center outward. A mounting table, large enough to hold eight or a dozen drawings, is of great assistance, and can be used for other purposes as well. The table, shown in the drawing, is covered with linoleum, an excellent top. When it is desired to mount drawings, a hook at each corner is unfastened, permitting an oak strip on each side to drop down, exposing a row of sharp points, as shown in the detail. The muslin is stretched over these points, which are hidden when the table is used for general purposes.—John D. Adams, Phoenix, Ariz.

----

❡A piece of corrugated cardboard is a convenient drier for photographic prints, the ends of the prints being arched in the corrugations, giving a current of air easy access.

----

# Horse Stalls of Concrete
### By W. E. FRUDDEN

Serviceability and sanitary considerations make concrete desirable for the building of horse stalls. The illustration shows stalls of this type that may be built into a new structure in various units, or fitted in an old one. The floor, drain trough, feed box, manger, and partitions are built as a unit, and wooden partitions are set above the concrete sections. A removable plank floor in the stalls gives the horses foot comfort, not possible upon even a heavily bedded concrete floor. The concrete partitions and the mangers are reinforced with wire mesh and steel pipes. The front edge of the manger is also guarded with a pipe, so as to prevent undue wear on the harness. The edges and corners of the exposed concrete should be rounded off so as to prevent injury to the horses from accidental contact in entering and leaving the stall. A stall in use and another in section are shown to the left in the sketch; a plan view is shown at the right, together with a detailed sectional view of the construction of the partitions and manger.

The floor is laid down first, and of the same material used for the other concrete portions, a 1 to 2 to 4 mixture. A weaker mixture may be used for the floors if there is a considerable area to be laid. The drain trough, 6 by 6 in. in section, is cast with the floor, a box of $7/8$-in. stock being fitted into the floor as a mold. The shallow drain grooves may be tooled into the surface, and the offsets at the top of the trough are provided by strips fixed

heavy wear on the harness. Bolts to support the upper portions of the par-

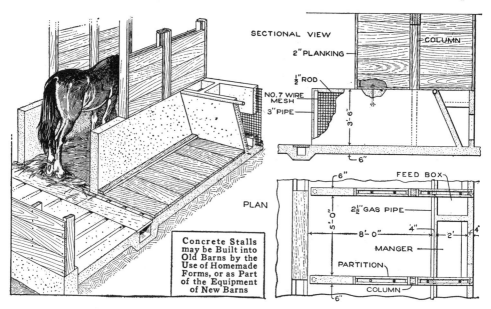

SECTIONAL VIEW
2" PLANKING
COLUMN
½" ROD
NO. 7 WIRE MESH
3" PIPE
3'-6"
6"

PLAN

6"
FEED BOX
2½" GAS PIPE
5'-0"
8'-0"
4"
2'
MANGER
PARTITION
COLUMN
6"

**Concrete Stalls may be Built into Old Barns by the Use of Homemade Forms, or as Part of the Equipment of New Barns**

to the trough mold. The 3-in. pipe, reinforcing the partitions at their rear ends, is set into the floor when the latter is laid, and it is desirable, also, to set the lower edges of the wire-mesh reinforcement into the floor.

Wooden forms are provided for the partitions and the manger. These should be built to be taken apart readily so that they may be used repeatedly. The form for the partition is a box in which the wire mesh is supported, taut and carefully centered, the mixture being poured into it and leveled at the upper surface. The forms for the manger and feed box should be set into place and fixed to the partition forms before any of the forms are filled. The inside of the manger is formed by a tapered box resting upon the floor. The feed box is poured around a similar but smaller form, and the portion below it is cast hollow by inserting a form, which remains in place after the concrete is poured into the molds. A 2½-in. pipe is set into the front edge of the manger, its ends being imbedded in the partitions, to protect the horses from the edge of the manger and to prevent

titions are set into the concrete, as indicated in the sectional view.

The mixture must be freshly mixed and thoroughly wet when being poured, in order that the molds may be filled properly. If necessary, the aggregate may be tamped into the molds slightly. The forms should be left in place three days, and then removed carefully, so as not to damage the concrete. Sprinkling the work occasionally, several days after the forms are removed, is also desirable as an aid in uniform drying. The surfaces should be smoothed by removing imperfections in the molds, and a mixture of cement and water should be brushed over them to produce a satisfactory finish, when the molds are removed. The work may be surfaced and troweled smooth if desired, but this is not essential.

The floor planking is laid crosswise and spiked to 2 by 4-in. pieces set at the sides of the stall. This arrangement makes it convenient to replace pieces of the planking where the greatest wear occurs, and the planking may be removed readily for flushing of the stall.

## Dirt-Collecting Corners Filled with Cement Grouting

Column footings and similar corners in a factory were filled with cement grouting, as shown, overcoming the unsightly dirt accumulations. The floor may be washed with water from a hose, in many instances, and the fire risk from inflammable materials collecting in corners is reduced, and sanitation promoted.—Roy H. Poston, Flat River, Mo.

## Vise Pads for Polished Tubing or Rods

If a length of highly polished pipe, or rod, is placed in a metal vise, it is usually marred or dented. The pads shown eliminate this. The holes are bored in a suitable board, about 1½ by 6 by 18 in., which is then sawed in two, as indicated, and hinges and a hook and eye are attached. It may also be given a coat of shellac. —Arthur W. Dahl, Superior, Wis.

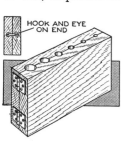

## An Electric Gas Lighter

For lighting gas burners used intermittently, the lighter shown in the sketch was found satisfactory. A piece of wood, ⅜ by ¾ by 3 in., was provided with two pieces of metal, and the two conductors were connected through a central hole to them. The other ends of the cord were connected to a 110-volt lighting circuit, in series with a small choke

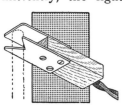

coil. When it is desired to light the gas, it is only necessary to turn it on and then place the lighter over the tip of the burner, moving it slightly to produce sparks. A coil of 10 or 15 ohms, having an iron core, will produce a sufficiently hot spark without endangering the usual 10-ampere fuse. The two metal contact pieces should be taped except on the ends projecting from the wooden handle.

## Soldering a Machine Nut to Sheet Metal

In fitting a can to receive a tap it was necessary to solder a nut securely to it and the method described was used. It has numerous other applications. The nut was placed on the metal and a line drawn around it, as shown. The center hole was cut and the six portions of the hexagon were cut and bent down. The nut was supported by them and soldered into place. A very strong fitting resulted. —J. H. S. Cronk, Woodstock, Canada.

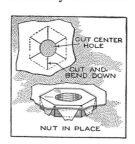

## A Flexible Socket Wrench

For use in places where an ordinary wrench cannot be applied, a flexible socket wrench is useful. It is a homemade device, the socket portion being formed from a short piece of iron pipe and the other sections from steel pipe. It may be made in various sizes and provided with several sizes and shapes of sockets, which can be fixed into place as desired, by means of the pin.—Charles C. Brabant, Detroit, Mich.

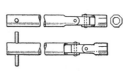

⟨Putty for glazing should contain 10 per cent of white lead to withstand the weather.

## Japanese Finish for Spruce

A finish used on spruce by Japanese craftsmen is produced by the application of dilute sulphuric acid, after which the surface is charred slightly. The acid is permitted to dry and the wood is then held over a hot stove, until the surface is well blackened. The charcoal surface is brushed off thoroughly, and the surface oiled with linseed oil and beeswax. The harder grain appears black and the rest has a rich brown tone.

## Preventing Oil Leakage in Gear Box

Occasionally trouble is experienced from leakage of grease or oil out of the ball bearings of an automobile gear box, as shown in the sketch at the left. This is usually due to the failure of the felt ring within the ball-bearing nut to press closely around the shaft. Such a condition was overcome by turning out one side of the nut that holds the felt packing, and threading it to receive

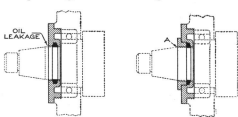

Leakage of Oil from an Automobile Gear Box was Prevented by Fitting a Pressure Nut against the Packing

another nut, A. The latter, when drawn up properly, forces the packing ring against the shaft, preventing leakage at this point.

## Compressed-Air Punch for Cutting Washers

A punch for making washers, and the automobile tires from which the latter were cut, are shown in the illustration. The punch is operated by compressed air. The cylinder is 6 in. in diameter and the piston has a stroke of 3 in. A heavy coil spring in the cylinder, directly under the piston, lifts

the punch after it has cut a washer. The lower spring strips the washers from the punch. The lever on the two-way cock controls the air, and when

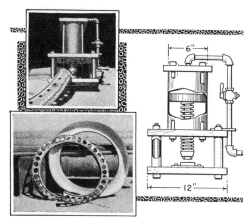

Old Automobile Tires were Cut into Washers with This Device

pulled down, permits the air to force the piston down for the cutting stroke. When the lever is raised, the air escapes as the spring lifts the piston. Tire casings were used with this device to make packing washers for oil-well pumps, and washers for other uses can be made similarly.—F. R. Shepherd, Fellows, Calif.

## Hand Drill Used as Lathe

An ordinary hand drill was used effectively as a small lathe in turning a number of brass pulleys, by rigging it as shown. Two wooden bearings with metal strips, A and B, hold the drill firmly on the baseboard. An arbor is held in the drill chuck, and supported on two metal angles, D. The pulley

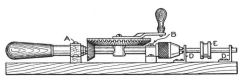

Small Brass Pulleys were Turned by Means of This Makeshift Lathe

E was drilled and forced on the arbor, and a suitable support for hand-turning tools was provided.—R. C. Fulton, Scarsdale, N. Y.

### A Garden Sprayer of Varied Uses

Primarily for use in spraying plants in a garden, the sprayer shown in the sketch, Fig. 1, and made at small cost

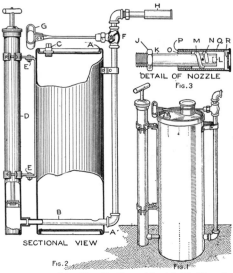

DETAIL OF NOZZLE
FIG. 3

SECTIONAL VIEW

FIG. 2

FIG. 1

A Revolver Cartridge Shell was Used in Making the Nozzle of This Handy Garden Sprayer

in the home workshop, is useful also in the garage, on the farm, and for other purposes. The tank A, Fig. 2, is 5 by 14 in., and operates satisfactorily at a pressure of about 15 lb., when used with ordinary liquids for plants. It is made of No. 26 gauge galvanized iron, the ends being riveted into place. It is filled at the pipe plug C. The pressure pipe B extends through the tank, and is connected to the pump D, a ball valve, originally in the connecting tube when the pump was used as a foot bicycle-tire pump, being at the junction, and controlling the back pressure. Straps E support the pump.

The liquid passes through the tube B to the valve F, controlled by the handle G, convenient to the pump, by which the sprayer is carried. When the valve is opened, the liquid is driven into the nozzle H, which is shown in detail in Fig. 3. The threaded $\frac{1}{8}$-in. nipple J fits into the elbow, and is soldered to the $\frac{3}{16}$-in. copper pipe K, which is plugged at the end L. A $\frac{1}{16}$-

in. hole, N, is bored in the tube, and two turns of brass wire, M, soldered into place, produce a spiral course for the spray. The brass tube O, soldered to the tube P, is set on the tube K, with a tight fit. The cap Q is a .38-caliber, long cartridge shell, sliding tightly on tube P. The end of the shell is drilled out, and the disk R, having a $\frac{1}{16}$-in. hole, is soldered into place. In filling the tank, sufficient air must be left in it to afford the proper possibility for compression. The parts, especially of the nozzle, should be cleaned after use.—T. T. Sturgeon, Los Angeles, Calif.

---

### Test of Steel Shelving for Deflection

A manufacturer of metal shelving desired to test it as to deflection under various loads. No special apparatus was available, and the arrangement shown in the sketch was devised for the purpose. The shelving, which was of various types, was supported on a wooden frame bolted to a bench. A scale was set into place below it, and a simple jack made by setting a bolt into a washer in the top of the tubing, as

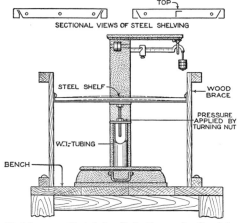

Shelving was Tested for Deflection under Load by Means of This Simple Rigging

shown. The pressure was applied by means of the screw and nut, and the shelves were deflected under a load specified for each size.—K. George Selander, Jamestown, N. Y.

## Painting Quick-Drying Cloth Signs

Where cloth, or muslin, signs are wanted for temporary use, exposed to the weather, letter them with a paint made without oil. Use dry colors of fine quality and grind them with varnish or japan to a thick paste; then thin out with benzine when ready for the work. If too thin, the paint will spread. Use a sign writer's one-stroke brush, and if especially good wearing qualities are desired in the paint, add a small quantity of boiled oil to the letter color.—A. A. Kelly, Malvern, Pa.

## Device for Tightening Fence Wire

A large length of loose fence wire was tightened by the use of the device 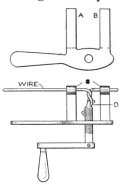 shown in the sketch, made for the purpose. A piece of ¼-in. iron was shaped to form a handle, and the two ends A and B were bent at right angles to it to form the upright parts. These may also be made by riveting pieces to the handle portion. Their upper ends, at C, were formed into eyes, left slightly open. A hole for the threaded crank was made in the handle section, and the pointed end of the screw bent into a hook, at D. The wire is tightened by looping it over the hook and turning the crank.—R. S. Matzen, Fort Collins, Colo.

## Collapsible Steps for Boarding a Boat

Boarding steps for launches and small yachts are often bulky to stow away on the craft. The type shown in the sketch packs flat, takes up little space, and is safe and substantial. The sidepieces, of ⅞-in. hard wood, are curved to fit the sides of the boat. Two iron hooks, the proper shape to fit over the gunwale, support the steps.

The treads are 18 by 10 by ⅞ in., placed 12 in. apart. They are set horizontally by hanging the sidepieces in

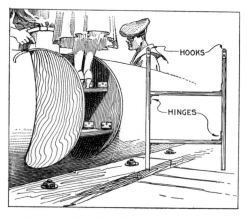

The Steps Fold Flat for Convenient Storage on Board the Craft

place, and marking the proper position. Strap hinges are fixed as indicated, and rubber treads provided.—L. B. Robbins, Attleboro, Mass.

## Support for Long Work in Vise

Blocking-up, or other makeshift, methods of supporting long work in a vise were discarded in a shop, in favor of the simple arm fitted to the sliding member, as shown in the illustration. The device is especially useful on a pivoted vise, since it revolves with the

This Simple Support Makes Unnecessary the Blocking Up of Long Work in a Vise

latter. The extreme end is provided with an adjustable screw to fit irregular work.—S. L. Wade, Montgomery, Alabama.

## Cushion for Charging Pan of Concrete Mixer

Cable breakages on the lifting rigging and damage to the charging pan of a concrete mixer were avoided by the use of a spring cushion made of two wagon springs, mounted as shown in the illustration. Sections of rubber hose were

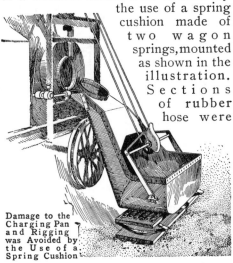

Damage to the Charging Pan and Rigging was Avoided by the Use of a Spring Cushion

nailed on the top of the upper board of the cushion as a further protection to the charging pan.—J. J. O'Brien, Buffalo, N. Y.

## Auxiliary Jaws for Center and Turret- Lathe Chucks

In turning a number of castings which were too large for the ordinary- size lathe chuck, it was found desirable

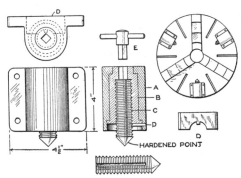

This Auxiliary Fitting for a Chuck Made Possible the Handling of Large Castings in a Lathe

to make a set of auxiliary jaws, which were fastened to the face of the chuck, as shown in the sketch. The casing A is made of soft steel, the sleeve B, of steel, tempered at the upper end, which is provided with a socket for the wrench E. The screw C is of tool steel, tempered at the point, and has a key- way, as shown, which extends longi- tudinally at the back of the casing. This keyway engages the key D, which is set in a slot at the back of the cas- ing and has its back edge flush against the face of the chuck. The screw is adjusted by means of the wrench E, which causes the sleeve B to revolve. —G. T. E., Pittsburgh, Pa.

## Tightening a Loose Bushing

Sometimes, after pressing bushings into their places, they are loose and turn when an attempt is made to ream them out. In this case, remove the bushing, and run a coat of solder around the outside of it. Force the bushing back into place and the excess solder will be scraped off and a tight fit will result, with no turning of the bushing in reaming it.—J. W. Reyn- olds, Mason, Ill.

## Kink in Cultivating Small Corn

When corn is small, it is difficult to do a good job of cultivating it, because of the tendency to cover it with earth. By wrapping the shovels of the culti- vator next to the row with binder twine, the dirt is not pitched on the small corn, and it is possible to work close to the plant, the binding aiding in breaking up the lumps of soil.—Irl R. Hicks, Moberly, Mo.

## A Polished-Black Wood Finish

A finish for woodwork in a high- polished black is produced as follows: Prime the work with linseed oil, tur- pentine, and white lead; apply two coats of black mixed with turpentine and copal varnish. Rub this down with pumice stone and water, and apply another coat of varnish. Rub again and polish to the gloss desired with rottenstone and oil.

# Shop Notes

## A Collapsing Bridge for the Movies

By RALPH CUMMINS

A MOVING-PICTURE bridge has one span so constructed that it can be broken away, precipitating an automobile, a carriage, or a horseman into the stream. Many movie fans are curious to know by what mechanical means this thriller is effected. Boys and others interested in making models, for play or diversion, will find a miniature bridge of this kind a novelty. A sure means of tripping the section is necessary, for the fall must be timed just right, so as not to spoil the picture and make necessary an expensive "retake." The tripping apparatus, shown in the sketch, is one that I have used successfully on bridges, towers, and walls. The principle is simple: Two hinges are placed on opposite sides of the trip post—a 4 by 4-in. piece upon which one end of the span rests. A piano wire stretched from the upper hinge to a point opposite the break-away section, forms the means of tripping. When an automobile is used, a wire can be run through pulleys in such a manner that the machine trips the break-away span at the proper instant.

---

### Painting Cold-Water Pipes

It is very difficult to obtain a satisfactory painted surface on cold-water pipes, because of the condensed moisture which collects on them. The water should be run out of the pipes and a thin coat of shellac applied after the surface has been dried thoroughly. Bronze aluminum, dusted over a preliminary coat of copal varnish, or over the shellac, which dries quickly, produces a neat finish.—A. Ashmun Kelly, Malvern, Pa.

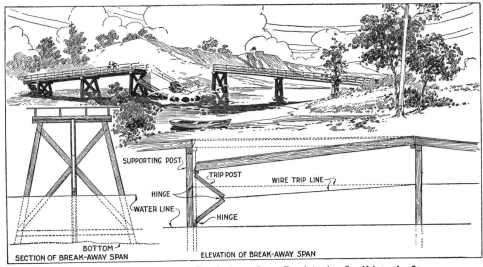

SUPPORTING POST

TRIP POST

HINGE

WATER LINE

WIRE TRIP LINE

HINGE

BOTTOM

SECTION OF BREAK-AWAY SPAN

ELEVATION OF BREAK-AWAY SPAN

**The Car Automatically Trips the Break-Away Span, Precipitating Itself into the Stream**

## Quickly Made Stand for Lathing

In lathing I found a stand built up on a horse and braced, as shown, to  be quite convenient. The laths were placed in a barrel supported near the end of the platform, and could be easily taken without stoop-

The Rapid Work of the Lather is Made Even More Speedy by the Use of This Stand

ing. The platform is light and easily moved. It is so cheaply made that after a job is finished it can be knocked down and only the horse taken to another job, if desired. The barrel used was a nail keg, like those obtainable at most buildings in construction.—John S. La Fleur, Haverhill, Mass.

## Safety Guard for Exposed Shafting

Suitable coverings for exposed shafting should be provided as a safety measure. If the shafting is already in operation and cannot be taken down

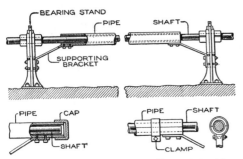

The Workmen are Protected from Exposed Shafting by Pipe Coverings

handily, a pipe may be cut into halves longitudinally in a keyseating machine and the parts clamped together with straps of sheet iron, when in position. A typical installation is that between bearing stands, to which the pipe is braced with brackets, as shown. Exposed ends of shafting are protected with a pipe and cap, as detailed.

## Locating Trouble in Automobile Starters and Generators

After a season's use, the automobile starter and generator should be carefully examined to make certain that its efficiency is up to standard. The starter may lack the necessary turn-over torque, especially when the engine is cold and spinning is difficult. The generator may heat up rapidly or fail to charge the battery properly. Before taking the motor or generator apart, go over every external connection to see that there are no grounds, breaks, or shorts. Examine the starter foot switch to make sure that the electrical contacts are in good condition. Note, also, the condition of the battery, whether it needs water or acid and that its voltage is sufficient. As for the generator, pay special attention to the relay to see that cutting-in occurs at the proper engine speed. This speed should average eight or ten miles an hour, for most generators. If trouble is experienced with the sticking of relay contact points, a small flat file should be used to smooth the contacts, care being taken to see that they meet evenly. An ordinary finger-nail file will serve the purpose. Still failing to locate the trouble, inspect the machine internally. As a rule, very little difficulty may be traced to the field coils, but a close examination of the armature and commutator is suggested.

Bad sparking at the brushes is generally a sign of high mica. A ground in the armature winding is caused by contact of the winding with the armature core. A careful examination should show the weak point in the insulation.

The last test to be made is for broken lead wires. Substitute a small piece of sheet metal for one of the brushes, so that only one commutator bar at a time is touched. A single dry cell should then be connected, through an ammeter, to the metal brush and to the next carbon brush. Turn the armature very slowly by hand, so that the metal brush may make sure contact with each commutator bar in succession. Unless the design is very special, there will be two lead wires soldered to each bar. A reduced deflection will indicate a break in one lead, and no deflection, a break in both, when the metal brush passes over the bar to which the faulty leads belong.—K. M. Coggeshall, Webster Groves, Mo.

## Triangle Holder Aids in Inking Drawings

It is often desirable, for rapid work in tracing, to draw ink lines with a triangle over lines that are wet. It is hard to do this without making blots. I made a protector, as shown, with which it is easy to move the triangle over wet lines, at the same time keeping it at right angles to the T-square. The device is made of metal,

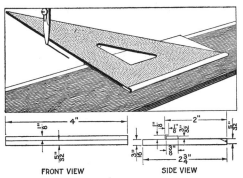

FRONT VIEW          SIDE VIEW

The Device with the Triangle in It is Moved in the Usual Manner

sheet aluminum being preferable. The size may be varied, that indicated being suitable for smaller triangles.—Howard Scott, Jersey City, N. J.

---

❡A smooth, well-tinned soldering iron transmits more heat than a rough or dirty one.

## Traveling Pulley-and-Hanger Support at Anvil

In the small forge shop where long pieces must be handled occasionally, as well as in the shop where drills and

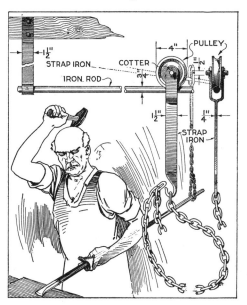

This Support was Made for Handling Long Rock Drills, and Has Many Other Uses

similar tools are sharpened, the pulley-and-hanger arrangement shown in the illustration is convenient. The rod on which the pulley travels is supported from the joists. A forged hanger supports a chain sling which is adjustable to various sizes and shapes of work.—John E. Cahill, Jr., New York, N. Y.

---

## Orchestra-Pit Rail Used as Speaking Tube

Musicians and the leader in an orchestra often wish to communicate with each other, which in a large orchestra is inconvenient. By cutting 1-in. openings in the pit rail at each player's chair in a local theater, and connecting the rail to a tube at the leader's station, means of communication was provided. At more expense, speaking tubes may be installed along the rail, but the plain openings proved a success.—Jack Wolmer, Marion, Ind.

## Remedy for Unreliable Auto-Oiling System

Many small automobiles are equipped with a constant-level splash system of engine lubrication in which a shaft-

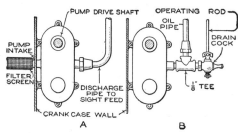

Frequent Stoppage of the Oiling System was Overcome by the Installation of a Drain Cock

driven gear pump draws oil from a chamber cast in one piece with the lower part of the crank case. This pump discharges the oil through a copper tube to a sight-feed fitting on the dash, from which it goes to the crank case by gravity. In one such case frequent stoppages of the oil flow were experienced, and when the parts were cleaned, little dirt was found, and the system worked temporarily on reassembly. An air lock was found to be responsible, and the change shown in the diagram was made to overcome the difficulty, the old arrangement at A, and the new at B.

A change in the piping was made, as shown, the other fittings being undisturbed. The regular discharge fitting was attached with a tee. A petcock was placed opposite the discharge and an operating rod for it was run up to the top of the engine. As soon as the oil feed stops, it is but a minute's work to open the petcock, and allow a small quantity of oil to be pumped out. When this is then closed, the oil flows through the discharge pipe, whether the stoppage was due to an air lock or to dirt.—Victor W. Pagé, Bristol, Connecticut

## Testing the Atmosphere in Polishing Rooms

A test for detecting metallic dust in the atmosphere of a polishing room may be made by placing a lighted Bunsen gas burner in the middle of the room, about 4 ft. from the floor. When steel and iron particles float in the atmosphere, the dust comes into contact with the flame, as indicated by the sparkling of the flame. The presence of brass dust is indicated by an intense greenish color. This simple device is valuable for the inspection of blower systems, intended to clear the air.

## A Workbench for Use Singly or in Multiple

This heavy workbench was designed for use in engine houses and small railroad shops where room is at a premium, and can be adapted for the use of machinists, carpenters, pipe fitters, boilermakers, and other mechanics who need a substantial bench. It accommodates four men, but can be arranged to be used in two sections. Two drawers are provided for each workman, and also a large cupboard with a screened door. The construction is such that the bench can be made quickly by machine or hand process,

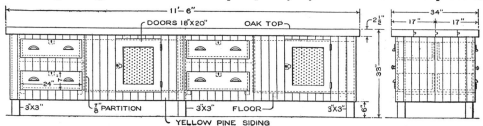

A Substantial Workbench of This Type may be Used in Single or Double Units for Heavy Shop Work

and there are no out-of-the-way corners to catch dirt.—Joseph A. Long, Sunbury, Pa.

# A Hydroplane Catamaran Built for Speed

By L. B. ROBBINS

THE building of this 16-ft. power boat of the catamaran type, involves no special skill in boat construction, and it is designed to be made without the bending of planks, ribs, etc., by mechanics having only a fair knowledge of handwork with tools. The craft is for use on fairly smooth water, and with a 4-hp. motor, develops a speed of 15 miles an hour. For greater speed with a more powerful motor, the size of the catamaran must be correspondingly increased. The bottoms of the hulls have steps, turning them into simple hydroplanes, and increasing their speed quality. The open structure simplifies the mounting of the power plant and its driving connections, as compared with conditions met in ordinary motorboats. The perspective sketch in the headpiece of this article, and the plan and elevations, Figs. 1, 2, and 3, show the general arrangement of the parts.

Cut the sideboards from ¾-in. pine. They fit between the top and bottom, and over the ends. Begin the construction with the hulls, detailed in Fig. 4. All of the wood used should be first-quality stock. Plane the edges square, and fasten the 1-in. battens into place with screws, applying white lead under them, on the inside of each sideboard, except at A, Fig. 4, where a bulkhead supports the structure. Coat the inside of the sides with marine paint.

The bow piece B is of oak, 2 in. sq. and 1 ft. 1½ in. long, and the stern piece C is of 1-in. pine. Fit the pine bulkhead A water-tight, the rear surface of it flush with the step. Fasten the end and bow pieces, and the deck board, painting the inner surfaces. Use 2-in. brass screws, countersinking

the heads, and place a strip of muslin soaked in white lead between all joints. Cut the holes D, and fit them with plugs. These holes are for filling in or pumping out ballast to distribute the weight properly. Scrape off the excess white lead, sandpaper the surfaces, and fill the screw holes with white-lead putty, and apply two coats of marine paint to the hulls. Next construct the deck of matched boards mounted on two 2 by 6-in. spruce timbers, 16 ft. long. These must be of fairly straight grain, and of very good quality. Set the timbers on edge and taper them to 5 in. at the ends, into a truss effect. Place the timbers, as indicated, 2 ft. apart, arched edges uppermost, and nail on the ¾-in. matched pine deck boards 3 ft. long. Leave 1 ft. of the timbers uncovered at the ends. Leave two openings forward, the size and position of them depending on the motor used. The center of the engine bed is 4 ft. 6 in. from the bow and heavy boards are laid for its support. Notch the timbers, 6 in. from the ends, and fit them with iron straps, bolted on, as detailed, to accommodate the supporting end shafts.

An old automobile seat and round gasoline tank is mounted on the frame, as shown, making certain that the bottom of the tank is higher than the carburetor of the motor. The seat and tank are set about 10 ft. 6 in. from the bow, to obtain an even distribution of weight. An auto steering wheel and column, fitted with a wooden drum, keyed in place, is used. A bracket near its base supports the post.

The deck is next fitted to the hulls.

The installation of the motor will depend upon its style and size. The usual connections of the gasoline sup-

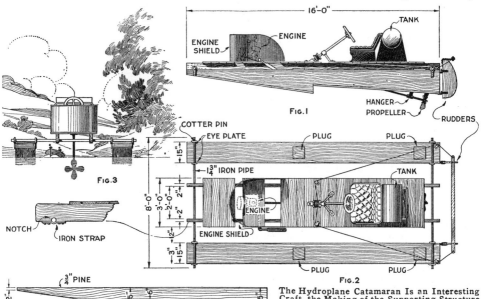

FIG.1

FIG.2

FIG.3

NOTCH    IRON STRAP

FIG.4

The Hydroplane Catamaran Is an Interesting Craft, the Making of the Supporting Structure Being Quite Simple as Compared with the Building of Ordinary Motorboat Hulls

Eye plates, as shown, hold the end rods carrying the long timbers. The plates are secured with screws, 6 in. from the ends of each hull. An 8-ft. length of 1¾-in. galvanized-iron piping is slipped through the sets of eyes, and through the notches of the deck timbers; cotter pins hold the piping in place. The straps at the ends of the timbers keep the deck frame in position on the piping.

Two rudders of thin oak or of sheet metal, as shown in Figs. 1 and 2, are hinged to the inner edge of each hull. An angle of strap iron at the upper edge of each rudder is bolted loosely to a bar of iron or wood, so that the rudders operate together. The steering rope is rigged through pulleys, as shown, and wound around the drum on the steering column.

ply and electrical equipment are, of course, provided. The batteries and coil are placed under the seat, and the wire connections carried in rubber hose. Heavy oak or ash engine timbers are bolted to the flooring for the engine bed, arranging the pitch so that the propeller will rest about 6 in. under water. Bolt the hanger for the propeller shaft to the floor boards, as shown in Fig. 1. A spray hood, of canvas over an iron frame, or of sheet metal, protects the motor.

## Punching Hard Sheet-Rubber Washers by Hand

Vulcanized, or hard, sheet rubber may be worked with shears or ordinary leather punches, using stock ⅛ in. in thickness, by gently heating the part to be cut, and sometimes heating the tool also. To cut a hard-rubber washer from a piece of flat stock, use two leather punches, a large one to cut out the blank, and a smaller one to punch out the center hole. Lay the stock on a flat piece of lead, or other fairly soft metal, heated just sufficiently to cause the rubber to become pliable, so as not to crack when the punch strikes it. The washer will cool flat if laid on a flat surface. Hard-metal tubing is suitable for cutting the stock, if properly sharpened, and other shapes may also be cut.—F. L. Whitaker, Olney, Ill.

## Padded and Flexible Paper Weights

For weighting large maps and drawings, standard square 2 or 2½-in. nuts, with a layer of cotton waste or cloth padding, about ¾ in. thick, evenly wrapped about them and covered with strong paper or cloth, are excellent and inexpensive. A smooth leather bag, 3 in. square, filled with small lead shot or dry sand and securely sewed, makes a good paper weight that is very flexible, and if accidentally dropped on a drawing, does it no injury.

## Tool Holder for High-Speed Steel

By the use of this tool holder, high-speed steel need not be broken into short lengths, but may be fed forward as required. The holder was designed for a medium-sized lathe tool post, and the device may be made strong enough for use on a shaper or planer, and to withstand heavy cuts. It consists of two sliding members of machine steel, grooved to fit the tool steel, as indicated at A, and is clamped in the tool post in the usual manner.—C. A. Gilson, Niles, Mich.

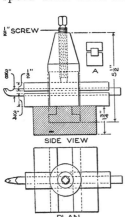

❡Undue forcing in photo development is indicated by a tendency of the fixed prints to sink in the wash water.

## Detachable Hauling Brackets on Passenger Auto

Two simple methods of adapting an automobile quickly for business pur-

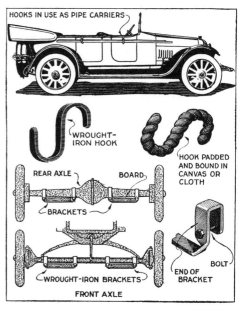

These Devices Are Useful in Carrying Pipes, Ladders, Fish Poles, and Similar Articles

poses are shown in the sketch. The S-shaped wrought-iron hooks, padded in cloth or canvas, are used by a plumber to convey long sections of pipe handily. The brackets are used by a paper hanger in transporting scaffolding. They are made of wrought iron, as shown, to conform to the axles of the car.—G. A. Luers, Washington, District of Columbia.

## Hay Carrier Rigged to Handle Excavation Dirt

In digging a cellar under my house, how to remove the dirt was a problem. I made a track for my hay-carrier tripping pulleys and hanger of 1 by 4-in. boards. I then made a strong box, 1 by 2½ by 3 ft. in size, and attached it to the carrier in such a way that by loosening a hook it would dump easily. With this arrangement one man took out an average of 7 cu. yd. a day.—J. H. Knight, Cumberland, Ohio.

## High and Low Water-Level Indicator

This easily made water-level indicator is in daily use and was worked out by me. Where the supply tank is located so that it is not visible from the pump house, such a device is reliable and convenient. Branch wires from an 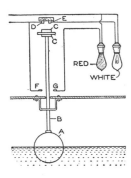 ordinary lighting circuit are run to the tank and to the pump house, office, etc., as desired. The copper float, at A, is fastened to a rod, B, to which are attached the plates C, with an insulating strip between them. The clamp and the hole in the tank act as guides to hold the rod in a vertical position. When the tank is full the lighting circuit is closed by bridging the space at the contacts D and E, lighting the white globe. When low water is indicated, the space at F and G is bridged, and the red globe is lighted.—James E. Noble, Toronto, Can.

## Device for Tapping Small Machine Parts

A machine which was found useful in tapping quantities of small parts is 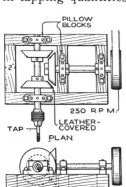 made as follows: Turn off one side of each of three 5-in. grooved pulleys, at an angle of 45°, making cone-shaped wheels. Remove the chuck from a breast drill, and thread one end of a ¾ by 12-in. shaft to fit it. Upon this shaft mount two of the pulleys, 4 in. apart, facing each other, and equally distant from the center. A second shaft, at right angles to the first, takes the third bevel pulley at one end, the pulleys being faced with leather. The leather is drawn tightly over the shellacked face of each pulley, bound down at the back with wire, and later trimmed off. A wooden frame of 2 by 4-in. stock forms the support of the two shafts, which run in pillow blocks. The shaft carrying the friction wheel is belted to the source of power and runs continuously, while the chuck shaft runs ahead when pushed in, and reverses when pulled in the opposite direction. The speed should be about 200 to 250 revolutions per minute.—Dexter W. Allis, Whitman, Mass.

## A Caliper with Locking Scale

Mechanics who have had experience with calipers will readily perceive the 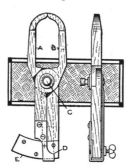 advantages of the indicating feature of this homemade caliper. I made this instrument of wood for gauging the top and back of a violin in course of construction, and it has many other uses. The legs A and B are fitted together at the lap joint C with a washer, and secured with a screw and knurled nut. The movable arm D is made of sheet metal, and is swung from the bolt that secures the legs, the thumbscrew locking the arm of the scale E. The latter is a piece of sheet metal fastened to the leg A, and its extension, with screws. A pointer is also fastened to leg B. When the caliper is completed, the pointer D is locked against arm A, and the indicating marks scribed deeply on the pointers. A scale may also be marked on the part E. Ordinarily, the arm D is clamped on E, as desired, the opening gauged by the pointers.—William A. Robinson, Waynesboro, Pennsylvania.

### Repairing Small Tire-Tube Punctures

Many automobile-tire repairmen, in repairing a pinhole puncture, use a patch several times as large as the injury. This requires very heavy pressure to obtain a smooth surface. A better way is to trim the hole just enough to remove all ragged edges. Clean it thoroughly and apply cement. When the cement has dried, force a small thread of gum through the hole with an awl, trimming it flush on the outside. In curing, use just enough pressure to hold the tube firmly on the tube plate; tracing cloth laid on the plate insures a smooth surface.

### Automatic Poultry Feeder with Clock Control

Uniform quantities of feed may be fed to poultry with a minimum of attention by the person caring for them, if the simple arrangement shown in the illustration is installed in the poultry house or yard. The grain or other feed is placed in the metal hopper, the device being supported on the rafters or other suitable support. The hinged door at the bottom of the hopper is controlled by a trigger, connected to the clock alarm winder by a cord. When the alarm is released, the cord is wound on a spool fixed on the alarm winder, and the trigger is freed. The feed falls to the conical spreader, and is scattered to the ground.

The hopper may be made in various sizes, and several may be rigged with the same clock control. It is mounted on a 7/8 by 9 by 18-in. board, on one end of which the clock is fastened, by a strap of iron. The spreader is supported from the board by metal rods. The hole in the bottom of the hopper is 2 in. in diameter, and the spreader is 12 in. wide.

A spool is secured to the alarm winder of the clock and the cord controlling the trigger is wound on it. The clock is wound up, and the alarm set for the desired time. When the alarm is freed, the spool turns with the alarm winder, winding up the cord,

and releasing the trigger, and feed. The fowls soon become accostomed to

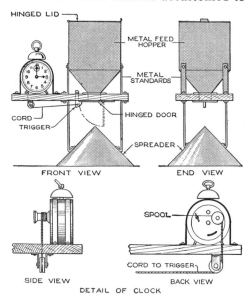

The Poultry Feed is Scattered on the Ground from the Suspended Hopper and Spreader, When the Alarm Mechanism Releases the Trigger

the ringing of the alarm, and respond to it quickly.—C. C. Holmes, Detroit, Michigan.

### Ball Bearings Overcome Thrust in Gear Shaft

The countershaft in the gear box of a motorboat power plant was subjected to a great end thrust when the gears were engaged. This caused considerable wear on the gear box, as indicated. Hardened steel balls were placed at each end of the countershaft, slightly countersunk holes being pro-

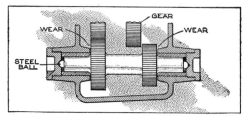

Steel Balls Set in Conical Bearings Take Up the End Thrust

vided in both the shaft and the housing. They took up the thrust in both directions, eliminating the wear.

## Handle Forms Coupler for Train of Trucks

By arranging the tongues of shop trucks so that they may be set in

One Man can Draw a Train of Small Trucks When They are Coupled Together

sockets on the rear of similar trucks, forming a train, one man can handle a number of them when empty. The end of the tongue and the socket are protected by metal fittings. — J. J. O'Brien, Buffalo, N. Y.

## An Adjustable Hay Shed

As a protection for hay stacked in the field, the hay shed shown in the illustration proved effective. It was built by setting four heavy cedar poles

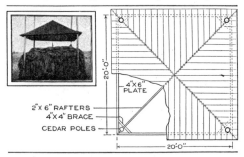

The Roof is Raised and Lowered by Sliding It on the Poles, in Which Heavy Supporting Bolts are Inserted

in concrete at the four corners of the stack and then constructing a roof to slide up and down on the poles. A desirable location for the haystack from year to year was determined upon, and the shelter built at that place. Holes were bored 2 ft. apart in the supporting poles, and the roof is set at various heights by means of bolts, placed in the holes. The roof is of comparatively light construction so that it is not difficult to raise or lower it. The tops of the poles are guyed together by means of wire braces.—W. E. Frudden, Charles City, Iowa.

## Fumigating Plants with Tobacco Smoke

The accumulation of insects or scale on plants should be held in check by fumigating them, at intervals. An efficient means of overcoming the pests is by the smoke of to-bacco. A suita-ble arrangement whereby this can be done

LIGHTING THE TOBACCO

either in the house or outside, is shown in the sketch. Bore 1-in. holes in the top of the box, and cut an opening in the end to admit a saucer. Make a cloth bag to be slipped over the box and tied closely, inclosing the plants, which are set on the box, above the holes. Light the tobacco on a saucer, and put the latter through the open-ing, so that the smoke may rise around the inclosed plants. The bag is care-fully taken out of doors to remove the smoke remaining in it. A light fumi-gating performed twice is better than fumigating heavily, with possible in-jury to the plants.—F. H. Sweet, Waynesboro, Va.

## Paper Drinking Cups as Containers for Wood-Finishing Materials

In a shop where many kinds of stains, paints, etc., are used, consider-able time and material are wasted in cleaning bottles, cups, or other con-tainers. A satisfactory solution of this problem is the use of paper drinking cups. They cost less than one-half cent each, and may be thrown away after being used once, or used several times for the same kind of stain.—P. Gaffney, Chicago, Ill.

## Leather Covering for Auto Magneto Coupling

In an automobile, a small leather covering over the coupling connecting the magneto to the engine is desirable. The dirt and grit will in this manner be prevented from working into the parts of the coupling. The boot is made of thin flexible leather, formed in the shape of a tube, and clamped to the two shafts by means of soft-iron wire.

## Extension for Drafting Board

A drawing board of considerable size was found too small for drawings which were to be made from time to time, and an extension was built, which could be removed quickly. The wood used was the same as that in the board, and the ends were fitted with cleats, to prevent warping, and to provide a good edge for the T-square. Metal straps hold the sliding pieces under the board. The extension is held rigid by two deep dowels, set in the joined edges. Hooks hold it firmly

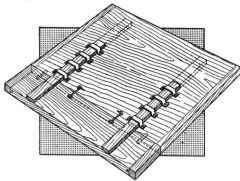

The Sliding Strips are Fastened on the Lower Side of the Board, and the Hooks Hold the Extension in Place

against the edge of the board. When not in use, the sliding strips are kept under the board.—Ralph W. Sherman, Burlington, N. J.

## Proper Care of Automobile Springs

A practical illustration of the care of automobile leaf springs is that frequently employed on racing cars, the

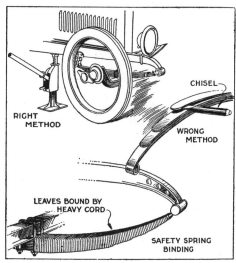

RIGHT METHOD

CHISEL

WRONG METHOD

LEAVES BOUND BY HEAVY CORD

SAFETY SPRING BINDING

The Leaves should be Properly Released, and Not Pried Apart with a Cold Chisel

springs being wrapped with heavy cords to crowd the faces of the leaves firmly together, increasing the frictional contact, as shown in the sketch. Mechanics, with a hammer and cold chisel or crowbar, sometimes pry apart the leaves of the springs to lubricate them. This method often produces permanent sets or bends. The correct method of separating the leaves is by releasing the clips and staybolts, and placing a jack between the frame and floor to raise the load. Beeswax, or this and powdered resin, heated, is suitable for the springs, if applied as suggested. The unsightly sagging rear of many cars is often caused by failure to maintain proper contact between the leaves, and in some instances by abuse through methods of lubrication. To insert a lubricant, such as oil, between them, may cause distortion and frequently broken springs.

❡A strip of canvas glued in several layers to the flanged driving pulley of a motorcycle overcomes the slipping of the belt.

## List-Printing Machine for Use with Rubber Type

It was found difficult to print a long list of names by the use of the flat type

This Printing Device was Made for Duplicating Lists of Names, and Has Other Uses

board ordinarily used with rubber type, and, since many copies were to be made, the machine shown was devised. It requires a comparatively small ink pad, and the rollers for the type can be used for many forms of this kind of printing. The rollers were spaced on their circumferences so that the lines of type registered properly in the forms to be printed, which were ruled. Ordinarily it will be necessary to space the type lines at standard spacings, or at spacings determined upon for special reasons. The type may be glued directly to the rollers, or to paper strips, which are then mounted on the rollers. The type rollers are inked by felt-covered ink rollers mounted in a hinged metal angle. The printing

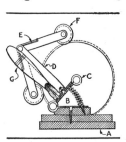

device is carried on a sliding block, fitted into a groove on the baseboard.

The detailed construction of the printing device is shown in the sketch. A is the sliding piece which engages the grooves of the baseboard. One butt hinge, B, and half of another, are fastened with screws. The half hinge carries the shaft C, which is the pin of the hinge. A strip, D,

holds the angle E, carrying the ink rollers F. They are held at proper pressure on the type by the spring at E, and are kept from dropping between the rows of type by small flanges at their ends, bearing on the wooden edge of the type rollers.

The printing roller is set firmly on the shaft. The first printing line is indicated on the side of the roller, as a guide in starting the impression, the roller being "spotted" by the fingers of the right hand, which holds the handle. The handle G is pushed forward, and the additional sheets are fed against the guide strip with the left hand. The coil spring holds the printing roller off the paper on the return stroke, and tends also to make the impressions more nearly uniform on the forward stroke. —T. T. Sturgeon, Los Angeles, Calif.

## Repairing Leaky Copper Heater Coils

Leaky or burned-out copper water-heating coils, such as are used in most

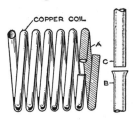

water tanks, can be repaired either by brazing a small hole, or, in case of large leaks, a new piece can be inserted. The burned-out part is sawed off, as at A, the shading indicating the burned-out section. Discarded coils from which good parts may still be cut, are used in repairing. One of the ends to be joined is spread with the round head of a machinist's hammer, as at B. The other end C is set into the funnel-shaped part, and, backed with asbestos sheeting, is put under the blowtorch flame. At white heat, using plenty of borax, the spelter is introduced about the joint, fluxing with the copper. At the same instant, the flame must be shut off, to avoid melting the copper coil. Heater coils repaired in this manner are nearly as good as new.—Ralph W. Tillotson, Erie, Pa.

## Keeping Down Dust on Concrete Floors

Mopping of some types of concrete floors is objectionable because the water is retained for a considerable time, causing dampness. In other instances the floor wears off, producing a disagreeable dust. By cleaning the floor thoroughly, and painting it with several coats of boiled linseed oil, allowing plenty of time for them to dry, the surface becomes filled. It wears to a smooth polish and the floor may be kept clear of dust easily, by mopping it.

## Steam-Operated Flue Cleaner

A handy labor-saving device was rigged up by a fireman in a local boiler room, the details of which are given in the sketch. The boiler it is used on is 16 ft. long, with 56 flues $3\frac{1}{2}$ in. in diameter, and it is quite a job to scrape the flues twice a week with the usual scraper. To make this steam-operated flue scraper, he used 2-in. seamless steel tubing, cut 17 ft. long. On each end he fitted a cap, and a packing nut on the forward end. Next he molded a piston of babbitt metal, 3 in. long, cutting grooves for two rings taken from a small motorcycle engine. A hole was then tapped at each end of the 17-ft. tubing for the steam pipes. A piece of $\frac{1}{2}$-in. pipe was attached at the back end, with a suitable fixture to fasten to a steam hose. Two three-way lever cocks were attached as shown, and $\frac{1}{4}$-in. pipe run from the lever cocks to the forward end. A $\frac{1}{2}$-in. pipe was used as a piston rod, to which the scraper was fixed.

In use, a rope is fastened to the end bearing the scraper, as shown, and run through a small pulley fastened to the ceiling. The scraper is started in the tube, and then the operator simply holds against the cylinder and opens the end cock, permitting the steam to drive the scraper through the flue. Then he opens the same cock to the exhaust position, and at the same time turns steam into the cylinder through

the other cock, which forces the scraper back. By means of the rope and pulley, all flues are quickly

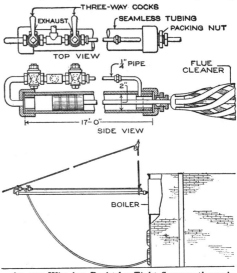

Anyone Who has Pushed a Tight Scraper through Boiler Flues will Appreciate the Labor Saved by This Device

reached. The device is used at from 40 to 90-lb. pressure, as the firemen find convenient.—R. S. Matzen, Fort Collins, Colo.

## Depth Gauge on a Hand Saw

In making the saw cuts for joints in timber, much time can be saved, and the job made more nearly uniform, by using a depth gauge on the hand saw. A simple contrivance for this purpose is made by clamping a steel square on the side of the saw, as shown. By adjusting the square properly, cuts may be made which are deeper on one side than on the other. When this kink was used by a carpenter recently, his fellow workmen immediately fol-

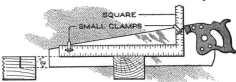

The Depth of Saw Cuts is Gauged Accurately by the Use of This Simple Device

lowed suit by rigging up devices in imitation of it.—J. V. Romig, Allentown, Pa.

# A Molding Head for the Circular Saw

### By CHARLES A. KING

THE modern circular-saw table, with its tilting top, its ripping, cutting-off, and mitering devices, and its movable throat, is an almost indispensable tool, but its possibilities either

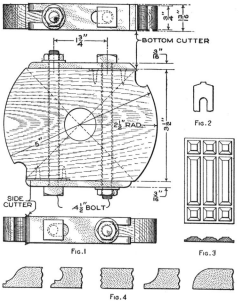

The Molding Head Is a Useful Addition to the Circular Saw Table, Especially in the Small Shop

are not realized or are ignored in many smaller woodworking shops. A variety of jigs and attachments for the circular-saw table may be made which will greatly broaden its range of usefulness. The head herein described, if accurately made, with knives properly shaped, tempered, and balanced, will be found efficient for many purposes.

The low cost of making a head of this sort, compared with the cost of the patented heads upon the market, will permit several of them to be made and kept on hand for special work; they are especially valuable in small shops, where there are no machines but a circular-saw table.

In making the head, select a well seasoned piece of maple, or other very hard wood, a little less in thickness than the width of the knife it is expected to carry, and cut it to a circle a little larger than the desired dimensions, about 5 in. Bore a hole in the center of this circle, to fit the spindle of the saw arbor. The roughly shaped head may then be placed upon the spindle and the collars set tightly up against its side. A rest for a turning tool should be devised, and, after starting the machine, the edge may be turned until the head is of the desired size.

Remove the head from the spindle and draw diagonals, as shown in Fig. 1, at angles of 45° with the direction of the grain, and indicate the portions to be cut off at the upper and lower edges. Cut away the segments, and straighten the edges until they are parallel with each other and square with the sides of the head.

Locate upon each side of the center, and 1¾ in. apart, the centers for two ⅜-in. holes, which pass through the head at right angles with the direction of the grain of the wood. These must be placed at exactly the same distance from the center, and bored carefully from each side until the holes meet. Cut out places for chip clearance, as shown, making the cut at right angles with the straight surfaces.

Fit a 5⁄16-in. bolt of proper length into each hole, and place a washer and nut on it. The head should now be put in place and the machine started up to see if the head runs smoothly. Usually there will be no trouble, but if the head jumps it should be balanced by boring small holes in the wood upon the heavy side until it runs with little or no vibration. If the bare head runs as it should, but vibrates when the cutters are in place, it will be known that the trouble is with them.

The cutters may be ground, or forged, from regular sizes of tool-steel blanks, as indicated in the sketch, but if such are not available, heavy worn-out files may be used. The knives should be slotted to permit endwise adjustment.

If it is desired to make a grooving head, the straight cutter should be ¹⁄₁₆ in narrower than the width of the desired groove; the other, being the lip, or scratcher knife, should project slightly beyond the edge of the straight knife, to perform the same function as the lips of an auger bit, which enter the wood ahead of the cutters, to prevent the latter from tearing the grain of the wood.

The points of the lips may be swaged so that only their ends will come in contact with the wood, as friction of the wood against the back of their edges may injure the temper. The form of the bottom cutter may be varied within a wide range of designs, suited to other work than cutting grooves. For instance, one shaped like Fig. 2, used with a lip cutter, will make a good design for a checkered panel, like Fig. 3; or the panel may be carried diagonally over the knives, making diamond-shaped checks, and by using different-shaped knives, the head may be adapted to a number of decorative and constructive uses. If a groove narrower than the thickness of the head is to be cut, the knives will have to be made long enough to cut the depth of the groove before the head reaches the surface of the wood.

Knives may be made in pairs, for molding the edges of shelves, for panel moldings, surface moldings, quarter-rounds, and scotias, as indicated in Fig. 4. One essential in the fitting of each pair is that they balance perfectly, as otherwise it will be impossible to make even fairly smooth work.

The head described is ¾ in. thick, but it may be made as thick as the distance between the collars upon the spindle will permit, and in some cases, the knives may project beyond the sides of the head.

A head of this type, 5 in. wide, if fitted with slotted adjustable knives, will make a satisfactory jointer or molding head, which can be used in many ways. An arrangement of springs, or pressure bars, may be devised which will hold the wood firmly against the knives and reduce the vibration of the wood to a minimum, besides giving added safety to the operator.

## Rack and Case for Sterilizing Shop Goggles

In a shop where the workmen were required to wear safety goggles at

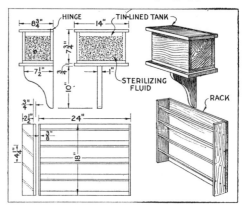

This Sterilizing Tank and Rack were Provided for the Care of Shop Goggles for General Use

various times, a number of pairs were provided for general use. For hygienic reasons these were sterilized before being used again. A tin-lined tank, mounted on a bracket support, contained the sterilizing fluid, and the goggles, after being removed from the fluid, were placed on a rack, made of ⅜-in. wood, as shown.—B. A. Donley, Renovo, Pa.

---

## Comb Used as Ruling Pen

In an emergency a fine-toothed comb will serve as a ruling pen for drawing two or more parallel lines at one operation. Five-lined music scores, cross-section and profile papers, borders for drawings, and various classes of decorative designs can be made with this

device. Bevel slightly the edges of the teeth in contact with the paper, to give straighter edges to the lines. The teeth on one side of the comb, cut down to half length, afford a multiple stylus for making carbon copies.—H. L. Wiley, Portland, Ore.

## Pair of Scissors Used as Envelope Sealer

A useful envelope sealer was made in an emergency, when a large number of envelopes were to be sealed. In an old pair of scissors a small piece of wood was inserted between the blades, as indicated, and the blades bound with electric tape. A string was wound around the top

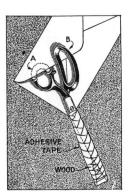

of one of the handles A. The string was moistened and inserted under the right end of the flap, and drawn along, the handle B pressing down the flap and sealing it.—Wilfred Reeves, Toronto, Can.

---

## Tray for Storing Mica Washers without Damage

Mica washers become ruined quickly if kept loosely in a box, or other container, and the tray shown in the sketch was made to care for an assortment of them. The box is 5 by 8 by 10 in. in inside measurements. The washers are placed on dowel rods, mounted in

a ⅞-in. board that is fitted loosely into the box. A long screw hook was fastened at the center of this board so that the assortment may be removed quickly, using the screw eye as a handle.—L. M. Drake, Daytona, Fla.

---

❏ Water made slightly acid with muriatic acid will clean and restore the brightness of gold-leaf gilding; this method is used by sign painters.

## Reinforcing a Light Wooden Triple Arch

I had occasion recently to make a wooden arch for the purpose of decorating with miniature incandescent bulbs. The arch, shaped as shown, was 7 ft. from B to C, with curves of 1¼ by 2-in. material. The standards were of white pine, but the arch itself was of yellow pine, a wood that is somewhat brittle. I secured a lot of thin wood from orange crates, and glued it on the curves with its grain

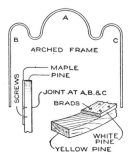

across the yellow pine. Brads were used to hold the strips. To facilitate handling in transportation I divided the arch at A, B, and C. The parts were joined with pieces of maple, secured with screws. This method of strengthening the arch was so effective that I carried it, in a bundle of four sections, a distance of 17 miles on the trolley car and erected it without a split developing.—James M. Kane, Doylestown, Pa.

---

## Erasing Shield Adjustable to Various Lines

The advantage of this erasing shield, which I made for my own use in the drafting room, is that it is adjustable to many shapes of lines, even in intricate drawings. It may be made of thin sheet metal, preferably aluminum,

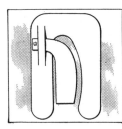

or of celluloid. The central piece is slipped through openings cut in the main portion and is prevented from falling out by a small knob, pressed into the surface at the end.—W. K. Creson, Newcastle, Ind.

## Bracing a Long Droplight Gas Fixture

On a long gas pipe, extending vertically from the ceiling, a brace was found necessary. It was provided by building up a right angle of lighter pipe and fitting it to the main pipe, so that the brace joined it about 4 ft. from the ceiling and extended vertically about 1 ft. from the main pipe. It was fastened to the ceiling with a pipe flange.—M. K. James, Chicago, Ill.

## Lead Form Varies Face of Concrete Blocks

In a homemade wooden form for making concrete blocks of the hollow type, used on porch and column foundations, the faces of the blocks were varied by making the corresponding side of the form a frame with a lead panel. The form was built up in the usual way, of $\frac{7}{8}$-in. wood. The core A was braced with angles, and the outer form B was hinged at two of the corners. The corner at which it opens was provided with catches. The lead face was made of a sheet of lead, $\frac{1}{8}$ in. thick. It was hammered into various forms, each block, or group of several blocks, being made slightly different.

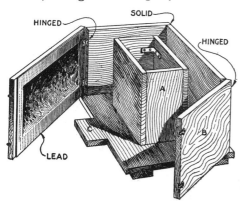

The Lead Panel is Shaped so as to Produce Various Faces on the Concrete Blocks

The cast block is set aside to dry on the base C. A block 8 by 10 by 12 in., with walls $2\frac{1}{2}$ in. thick, is suitable for porch columns.—Fred Quantmeyer, River Vale, N. J.

## Nonwarping Frying Plate for Electric Stove

An electric stove was provided, when purchased, with an aluminum pan, as shown at A. The first time it was used

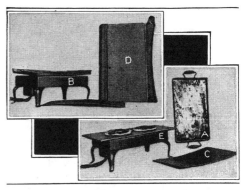

The Cast-Iron Hearth of a Stove Proved to Be Better than an Aluminum Pan and a Sheet-Iron Plate for Making Hot Cakes

for hot cakes it warped diagonally across the middle, as at B. This made cooking with it very slow, and to straighten it so it would not warp seemed impossible.

A piece of No. 20 gauge sheet iron was cut a little larger than the stove, and used as a plate. However, it warped, as at C. The hearth of a discarded wood cookstove was then used. The sides, as shown at D, were sawed off, leaving a cast-iron plate, $\frac{1}{8}$ in. thick. The edges were filed straight and smooth and the top smoothed as much as possible. This plate did not warp and has given satisfaction, as indicated at E.—C. F. J. Charliss, Houston, Tex.

## Directions Painted on Machine Save Cleaning

The floor around the spot where a lever shear was located in a sheet-metal shop, was frequently littered with cuttings. A box was provided for them, but little used. A sign "Put Cuttings in Box," painted in white letters on the lever of the machine, furnished the necessary constant reminder. Thereafter the floor was clean, and the expense of gathering up the scrap was eliminated.

## Padded Compartments in Auto for Small Equipment

Tool compartments, under the seats, in automobiles are usually of rough

A Lining in the Tool Compartment Protects the Contents and Overcomes the Annoyance of Rattling

wood or sheet-iron construction, which exposes their contents, such as curtains, top cover, inner tubes, spark plugs, electric bulbs, tools, and other equipment, to the damaging effect of jostling over the roadways. If a lining of felt, canvas, or carpet is provided, it eliminates this to some extent, and overcomes the annoying rattle of the loose parts. It is a good plan to provide separate compartments in one side for storing inner tubes and electric bulbs.

For those who carry an emergency can of gasoline or oil, a similar covering will protect the container. A convenient foot rest is provided where the emergency can is padded, and then strongly covered.

## Electric Switch Controlled by Hinged Stair Tread

Electric lights in the cellar, or attic, are often left burning by accident, but

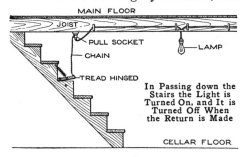

In Passing down the Stairs the Light is Turned On, and It is Turned Off When the Return is Made

by arranging the light to be turned out automatically when a person leaves the

place, no special attention need be given to the light. In the use of such a scheme for a cellar, as shown, a pull socket was fixed to the joist above the stairway. The socket chain was adjusted carefully and fastened to the edge of a hinged tread, kept slightly raised by a spring. Pressure on the tread controls the light socket.—Albert Bourget, Lauzon, Que., Canada.

## Large Grease Gun for Garage or Shop

In a shop or garage the ordinary grease gun is often inefficient, because

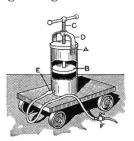

of its small capacity. A portable machine that I made holds 15 lb., sufficient for a large number of cars. The work is also done very quickly with the device, which is mounted on a truck. It was made as follows: An old engine cylinder, A, and piston, B, were fitted with a ¾-in. rod, 14 in. long, C, threaded as shown. A handle was fixed to it, and the yoke D, threaded to engage the rod, was bolted to the cylinder. An outlet was fitted with ½-in. hose, E, and a valve, F, with a nozzle. The nozzle should be long enough to reach the machine parts to be greased, and is made of ⅛-in. pipe. To use the gun, fill the cylinder, screw the piston down tightly and open the valve to the feed desired. —M. R. Landin, Denver, Colo.

## Care of Chamois-Skin Wash Leather

So-called chamois skin, or wash leather, should be wrung out at once after using it in water. Spread the leather out carefully, and hang it up to dry. Hot water makes it harsh. Wash the leather in soapsuds, using a good white soap, and permit some of the suds to remain in it. If properly cared for, a wash leather, used considerably, is better than a new one.

# The Making of an Eye Magnet

## By JOHN D. ADAMS

When one considers the number of accidents to the eye that occur in machine shops and factories from flying chips of iron and steel, it is remarkable that the eye-magnet method of extracting is not more commonly used. It is the purpose of this article, therefore, to describe the construction of a strong eye magnet that may be connected up directly, without any additional resistance, to the ordinary 110-volt alternating-current supply. The device may be made at a cost of about $1.50 for materials.

The sketch shows the essential dimensions. A stiff paper tube is first formed by wrapping a strip of strong paper, about 18 in. long, on a round smooth rod, about 5/8 in. in diameter.

The core is composed of soft-iron wires, neatly packed together and temporarily wrapped with wire near each end to hold them together. Dip the ends in soldering fluid and then in a small pot of melted solder, in which they should be held until the solder works well in among the wires. Before unwrapping, file off the ends, one to a dull point and the other quite sharp.

The temporary core upon which the tube was formed is then mounted on the bench in a pair of blocks, so that it may be turned readily with an improvised crank fastened on the end. The tube is then forced on tightly, after which the winding is begun. This preliminary work will save time, as it is impractical to wind wire by hand, and winding in a lathe is often unavailable for amateurs. Secure the end of the wire to the mandrel; about 1½ lb. of No. 20 wire will be necessary. Wind on the first layer tightly and shellac it. In beginning the second layer pull the wire tightly, and then wind it in the hollows of the first layer. By continuing this method the ends of the coil will build up at an angle of 60 degrees.

To mount the coil, a wooden yoke should be prepared and fitted to match the curve of the coil. In the center of

this, a wooden handle, having a central hole large enough for the usual flexible cord, is fitted and glued into place. A

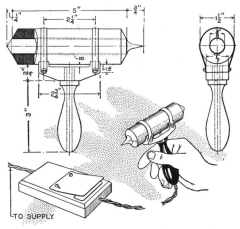

A Powerful Eye Magnet may be Made at a Cost of $1.50 for Materials, and Is Useful in Shops Where There Is Danger from Flying Chips

pair of brass or copper bands are fitted and drilled at each end. Run the flexible cord up through the handle and connect it to the coil, soldering the two joints, after which place the bands in position and tighten the screws.

The floor switch is a block of hardwood, 1 by 3 by 4 in., hollowed out underneath. The spring is made of a wide strip of brass or heavy tin, which is screwed down at one end while the other stands about 1/8 in. above the block. The lower contact is a strip of the same metal, about 1/2 in. wide and screwed down directly below.

## Angle Strengthens Loose Auto Fender

The connection between the fender and running board on an automobile became loose, and caused considerable racket, and in addition the fender became badly distorted. An angle of 1/8-in. sheet steel was riveted below the break. It served as a rigid connection, and was scarcely visible, also making possible the continued use of the old fender.

## Compressed-Air Motor Drill Operates Windlass

In repairing a 500-ft. well, a portion of the casing was dropped to the bottom. Two men were required to turn

A Socket Wrench was Gripped in the Air-Motor Drill and Set on the Windlass Shaft

the crank of a windlass alternately while "fishing" operations for recovery of the section were in progress. The use of the air motor of a drill, as shown, greatly reduced the cost of labor and the time required. The air-motor drill was clamped to the windlass with U-clamps and angle irons. A socket wrench was tapered and slipped into the drill holder. The wrench was put in place over the square end of the windlass crank, operating the windlass at a moderate speed. The air motor may be used similarly for other winding or shaft-driving operations.—C. E. Eurit, Indianapolis, Ind.

## Strike Board for Tamping and Crowning Roadway

A combined template and tamper, used in the laying of a one-course concrete pavement, is shown in the illustration. The street being only 37 ft. from curb to curb, the concrete was placed across the entire width as each

batch came from the mixer. The template conformed to the 8-in. crown, and was constructed of 2 by 12-in. planks, joined to make the implement the required length. Two such sections were bolted together, and the bottom shod with 1/8 by 4-in. steel. A system of trussing supports the template, and a set of plow handles is fitted at each end. This device was handled by two men throughout the entire job of 102,800 square feet.—A. C. Francis, San Diego, Calif.

## Double Ventilator Hood Draws Fumes Away Quickly

If a ventilator over a stove, furnace, or for similar uses, is made with a double hood, the fumes are drawn away more quickly because of the increased draft. The hood is formed like an inverted funnel having a smaller cone of sheet metal fitted inside of it, the lower edges of both being on a level. The inner cone has a small opening at the top, and a space of about 6 in. is allowed between the outer and inner hoods. The draft through this outer ring is considerably increased.—B. J. Ryan, Buffalo, N. Y.

## Sawdust Foundation Levels Floor Linoleum

Occasionally it is desired to lay linoleum on floors, that, by the warping of the boards, have acquired ridges which would be hard on the linoleum. Instead of ruining a plane, and perhaps ruffling one's temper, by attempting to plane down a painted or hardwood surface, it is better to put about 1/2 in. of fine sawdust on the floor, leveling it off with a straightedge and laying the linoleum over it. The sawdust makes the floor level and adds to the resiliency of the linoleum.

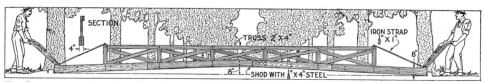

The Concrete was Tamped and the Pavement Crowned in One Operation by the Use of This Strike Board

# Miniature Landscape Built Up of Concrete

### By A. J. VIKEN

AN interesting use of concrete is in the making of models of landscapes, for practical uses as well as for pastime or in scientific work. One of the widest applications of this form of model construction is for display and advertising purposes, where small lakes and picturesque natural effects are desired. The photographs show a miniature landscape which I made principally of reinforced concrete. It measures 20 by 30 in. and is built in a box 5 in. deep. The trees are Japanese air plants. The log cabin is built of matches and toothpicks. Window wire screen was used for fences and bridge railings. In the lake are gold fish, a submarine, a row-

General View of the Rugged Mountain Lake

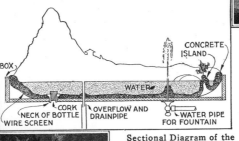

Sectional Diagram of the Construction

The Match and Watch Give a Basis for Comparison with the Cabin

to make the landscape as light as possible. The bottom of the lake was also formed with the aid of wire screen and the concrete put on top of it. After the concrete had dried, the whole landscape was painted in natural colors. The bottom of the lake was given two coats of dark-gray paint, and when thoroughly dry, a coat of paraffin wax was added to make it waterproof, and to prevent the paint from affecting the water. The whole landscape is mounted on a stand like a rectangular mission table.

boat, and a ship. The lower photograph shows the size of the log cabin and people compared with a match and a 16-size watch.

The mountain and hills, as shown in the sectional diagram, were built on a skeleton of iron wire, and wire screen,

## An Artist's Palette Supported by the Easel

Artists and others who sketch out of doors can make good use of a palette which hooks to the easel and is supported by a stick, as shown. The shelf keeps within easy access the several articles of a painter's outfit, while he is working. It eliminates some of the distractions of outdoor work. The hand is free from holding the usual thumb-hole palette, a comfort appreciated

The Artist can Work More Freely When His Materials are Kept on the Palette Shelf, Making a Thumb Palette Unnecessary

especially in hot or cold weather, and in mosquito-infested regions.

The palette consists of shellacked canvas tacked on a wood stretcher. Hooks on the easel and screw eyes on the palette provide a support. The brace is inserted in a slot, and held by a large screw eye.—Phil Bierdemann, Chicago, Ill.

## A Safety Window-Cleaning Seat

In the home, and in many shops or buildings where window washers are not employed and the usual safety de-

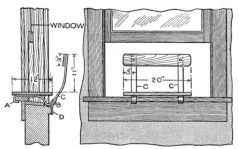

SECTION                    ELEVATION

This Homemade Seat Is Comfortable for Window Washing and Insures Reasonable Safety

vices are not used, a small window-cleaning seat is practical as a safety

measure. One like that shown can be made easily by the home mechanic. It hooks over the window stool, at A, and rests on the sill, at B. The main supports C are of ¼ by 1½-in. band iron, shaped as shown, and riveted to a seat of wood, 12 by 20 in., and braced at the top with a wooden rest, 3 by 20 in. The safety strips D are of ⅛-in. band iron, riveted to the pieces C. The position of these strips should be determined carefully for the windows on which the seat is used. The back rest makes the work of window cleaning easier.

## Hints on the Making and Use of Coil Springs

The experimenter or mechanic often spends time trying out springs that could not possibly do the work expected of them, owing to a lack of knowledge on this important subject. First as to coil springs: Compression springs have open coils and the pressure on each end is toward the center. Tension springs have their coils wound close together; the working pressure on their ends is away from the center. A compression spring of greater strength is made by increasing the size of the wire; making fewer coils per inch of length, or decreasing the outside diameter of the coils.

When this kind of spring is compressed, its outside diameter is slightly increased. Where a spring fits in a hole, this should be allowed for. A given weight will compress a long spring more than a short spring, otherwise of the same dimensions. In building a mechanism with a spring that is to be compressed, see that in the extreme closed position there is room left for the spring itself.

A stronger tension spring is made by increasing the size of the wire, or by decreasing the outside diameter of the coils; and a weaker one by changes in the opposite direction. A compression spring of fair quality may be made from a tension spring by spreading the coils with a screwdriver. The loop on the end of a tension spring can be made, with pliers, from the end of the spring wire. Springs may be coiled from spring wire, brass or steel, or from piano wire. Spring wire comes annealed or tempered; if the former is used, the spring has to be tempered after coiling.—Donald A. Hampson, Middletown, N. Y.

## Homemade Power Hoist for Loading Hay in Barn

Having a gasoline engine for use on the farm, I rigged it up to aid in loading hay into the barn, by building a hoist for it. An ordinary hay carrier, or fork, was used, with the same tackle commonly used with a team in hoisting the hay into the mow. I built a frame of 2 by 4 and 2 by 6-in. lumber, bolting it together strongly, as shown. The check reel from a corn planter was mounted in it as a drum. On the end of the center shaft a drive pulley was mounted and belted to the engine, which was set in the barn on its usual skid. The clutch for checking the hoisting of the load quickly was on the engine. The arrangement proved more

This Hoisting Arrangement was Devised on the Farm for Use with an Engine, in Putting Hay into the Mow

dependable than horses and made it unnecessary to unhitch the team, or to use an extra team for the hoisting.—Ralph A. Page, Urbana, Ill.

⁋A worn broom can be used handily for cleaning corners by cutting it to a sharp point at one side.

## Warning Horn at Sidewalk Garage Door

A garage, situated on a much-traveled street, uses an effective scheme

The Warning Horn Set in the Metal Window Pane Is Effective in Safeguarding Pedestrians

to warn pedestrians on the sidewalks when a car is about to leave the garage. A circular hole was cut in a sheet-metal pane set in one of the sections of a window at the doorway, and a large electric automobile horn was set into it. The mechanism of the horn is supported on a bracket, fixed to the wall. When a car is ready to leave, the employe, who opens the sliding door, touches a push button, sounding the horn. Passers-by "wake up" without fail at the blast, whereas the car horns, sounded inside, cannot be heard readily outside.—John Miller Bonbright, Philadelphia, Pa.

## Cementing Gaps around Machinery Tension Keys

There are usually unsightly gaps around tension keys used to hold together sections of large flywheels, and other heavy machinery parts. If this space is filled with neat cement, a smooth, workmanlike finish is obtained that will not crack nor crumble. After painting it the same color as the machinery, the joint is hardly discernible. The cement can be chipped out when desired.—H. P. Roy, Kansas City, Mo.

## A Drop Plumb Bob of Weighted Tubing

A plumb bob which may be dropped so that its point will indicate a "plumb spot" is handy as a part of the equipment of a home tool chest. An easy way to make a plumb bob of this type is as follows: Cut a piece of ¾-in. bicycle tubing 6 in. long. Turn a piece of steel to fit the bore of the tube and point it for the bottom of the bob. Turn the other end of this plug with several grooves around it, so that when the lead is poured into the tube with a point in place, the grooves are filled with lead. Pour in about 3 oz. of lead, holding the tube perfectly vertical. Turn a metal plug, as shown, for the upper end of the tube. Secure it by a rivet through the tube. It is best to make this plug so that it can be removed and the plumb line knotted through a vertical hole.—J. H. Beebee, Rochester, N. Y.

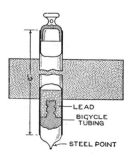

---

## Shelf for Order Books on Auto Dash

A shelf, made from ⅝-in. surfaced stock, painted to match the dash of a delivery, or collector's, automobile, makes an excellent place for order books and the like. The books are always in convenient position; they cannot easily be bounced out of the car and lost, nor thrown on the floor and walked on, becoming soiled and dog-eared. The shelf is set across the dash at an angle, so that the books lie nearly vertical, in a slotlike rest.—Francis W. Nunenmacher, Berkeley, Calif.

## Indicator for Centering Faceplate Work

Some means for accurately locating the center of faceplate work in the lathe is a great convenience to machinists or tool makers. An effective device for this purpose is shown in the sketch. The rod A is of ⅛-in. cold-rolled steel, 12 in. long. One end is turned to 3/32 in., for a length of 1¾ in., and pointed to an included angle of 60°. The other end is filed to a sharp point, and both ends are casehardened. Two 5/16-in. bearing balls, B, are annealed, and drilled 3/32 in. to fit the end. The spring C is made from .020 music wire ⅝ in. long, and wound on a 3/32-in. core. The inner ball is free to slide, while the outer one is fastened to the rod with a pin, the spring separating them.

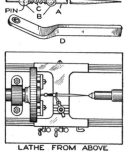

The stock D, for holding the testing bar, is used in a tool holder, and is made of 5/16-in. square cold-rolled steel. A 7/32-in. hole is drilled and chamfered in the flattened end. The view of the lathe as seen from above shows the tester in use. The stock is fastened in the tool holder, the bar A is pushed through the 7/32-in. hole in the flattened end, and the carriage advanced until the 60° end of the bar is in contact with the job. This pushes the loose ball against the spring and holds the end against the work. By starting the lathe and observing the relation of the pointed end to the tailstock center, it is easy to determine how much the piece is off center.—William E. Jewett, Jersey City, N. J.

---

⟪Time may be saved in drafting I-beams, and other duplicate parts, by making a triangle having special angles, or a hole in it, for marking these standard shapes.

# Structural-Steel Sliding Base for Motors and Machinery

By A. L. FENTON

A STRUCTURAL-STEEL sliding sub-base is often convenient for belt-drive electric motors and machinery, and may be arranged substantially as shown in the photograph and detailed in the sketches. These sub-bases are desirable especially where the service is severe, and the belt requires frequent tightening. Provision is usually made on the bases of belt-drive motors to permit take-up for belt tightening, but in some cases the adjustment provided by the manufacturer of the motor is not sufficient. Where a sub-base of the type shown is used, the base can be made long enough so that any reasonable amount of take-up will be provided.

The structural-steel members of the base are I-beams, held together with plates, riveted to their lower flanges, as detailed in Figs. 1 and 2. Holes for the anchor bolts are provided in the plates. Channels may be used instead of I-beams with a decrease in cost, but an I-beam has two flanges as against one for a channel, and hence is capable of being riveted more securely to the

A Substantial Foundation for Motors and Machinery Which Permits of Easy Adjustment or Removal of the Machines

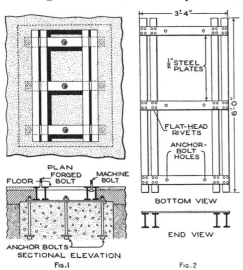

The Frame is Built Up of I-Beams to Which Steel Plates are Riveted

plates, and held more rigidly upon the top of the foundation where it is to be installed.

In installing the structural-steel sub-base, it is mounted on top of the foundation prepared for the motor, as shown in Fig. 1. The height of the foundation should be such that the top faces of the I-beam members will, after the sub-base has been installed, lie flush with the face of the top floor. The surfacing of the floor should be built up close to the sub-base, as indicated in the sectional elevation.

The motor base is bolted to the sub-base by means of bolts set in the slot between the pairs of I-beams, as shown in two forms in Fig. 1. The bolts for this purpose are made as detailed in Fig. 3, or ordinary machine bolts can be used in combination with a casting similar to that shown in Fig. 4. The casting is shaped to fit the I-beam flange, and the head of the bolt is held in a recess, preventing the bolt from turning. The T-bolt is forged by welding a piece of stock of suitable dimensions to the head end of an ordinary machine bolt. The under side of the T-head should be given a 6 to 1 pitch to correspond with the pitch on the flanges of the I-beam, or channel members, in the sub-base, against which it is clamped. The thickness T of the head should be such that the

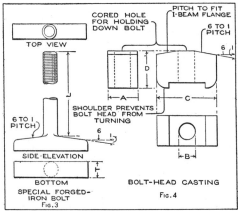

A Forged Bolt with a T-Head, or a Machine Bolt, may be Used to Secure the Machine Bases

bolt can be dropped into the slot between the I-beam members of the sub-base, so that if a bolt breaks, a new one can be substituted, and so that it will not be necessary to place the bolts in the sub-base until all of the rough work involved in building the foundation and setting the sub-base has been completed. The length L of the bolt will be determined by the thickness of the motor base, and by the general proportions of the particular installation.

Where a bolt-head casting, like that of Fig. 4, is to be made, its thickness, A, should always be such that the casting can be inserted in the slot between the I-beams in the sub-base. Hence, these I-beams must be spaced a little farther apart than the thickness T of the head of the forged bolt. The diameter B of the hole should be just large enough to produce a good sliding fit on the bolt. The length C should be about twice the thickness, and the height D proportioned as shown.

### Filing Down a Thin Washer

It is difficult to hold a thin washer in a vise while filing it on the face, and a good method of accomplishing this is to file the washer flat on the bench, or on a block. Drive a nail into the bench

top, or into a block, so that its head is just below the surface of the washer, and place the latter over it. Lay the file flat across the washer, a little to one side of the center. File with a forward stroke only, causing the washer to turn slowly. An even cut will be removed from all parts of the surface.— Walter B. Raynor, Patchogue, N. Y.

### Repairing a Large Reamer

An apprentice drove the expansion screw of an expensive, large hand reamer in too far, causing the reamer to crack, as indicated at A. A satisfactory repair was made by first removing the pin B, separating the shank D and the body. The screw C was then taken out, and a tight push-fit collar, E, was forced on the blades, to hold down the broken ones. The reamer was put on centers in the lathe, and the groove F was ground in. The portion between the new groove and the old one at G was ground down to a diameter slightly smaller than before. A steel bushing, H, was made, the hole in it being .003 to .004 in. smaller than the newly ground part at G. The bushing was heated and shrunk on the reamer, the old groove beside it being made as wide as the original one, at A. The bushing held down the broken blades, and was

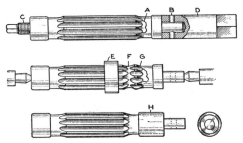

An Expensive; Large Reamer was Saved by Making a Skillful Repair for It

ground down to the size of the shank D. The reamer was then reassembled. —Richard H. Jehlicka, Worcester, Massachusetts.

¶A machine bolt is usually screwed down 2½ times its diameter.

## Shop Bin Economizes Short Lengths of Steel

It is customary in some machine shops to discard short lengths of cold-rolled and machine steel into a box provided for this purpose, and when a sufficient quantity has accumulated to sell it as junk. This frequently results in the throwing away of useful pieces. Particularly when steel is high-priced, care should be exercised to cut down material costs. An economical plan is to provide two bins, one for cold-rolled steel, for the screw-machine operators, etc., and one for the machinery steel. These bins are divided into compartments, 9 in. square and about 3 ft. deep, and their size and number depend on sizes used in the plant. Each compartment is for one size of steel, ranging in length from 6 in. to 3 ft., the smaller lengths only being thrown away as scrap. Time is also saved in finding short lengths for various small jobs.—Joseph Plogmann, Cincinnati, Ohio.

---

## Glass Rod Used as Parallel Ruler

A useful drafting-room tool is a parallel ruler made from a piece of glass tubing or rod, 6 to 8 in. long and about ½ in. in diameter, and two short sections of rubber tubing of a size to fit snugly on the ends of the tubing or rod. The rubber ends keep the glass

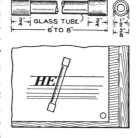

part off the tracing, enabling the ruler to be used over wet ink. The ruler is especially useful in large lettering. It is steadied with the left hand, and rolled to a new position carefully so as not to change its direction.—R. L. Templin, Champaign, Ill.

## Rack Safeguards Surveyor's Instruments

After a floor sweeper had overturned a surveyor's transit set in a corner of

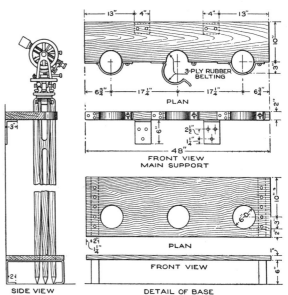

The Expense of Making This Rack was Found a Small Premium on the Assured Safety of Valuable Instruments

an office, causing $35 damages, a rack was designed for it and two other instruments. The top portion serves as a holder for the upper part of the instrument, and the lower fixture keeps the tripod legs from spreading, as detailed.

In placing the instrument in the holder, the legs are first folded together and placed in the lower fixture. The hinged piece of the upper holder is swung out, the instrument set in place, and the hinged piece closed, and padlocked, if desired.—Roy H. Poston, Flat River, Mo.

---

## Bushing in Handle of Soldering Iron

The constant heating and using of soldering irons causes the handle to become loose, making it difficult to do close work. In this case, remove the handle and insert a bushing of heavy tin, where the shank enters the wood. This holds the handle firmly, and keeps it from burning.—Stanley Radcliffe, Laurel, Md.

## Machine Clamps Made from Hexagon Nuts

I made a set of hexagon clamps which are strong and useful for many kinds of small work, by fitting 1-in. cold-pressed nuts with thumbscrews, as shown in the sketch. One side of the nut is cut away and

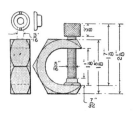

a $\frac{5}{16}$-in. knurled thumbscrew, provided with an adjustable cap at its lower end, is fitted to it, as shown. These clamps may be laid flat on work and can be used like parallel clamps in many cases.—J. Harger, Honolulu, Hawaiian Islands.

## Fans on Machine Shafting Cool Workman

Lacking an electric, or other common power fan, an ingenious workman in a machine shop attached two ordinary paper hand fans to the line shafting, securing them with cord, as

shown. The result was a rather unique fan, which cooled him at his machine, nearly as well as the boss's elegant brass fan cooled him, in his private office.—M. J. Doyle, Cleveland, O.

## Skimmer for Removing Slag from Molten Metal

In using molten lead or other metal, especially in the workshop where it is gathered in many small pieces, it is important that the slag be skimmed off carefully. A handy tool for this purpose was

made by hammering a piece of iron rod out to the shape shown in the sketch, the small end serving as a handle, and the rounded edge of the skimming end fitting against the curve of the ladle in which the metal is melted.—E. K. Marshall, Oak Park, Ill.

## Device for Wrapping Small Articles of Uniform Size

A block for wrapping small articles, such as typewriter ribbons, in tin foil,

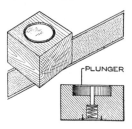

can be made from wood with metal fittings, as indicated. The hole in the top is cut $\frac{1}{16}$ in. larger than the width of the article to be wrapped. The foil is laid on the top of the block, then the article is pressed down, and the foil drawn from the sides and pressed with the palms of the hand. When released the article rises above the top, so that it can be handled easily. Articles wrapped in this form are neater and more uniform than when wrapped by hand. The shape of the hole in the block can be varied to suit special needs.—A. H. Hale, Brooklyn, N. Y.

## Reaming a Bushing or Collar without Reamer

To enlarge a bushing properly, where a reamer is not obtainable, take

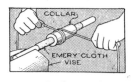

a round rod, or a piece of wood, somewhat smaller than the bushing; wrap emery cloth around the rod and place one end in a vise. Place the bushing over the emery cloth. By coiling a cord twice around the bushing, and pulling on the ends of the cord, first one, then the other, the bushing is dressed to a perfect fit. In reaming a bushing by this method, for piston pins, etc., it should be made to fit rather loosely, because of the tendency to tighten when in place.—J. W. Reynolds, Mason, Ill.

## Saving Overall Buttons That Pull Through

The buttons used on mechanics' overalls and jumpers sometimes pull out. Examine the buttons used; if in the center two bent wires hold on the button, they can be sewed on again. With a pair of cutting pliers cut off the rivet head of the button that pulled through the cloth; remove the wires from the center of the button, and it may then be sewed on. If it is the type of button that shows a round rivet-head center, it cannot be so used again. Keeping these buttons saves hunting up other suitable ones.—John Hoeck, Alameda, Calif.

## Incandescent Lamps Used in Stereopticon Lanterns

The electric arc lamp has been used to a great extent in stereopticons and moving-picture apparatus, where an intense light is essential. However, the newer high-candlepower incandescent nitrogen lamp, from 300 to 1,000 watts,

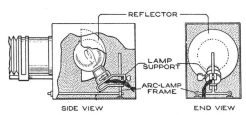

SIDE VIEW          END VIEW

The High-Power Nitrogen Filament Lamp Is Safe and Efficient for Use in Stereopticon Lanterns

provides a satisfactory substitute for the arc lamp. The former requires little attention, and is more economical of current. It is also safer than the arc lamp, and is easily adapted to stereopticon equipment.

A special support of $\frac{1}{8}$-in. sheet iron is provided for the arc lamp, as shown, and is clamped on the vertical rod. A 300-watt lamp is satisfactory for small stereopticons, and the 500-watt size for larger ones. Round-bulb lamps are used, and a reflector, placed behind the lamp, increases the light efficiency. The old housing and lamps are used.—E. A. Binney, St. Louis, Mo.

## Valve and Stand for Inflating Tires Quickly

Much time is spent in inflating tires in automobile factories and garages, and the device described reduces this opera-

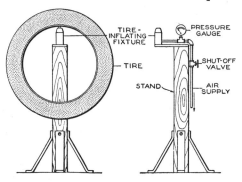

Fig. 1

The Tire is Inflated After It is Mounted on the Rim, and Before the Rim is Placed on the Wheel

tion to a minimum. The tire is inflated after it has been placed on the rim, and before the latter is placed on the wheel. A stand is used, as shown in Fig. 1, and a special valve is arranged on the tire-inflating fixture. This is shown in the detail sketch. The weight of the tire and rim presses down the plunger, which bears, at its lower end, on a ball and a spring, controlling the air at the inlet. The air passes around the spring and the ball and up into the tire valve. A pressure gauge and a shut-off valve

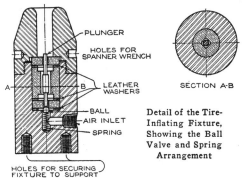

Detail of the Tire-Inflating Fixture, Showing the Ball Valve and Spring Arrangement

are provided in the air line, so that the air may be regulated easily.—William J. Outcalt, Detroit, Mich.

⊄A piece of tin, fixed to the lower edge of an ax handle at the head, saves wear.

## Barrel Sprinkler for Oiling Roadway

In summer, the suburbanite is often confronted with dusty driveways and walks that are easily improved with a

Occasional Oiling of Roadways with a Homemade Sprinkler will Keep Down Dust around the Home

homemade oil sprinkler, like that shown. A steel frame, mounted on wheels, was rigged up to hold an ordinary oil barrel. Inserted in the bung is a short piece of pipe equipped with a shut-off. To this is attached the sprinkling pipe, having perforations, about 1½ in. apart, of sufficient size to allow the oil to flow freely. The cart may be drawn, or pushed, the latter being more convenient, discarded shoes being worn, and a thin layer only applied.—J. C. Grindell, St. Louis, Mo.

### A Solderless Extension Drill Rod

In using an extension drill, a common practice is to sweat the shank of the drill into a brass tube, or a rod bored

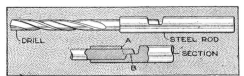

The Drill is Held in the Extension Rod by the Shoulder Joint

out. This process fixes the drill more or less permanently in the rod or tube, and requires special heating for the soldering. By making a special drill rod with a simple chuck arrangement, as detailed in the sketch, it is unnecessary to solder the drill into place. The end of the drill rod is bored out to receive the drill, and a groove, A, is filed across the rod and into the drilled hole. This provides a small, slightly beveled shoulder, B, which grips a corresponding shoulder on the end of the drill. The fastening is very strong if carefully made, and the drill can be quickly removed.—V. Arkin, Chicago, Illinois.

### Hidden Screw Rivets for Woodwork

When one has done a fine bit of gluing, as on the neck of a violin, some not unsightly reinforcement is often desirable. I proceeded in the following manner in making such a repair: Using No. 17 brass escutcheon pins of a suitable length, I cut off the heads, and gripped the

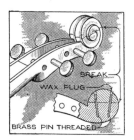

pins in the chuck of a small hand drill, and threaded them. Taking another light hand drill, and with a drill about two sizes smaller than the pin, I bored through the glued parts as many holes as were necessary. I cut off the point of the pin, and, with it still in the hand drill, screwed it into the hole. To hide the screw pins, I cut them off on the top side and dressed it smooth. Carefully pricking a center mark, and taking a drill the size of the brass wire, I drilled out a little of the end. By waxing these holes and staining the spots properly I had a strong and neat job.—L. M. Drake, Daytona, Fla.

❡A bearing for moderate speeds and light duties should be of a length at least two diameters of the shafting. High-speed shafts should have bearings of a length four times the diameter of the shaft.

# A Direct-Reading Lever Micrometer

By H. L. WILEY

THICKNESSES of paper, sheet metals, rubber and cloth fabrics, wire, and similar materials, can be read directly to .0001 in. with this lever mi-

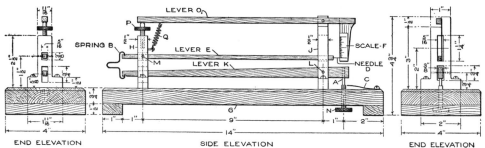

When the Operator becomes Accustomed to This Homemade Lever Micrometer, He can Read to Minute Accuracy with It

crometer. It can be operated much more rapidly than a screw micrometer of the usual type, over 30 readings per minute being possible after a few minutes' practice. To operate the micrometer, the anvil A is raised by placing the finger lightly upon the spring link B, the object to be measured being guided to its position under the anvil by means of the guide spring C. When the object is between the jaws of the micrometer, the spring link B is released, and the needle D, at the small end of the lever E, immediately indicates the thickness of the object upon the scale F. Upon the base G are mounted two supports, H and J, through which run the levers K and E. These levers, K and E, work respectively on the pins L and M. The upper anvil A is set into the end of the lever K, and forms a contact with the lower anvil, which is the end of the screw N. The small end of lever K is connected to lever E by means of the spring link B, which is made out of a piece of clock spring, or other thin, flat spring steel. The small end of the lever E terminates in a fine needle, working close to the scale F. This scale is carried on the end of lever O.

Base, supports, and levers are made of cedar, or other light-weight wood, as the machine is delicate in its action, and superfluous weight in the moving parts, especially in lever E, should be avoided. The levers K and E are car-

ried on fine needles thrust through them at points M and L. The levers work through slots cut in the supports H and J. To keep the levers from touching the sides of the slots in the supports, washers, or fillers of fine glass beads, can be used on both sides of the levers.

The scale F is 1 in. long, graduated to hundredths of an inch. If desirable, a reading glass can be mounted on support J, directly focused upon the scale. With the upper and lower anvil jaws in contact, the reading on the scale should be zero. If such is not the case, adjustment is made by means of the screws N and P. Both of these screws work directly in the wood. In placing them, holes, slightly less in diameter than the screws, are drilled into the support H, at the top of which is located the screw P, and into the base G, through which passes the screw N. The coarse adjustment, by means of which the indicator needle D is brought within .01 in. of the zero line on the lower end of the scale F, is made with the screw N. The finer adjustment is made with the screw P. The lever O is held lightly against the screw P by means of the small coil spring Q.

This machine is accurate, by close observations, to .00001 in. and will stand considerable hard use without requiring adjustment. As soon as the operator becomes accustomed to its use he can read to $\frac{1}{50,000}$ part of an inch without difficulty. The machine will indicate the thickness of a pencil mark on paper.

## Tool for Soldering Automobile Radiators

An attachment made in the shop to be used with a common gas-and-air torch is the best arrangement for soldering auto-mobile radiators I have ever used. When the leak occurs in the cells of a honey-comb radiator, little difficulty is experienced in soldering it. A tube radiator can also be soldered, without moving the webbing.

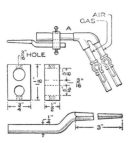

The soldering iron is made of ¼-in. round-iron stock, bent as shown in the sketch, ground square and slightly tapering from the curve to the point. The length of the iron depends on the depth of the place to be soldered, 3 in. being practical. The torch unscrews at A, allowing the device to be slipped on through the ⅜-in. hole in the clamp, provided with setscrews.— Charles G. Moon, Des Moines, Ia.

## Boxes for Small Hardware Display Contents

A convenient way to keep nails, screws, and other small parts, is to place them in tin boxes of uniform size, which may be stacked without the use of shelving. It is desirable to mark the boxes so that the con-tents may be identified easily. A good way to do this is to make a depres-sion in the top or front of the box, large enough for one of the articles contained. The sketch shows how a screw was fastened in the top of the box. The part A was bent to hold the head, and the part B ham-mered in.—H. K., West Nyack, N. Y.

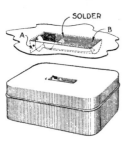

## Washer Holds Bolt from Turning in Clamping Grooves

To keep the head of a bolt from turn-ing in the clamping grooves of a planer, miller, or other shop machine, on which machine parts are bolted down while in process, take a washer of the same size hole as the bolt diameter, and turn over two opposite edges of it so that the head of the bolt fits between them. Then slip the washer under the head of the bolt, so that it rests in the clamping groove, almost as a part of the bolt head. This takes up the looseness.—J. Fast, Denver, Colo.

## Preventing Rapid Wear on Horseshoe Calks

An efficient method of fixing a horseshoe calk so it will stay sharp is to have the blacksmith split the toe calk lengthwise and insert a strip of steel cut from a worn-out mow-ing-machine knife. This is done after the calk is welded to the shoe. The inserted strip of steel, ready for welding, is shown at A, and the calk with the strip of steel welded in place, at B. The hard steel will not wear away as fast as the softer part of the calk, hence the calk wears in a V-shape, remaining comparatively sharp.—Clarence H. Green, Columbus, Ohio.

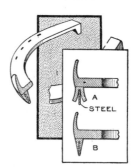

## Toothed End Prevents Screwdriver from Slipping

The troublesome slipping of an auto-matic screwdriver, often experienced when driving is unusually light or hard, can be avoided by filing small teeth in the edge of the blade. About 24 teeth to the inch, or about seven teeth to a medium blade, is suitable, and they should be kept sharp as saw teeth.

## Handy Plier Vise Used on Piston Rings

An effective method of securing additional usefulness from an ordinary combination adjustable plier, is to drill two elongated holes through the handles, inserting a $\frac{3}{16}$ by 3-in. screw or stove bolt, as shown. A thumb nut controls the adjustment, providing a hand vise that is useful for light work. A C-clamp fastens the plier quickly on an automobile running board, for roadside repairs.

One of the many novel uses to which the vise may be applied is as an aid in a one-man method of inserting pistons in the cylinders of a gas engine. A wire band of the diameter of the piston is made, as shown, with loops at the ends for the nose of the plier. The vise in position, as indicated, compresses the piston ring and holds it clamped until the piston is slid forward into the cylinder. The end of one handle of the plier is forged and filed into a convenient automobile-

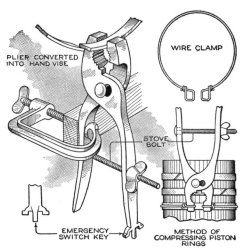

The Automobilist and Mechanic can Make Better Use of a Plier by Applying These Simple Kinks

starting switch key, which cannot easily be mislaid.—George A. Luers, Washington, D. C.

---

¶A few drops of oil applied to the joints of a folding rule greatly facilitate its use.

## Emergency Sash for Railroad-Car Doors

Window sashes are frequently broken on railroad coaches, and it has been

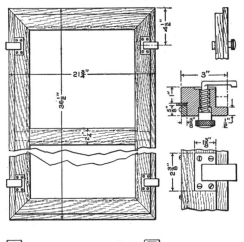

This Emergency Sash was Designed for Use on Railroad Coaches

found desirable to have emergency sashes on hand at the repair shops of divisions. The sketch shows the detailed construction of such a sash that can be installed in a few minutes. The glass is held in a wooden frame which is locked in place by means of four catches. The latter are shown in detail in the sketches at the right. The catch consists of a brass fitting, cast with an angle plate at one end and a round rod at right angles to it. The rod is machined and fitted to a plate fixed to the sash. A spring acting against a knurled knob, sliding over the end of the rod, draws the angle end firmly against the window casing.—John W. Shank, Renovo, Pa.

---

## Boiler-Furnace Stokers' Inspection Glass

A piece of blue glass, about 4 in. square, mounted in a small frame having a handle, is useful for stokers in examining the condition of the fires in large boiler furnaces, which require close and repeated inspection to maintain efficiency.

## Self-Opening Garage Door

It is often annoying, especially in rainy or winter weather, to get out of an automobile at the garage in order

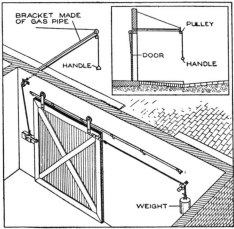

The Driver of the Car Pulls on the Handle, Releasing the Catch, and the Door Opens Automatically

to open the door. Customers at a public garage usually toot their horns until the door is opened, and in order to make this unnecessary I built a self-opening arrangement for the garage door. The auto driver pulls on the handle suspended in front of the door, releasing the door catch. The door is then automatically opened by the counterweight. The garage attendant can easily close the door, and adjust the catch for the next patron. This device is also handy on private garages. A section of gas pipe, braced with strong wire, was used to support the pulley and the unlocking cord.—R. S. Matzen, Fort Collins, Colo.

## Hammering Tightens Worn Brass Thumb Nuts

When brass thumb nuts used on drawing instruments, and for similar purposes, become worn, they may be tightened by hammering them slightly to make the threaded hole smaller. Place the nut on a metal plate and strike it a level blow with a hammer. Try the nut in its original position, and repeat the hammering until a tight fit results. —E. C. Griess, Grand Forks, N. D.

## Shop Device for Addition of Fractions

Draftsmen, machinists, and many other mechanics, will find the home-made instrument shown in the sketch almost indispensable after giving it a trial. A disk, A, of heavy white cardboard or opaque celluloid, is graduated as indicated. A smaller transparent disk of celluloid, with small holes drilled in it to correspond to the graduations on the disk A, is riveted to the latter, at C, permitting the disks to turn. The arrow is scribed on disk B.

To add two fractions, such as $\frac{5}{16}$ and $\frac{7}{32}$, set B so that the arrow is at 1, place a pointed, pencillike stick in the hole in the arrowhead and turn this disk until the arrow is at the fraction $\frac{5}{16}$; then place the stick in the hole now opposite 1, and turn B until the stick is at $\frac{7}{32}$. The arrow will then be at $\frac{17}{32}$, which is the sum of the two fractions. This process may be carried on indefinitely, and each time the arrow passes the unit graduation, 1 is added to the sum. To subtract two fractions the operation is reversed. The arrow is placed at the larger fraction; the stick is placed in the hole opposite the smaller one, and disk B is turned back to 1. The arrow will then be found to point to the difference of the two. Disk A may be graduated to suit the uses

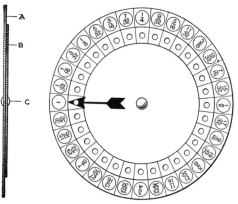

Much Time is Saved and Errors Minimized by the Use of This Handy Adding and Subtracting Device

for which it is intended, and decimal equivalents to the fractions placed underneath them.—James F. Boyd, Detroit, Mich.

## Rapid and Accurate Repair of Broken Tapeline

When the only available steel tapeline on a job broke it was necessary to make a repair immediately. A piece, about 1 in. long, was broken out and it was replaced and a good joint made as follows: A piece of steel was cut from an old stovepipe, to the same width as the tape and 3 in. long. It was marked carefully to correspond to the broken part, and riveted into place with ordinary carpet tacks, cut down to the proper length.—P. A. Midland, New York, N. Y.

## Removing Dents from Auto Fenders or Sheet Metal

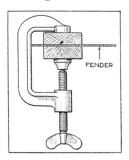

A simple and effective means of removing dents from automobile fenders or sheet metal is to clamp the damaged part between two wooden blocks, as shown in the illustration. An iron cabinetmaker's clamp is best suited for this purpose, but various other means of applying pressure may be used. Where the damage is considerable, this method will, of course, restore the surfaces only partly.—Arthur E. Miller, Evansville, Ind.

## Cushion-Seat Folding Stool of Metal

This compactly folding stool was made of high-grade materials shaped by the use of a forge. If softer metal is used the parts may be bent cold. Strap iron, $\frac{3}{16}$ in. thick, was used for the pieces A and B. The brace C is a bolt. The pieces D and E are made to snap together, the shoulders on the ends of each checking the motion of the other. The upper supports are made similarly of $\frac{5}{16}$-in. cold-rolled steel. The rigidity of the stool depends on the care with which these parts are made and fitted. The padded top is built up around a wooden frame, one of the upper supports being hinged to it, as shown in the bottom view.

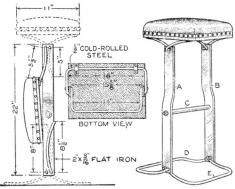

The Upper and Lower Supports Brace Each Other, and the Stool can be Folded Compactly

The method of folding the stool is indicated at the left.—Hubert Kann, Pittsburgh, Pa.

## Repairing Broken Teeth in Fiber or Paper Gears

A repair of broken teeth in gear wheels made from fiber or compressed paper, by replacing the broken teeth with lead reinforced by screws, proved satisfactory. The broken tooth stub was dressed down with a file, and holes for machine screws were drilled as indicated in the sectional views. The bolts were given a brushing with soldering acid, and the tooth was built up on them, with solder and a soldering copper. After roughing in the tooth, it was finished with a file. The heads of

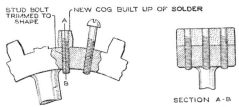

The Broken Teeth were Replaced by Building Up New Ones of Solder around Machine Screws

the bolts were cut off flush with the curved surface of the gear. Such a repair, properly made, will last practically as long as the other teeth.—Logan E. Anderson, Cove, Ore

## Spider for Cutting Large Pipe in Lathe

A machinist in our shop, having to turn out a lot of 8-in. pipe for coup-

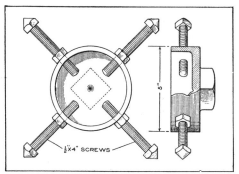

The Work was Turned Out in Record Time with This Tool

lings, had no tool large enough to center the pipe in the lathe. He obtained a 5-in. plug and drilled four holes in it, and tapped them out for ½-in. screws, as shown. Taking four ½ by 4-in. machine screws, he ground the heads to a point, leaving just enough to put a wrench on. He fitted four locknuts to the screws, and put them in place. The tool is inserted into the end of the pipe, adjusted, and centered, and the locknuts tightened up. The other end of the pipe fits into the chuck of the lathe.—Charles K. McCluskey, Wheeling, W. Va.

## Holder for Wood-Turning Tools

Instead of having handles for each wood-turning tool, a mechanic made a

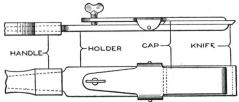

This Holder Provides for a Number of Knives or Bits for Wood Turning, with a Single Handle

simple holder which makes it necessary to have only a single handle and a number of bits, which are inserted as required. The bits, or knives, are thin, making it easier to grind them to

various shapes. The detailed construction of the holder is shown in the sketch. A sheet-metal clamp is pivoted over the main support of the holder and clamps the knife by means of the thumbscrew.—M. E. Duggan, Kenosha, Wisconsin.

## Copper Covering Transmits Heat to Auto Intake Manifold

A practical means of heating the intake manifold of an automobile from the hot exhaust manifold, to increase the efficiency, is to cover the entire intake manifold, and part of the exhaust manifold, with No. 20 gauge copper, bending well around each, and making it meet in the rear of the intake manifold. This copper plate is held in place

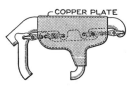

by boring holes through it to correspond to the bolts on the engine block, slipping it over these bolts, and then setting the pipe clamps in place, tightening them with the nuts, as usual. The copper plate conducts the heat from the hot exhaust manifold to the intake manifold. After running the engine 10 minutes, the intake manifold becomes so hot that the hand cannot be held safely on it, thus preheating the gas, and making it more combustible.— Charles A. Pettit, Rossville, Md.

## Ropes Fed through Floor from Basement Stock Room

Coils of different-sized rope lying around the main floor of a hardware store look untidy, to say nothing of the valuable floor space they occupy and the dust they collect. A good way to do away with this nuisance is to place the coils in the basement on a shelf, bore holes in the floor for the different sizes, and pull the rope through, as required. A single loose knot will prevent the rope from sliding back. A measuring scale is laid out from the hole, the rope being pulled out and measured off in one operation.

### Filing Cork in a Lathe

Cork cannot be turned in a lathe in the usual manner, but can be cut down quickly by filing it, much as metal spindles are finished in a speed lathe. A coarse file, preferably of the type used for filing wood, is used for the roughing out. Special care must be taken that the file is applied only on the forward or cutting stroke. If the cork is of a fairly solid texture, it can be worked quite smoothly. To finish the surface, apply a fine file, gradually applying greater pressure. To give the cork a polished surface, burnish it with a smooth piece of steel.

### Beveled Piston Ring Overcomes Excess Oil in Cylinders

Many automobile and similar motors have a tendency to pump oil into the compression chamber, which causes rapid accumulation of carbon. I have found the first cylinder usually the worst. After some experimenting I filed off the lower, outer corner of the piston ring at the bottom of the piston, beveling it slightly. The ring was replaced in its normal position, and reduced the pumping of oil. The opening around the corner of the ring prevents the oil from being sucked up into the cylinder. When a piston fitted quite loosely, an oversized piston was substituted with very good results, the lower ring being beveled as described.
—J. W. Reynolds, Mason, Ill.

### Remover and Wall Receptacle for Bottle Caps

In a store, or other place, where drinks or bottled goods are sold in bottles having metal caps, a convenient way to remove the caps and prevent them from falling on the floor is to install an arrangement like that detailed in the sketch. The caps are removed quickly by means of the small device fastened to the wall, and dropped into a chute and a box made of cigar-box or other thin wood. The box is suspended on screws and can be quickly

removed and emptied. The cap remover, as detailed, is made of a strip of galvanized sheet iron, bent over a

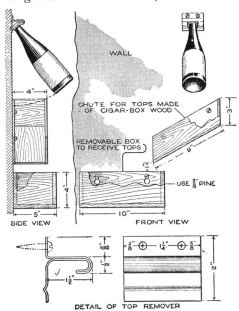

The Bottle Caps are Quickly Removed and Dropped into the Receptacle, Avoiding the Danger of the Slippery Caps on the Floor

½-in. pipe held in a vise. It is fastened with screws.—P. P. Avery, Garfield, New Jersey.

### Belt Guard Pivoted for Easy Removal

A belt guard on some machines, while desirable for safety, is considered a necessary evil, especially when it interferes with making quick adjustments of parts of the machine, which it makes inaccessible. A swinging guard that can be moved out of the way in an instant is shown in the sketch. It is supported by a pipe column, which may extend from the floor to the ceiling, if desired.—J. J. O'Brien, Buffalo, N. Y.

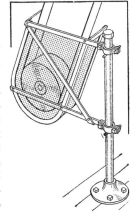

# Suggestions on the Care of Automobiles and Motorboats

### By HAYES BIGELOW

INEXPERIENCED automobile and motorboat owners may find the following suggestions helpful: Almost all nuts, bolts, and screws have right-hand threads. They tighten as the hands of a watch turn, and loosen in the reverse direction. If a nut or bolt fails to turn on applying moderate pressure, remove the wrench, and tap the part firmly, several times, with a hammer. By using wrench and hammer alternately, almost any "frozen" nut or bolt may be started. With slotted screws, tap on the head of the screwdriver with a block. When the screwdriver shaft is square a wrench or pliers used.

The application of oil, or, in some cases, heating the surrounding metal, facilitates the work. Be sure the wrench fits snugly, and does not cause burrs. Left-hand threaded nuts are usually placed on axles, or other bearings, where the motion might tend to remove a right-hand threaded nut. Propeller-shaft stuffing boxes in boats may have left-hand threads. A left-hand thread loosens as a right-hand thread tightens, and vice versa.

Graphite, No. 1 or finer, is often useful. Mixed with oil or grease and applied to threads, it prevents sticking, and is particularly useful in making up pipe joints and union nuts which will be subjected to heat. Candle wicking, rubbed full of grease and graphite, makes a good packing for propeller-shaft stuffing boxes, setting up little friction—a good point to remember when dealing with a hard-starting, two-cycle engine not equipped with a clutch. Plain graphite, thoroughly rubbed over wheel rims, tends to prevent rusting.

Shellac is not dissolved by gasoline. Always use shellac on the threads of gasoline connections. Gasoline-supply tubing sometimes develops leaks suddenly; a cloth soaked in shellac provides a temporary repair when wrapped around the leaky pipe. Tire tape will not hold gasoline long unless shellacked. Soap is a fair substitute when shellac is not at hand. Gasoline cuts the oil in white and red lead, and many kinds of varnish.

Storage batteries need distilled water frequently, and lack of water ruins them. Some cells lose water more rapidly than others in the same battery. Sulphuric acid weakens slowly, and should never be introduced into the cells except by an expert. Acid fumes rise from the cells, and if given a chance to work on battery connections, will cause corrosion, which may put a self-starter, operated from the battery, out of commission. All connections should be bright, and assembled with vaseline, which is impervious to acid fumes. Corroded bolts and lead-cased nuts can be cleaned by boiling them in a solution of cooking soda and water. Such connections, if corroded, are likely to stick very tight, and can best be loosened by applying a pair of hot tongs to the nut before attempting to twist it.

If the self-starter operates sluggishly, run it 30 seconds and then feel its battery and line connections. If a connection is warm, its contact is either loose or corroded, and the full current is not able to pass through it. Generator armatures should be clean and not sticky, and the brushes free and smooth.

Blue smoke pouring from the exhaust indicates too much cylinder oil, and this condition produces carbon trouble. Only a stiff, new engine justifies the use of much oil, and even then the smoke should be a trail rather than a cloud. Black smoke indicates too much gasoline in the carburetor mixture, and will result in sooted and irregular sparking plugs. If the engine chokes and emits black smoke when suddenly given more throttle, the carburetor is usually at fault, and it is best to consult an expert carburetor adjuster.

When descending steep hills, shift into middle or low speed, cut out the spark, and let the car operate the engine, as much brake wear is thus avoided. With practice it is possible to see reasonably well around a corner. Show windows frequently afford reflections of the side street.

On motorboats, carry adequate life-saving apparatus at all times when the craft is in commission. Even though willing to assume a dangerous risk, it is well to remember the government requirements, and that inspectors are paid to guard boat owners from their own recklessness in disregarding dangers.

Have at hand in the automobile, or motorboat, the following items of equipment: Shellac, tire tape, graphite, rubber and asbestos packing, cotton wicking, waste, overalls, hand soap, towel, dry-battery tester, extra spark plugs, matches, and a trouble lamp. Lastly, know the rights on the water or the road, use caution, and have consideration for the "other fellow." Happily, friendliness and rendering of assistance are quite common among drivers of gasoline motors on the road as well as on water.

### Temporary Pump for Cooling a Gas-Engine Water Jacket

A pumping engine for flooding a cranberry bog at a critical time was put out of commission by the breaking down of the circulating pump supplying the water jacket. The owner devised a substitute as follows: Two barrel heads were nailed together so the beveled edges formed a grooved pulley wheel, as shown. The pulley was then mounted on a pipe shaft in a wooden framework, and lined up with one end of the engine flywheel shaft. The belt was a piece of spliced rope.

A pitcher pump outside the engine house was driven down, as indicated, opposite the wooden pulley, and a wooden arm was bolted to the pulley. The upper end of the arms was slotted to fit the pump handle, this arrangement giving a 2-in. stroke to the pump.

The old circulation pump was disconnected, and the water pumped was

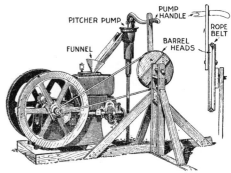

This Emergency Water Supply for a Gas-Engine Water Jacket Proved Serviceable for Several Months

conducted to the engine by means of a trough.—L. B. Robbins, Harwich, Massachusetts.

### Roller-Bearing Reel for Electrical or Other Wire

To replace cumbersome horizontal-drum wire reels on his various jobs, an electrical contractor designed the reel shown. It feeds out the wire in various directions without jamming. The framework is a wooden cross, and rods serve as a drum for the wire coil. Casters are provided to operate on a disk of heavy sheet iron, bolted to a wooden foundation. The reel is held

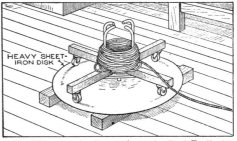

The Wire may be Drawn from the Reel Easily in Various Directions

in position by a long bolt, and is free to turn. The coil is placed in position quickly, and the device is readily portable.

¶A pocket in the front cover of a schoolbook is convenient for carrying notes and papers.

## Artist's Cabinet Made from Old Sideboard

The great miscellany of material, tools, paper, sketches, etc., with which

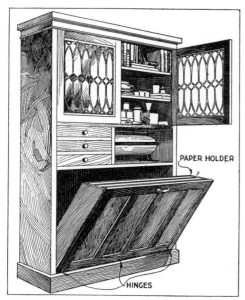

Instead of Using Various Makeshifts, an Artist Rebuilt This Cupboard to Suit His Special Needs

an artist works were cared for economically by providing a cabinet for them, which was adapted from an old sideboard, or china cabinet. Adjustable shelves were fitted into the upper cupboard for books, tools, etc. Three shallow drawers were built into the center section, which was an open shelf. At the right of this shelf a roll of paper was mounted in a holder. The lower section was provided with a hinged door to which the cupboards for mats, paper, etc., were fixed.—John T. Bowe, Chicago, Ill.

## Hand Tool for Making Mortise-and-Tenon Joints

One of the chief causes of failure in home woodworking by intelligent, though inexperienced, persons is lack of knowledge in the proper use of chisels in making joints, particularly the common mortise-and-tenon variety. This joint must be exact in its con-

struction or it is almost worthless. Having to build with the aid of inexperienced helpers, several pieces of furniture in which were many mortise-and-tenon joints, to be made by hand, I made a device that did the work rapidly and accurately.

First, I had made two tools, A and B, of ½-in. tool steel, grinding them carefully. Tool holders of maple, as detailed, were made, the screws D preventing splitting, when the wing screw, which holds the cutter, is tightened. The 1½-in. hole is an outlet for chips. The various steps in making a mortise and tenon with this router are: First, saw and chisel for the tenons, as detailed, leaving strips E as bearings for the router and removing them later. Trim both sides of the tenon at one setting of the tool.

To make the mortise, use the tools as shown. The two tools make it possible to cut both sides of the mortise from the same side of the piece. Make all of the similar cuts with one setting of each of the tools, using a chisel for

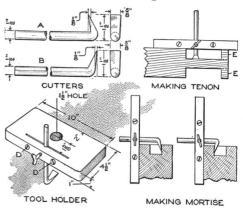

By the Use of This Homemade Router Mortises and Tenons were Cut Quickly and Accurately by Inexperienced Workers

preliminary work, as usual, to within a scant $\frac{1}{16}$ in. of the lines.—D. D. Gurnee, Hempstead, N. Y.

❡Indicators having a metal point require a specially coated paper of good quality. Apply a thin coating of this mixture, by weight: 1 part zinc oxide, 4 parts water, $\frac{1}{10}$ part gum arabic. Permit it to dry thoroughly.

# Shop Notes

## A Submarine Chase in a Display Window

### By HARRY MARCELLE

DIPPING in the waves, now submerging, only to reappear and continue the pursuit of the giant liner tossing on a choppy sea, a daring submarine holds the attention of spectators before a novel window display, depicting "Somewhere off the Irish Coast." The endless water stretches out in the background, and the chase continues while the faithful electric motor keeps the "wheels going round." The rolling cardboard waves, and the pitching vessels on the ever-changing scene, produce the effect of a ship attempting desperately to elude its submarine enemy.

A painted background of a marine view, in water colors, or flat oil colors, is set up behind the display. The waves are painted on heavy cardboard, or better still, beaver or compo board, 18 in.

wide, and of a length to suit the size of the window. A strip, 2 in. by ¾ in., extends along the bottom of each wave, holding it in an upright position, and forming a base for the wave, when riding on the cams, as shown in detail. Five waves are shown in the illustration, Fig. 1. A stationary one is in the front of the window, to hide the mechanism, which is 2 ft. in width. The other four travel on the cams, mounted

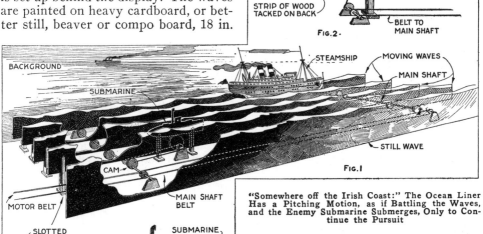

FIG. 2.

STRIP OF WOOD TACKED ON BACK

BELT TO MAIN SHAFT

BACKGROUND

STEAMSHIP

MOVING WAVES

MAIN SHAFT

SUBMARINE

STILL WAVE

CAM

FIG. 1

MOTOR BELT

MAIN SHAFT BELT

SLOTTED GUIDE POST

SUBMARINE

MAIN SHAFT

FIG. 3

"Somewhere off the Irish Coast:" The Ocean Liner Has a Pitching Motion, as if Battling the Waves, and the Enemy Submarine Submerges, Only to Continue the Pursuit

on shafts, as shown. The cams are set so that their high points are opposite those of the adjoining cams, to produce alternations in the wave motion. The ship is made of the same material as the waves, is 3 ft. long, and placed in front of the last wave. The ship also has a strip tacked to the bottom to strengthen it. The submarine is built similarly, and is 24 in. in length.

The wood disks for the cams are cut

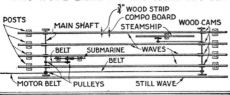

**Plan View Showing Details of the Driving Mechanism, and the Relative Positions of the Waves, Boats, and Other Parts**

8 in. in diameter, out of 1-in. lumber. Two shafts are provided, and in each disk a hole is drilled, 3 in. from the edge, to fit the shafts tightly, thus making cams of the disks. Seven grooved wooden pulleys, of proportionate sizes, as shown, are also placed on the shafts. Eight uprights, as detailed, are provided, in which the waves ride. One upright is used on the large ship, which is balanced on a nail shaft, placed in the end of the upright support, as

shown. A small countershaft, belted from the main shaft near the liner, oscillates the steamship, by means of a wire crank, as detailed in Fig. 2. The submarine rides on the cam only, and is not pivoted in the center, as shown in Fig. 3. It is also driven from a countershaft. This gives it the effect of being submerged, and slowly rising to the surface. The ship has a pitching motion, as if battling with the sea. A large cam is used on the submarine countershaft, and a small pulley belted from the main shaft, so that the action of the submarine is not as frequent as the tossing and pitching of the steamship. The submarine is placed to the left of the display, between the second and third waves. The display is operated by an ordinary electric-fan motor, and can be driven by various other kinds of power. Of course, much depends upon the artistic and mechanical ability of the maker in painting the background, waves, and boats, as well as in making the parts.

---

### Automatic Hammer for Light Work

Electricians, tinsmiths, gas fitters, and others doing light riveting, chipping, and the like, will appreciate the advantages of this automatic hammer. It can be used in places inaccessible with a hand hammer, it will not split or smash a rivet, and all of them will be

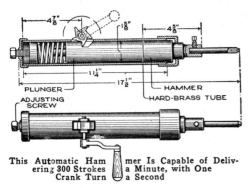

**This Automatic Hammer Is Capable of Delivering 300 Strokes a Minute, with One Crank Turn a Second**

hammered uniformly. By using form dies, the rivet head may be formed round, square, oval, star-shaped, or in

other designs. It has no valves to get out of order, and no joints to regrind, or glands to pack. As there is no pressure used, save that of a spring, very accurate fits are not essential in its construction, and only a few simple parts are required.

In use, the tool is held in one hand, and the riveting die is pressed against the rivet; then the crank is turned as indicated. The star wheel engages the plunger, and forces it back against the helical spring, compressing the latter. The tooth frees itself from the plunger, and the latter is driven forward by the spring, and strikes the hammer and tool holder, delivering the blow to the rivet. The force of the blow is regulated by tightening or loosening the adjusting screw; the length of stroke is not variable, being controlled by the size and number of teeth on the star wheel, and the depth of the recess in the plunger. On a short stroke a heavier plunger must be used, since the direct weight must be made up in the weight of the plunger. The hammer is proportioned for work up to riveting ¼-in. soft-brass rivets.—J. B. Murphy, Plainfield, N. J.

## Inclines to Platform Scale Save Lifting

Many shops cannot afford a large built-in scale with a platform on a level with the floor. Such scales save much labor of lifting, since crates or barrels can be pushed or rolled directly onto the platform. An ordinary platform scale can be made to serve as a good substitute if inclines are built up to its side. These inclines, made from wood and well supported, should be portable, so that the scale may be used in various parts of the shop. Barrels, heavy crates, etc., can be moved to the platform with rollers, instead of the block-and-tackle arrangement otherwise required.—F. M. Ball, Kansas City, Mo.

## Bell Signal Calls Automatic-Machine Operator

A signal bell is used in connection with an automatic machine which fills cans and deposits them in the trough, as shown. When the trough is

The Clapper is Automatically Tripped against the Bell, Warning the Operator

full, the front can actuates the clapper, which falls through the slot, striking the bell. This calls the attention of the operator, who removes the cans from the trough. The handle beside the trough is used to return the clapper into position for the next batch of cans.

## Charcoal Forge Made of Washbasin and Concrete

While engaged in some experimental work at home, I made a small forge,

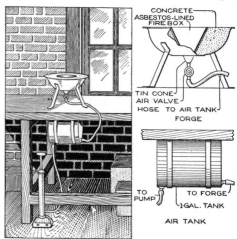

This Concrete and Asbestos-Lined Blast Forge, Made for Temporary Use, Became a Permanent Shop Fixture

and it worked so well that I pass the method on to others. Its construction is very simple. An old granite basin from the kitchen was filled with concrete, and a hole left for the fire box. While the concrete was still wet, a sheet of asbestos was laid around the inside. This keeps the cold concrete from the fire, and makes possible a greater heat. An old fixture from a discarded oil stove was connected to the tin funnel extending to the rubber tubing from the forge, to regulate the air flow. A gallon can, with the proper accessories, was used to regulate the otherwise uneven flow of air from the pump, and to store a pressure supply. The pump was an ordinary tire pump. Legs for the basin were made of strap iron and riveted to the basin, so that it may be more easily handled and the regulating valve underneath reached handily. Charcoal is used in the forge, homemade wood charcoal being prepared with little trouble. The forge melts most of the common metals in small crucibles, and the heat is localized so that it does not heat the room to any considerable extent.—Dale R. Van Horn, Milton, Wis.

## A Handy Sheet-Metal Bench Dog

The carpenter's workbench is not complete without a bench dog and a bench stop.

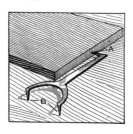

When cutting a mortise, or using a router plane, scraper, or sandpaper, it is often necessary to hold both ends of the board rigid. The bench dog shown is especially handy, being cut from a piece of sheet steel, ⅛ in. thick. It is 6 in. long, and the points B are 2 in. apart. To use it, place the board on the bench with one end firm against the regular bench stop, then drive point A into the other end as far as necessary, being careful to hold points B close to the top of the bench. Next drive points B into the bench, holding the board perfectly.—John Countermine, Vinton, Iowa.

## Can for Recovering Oil from Chips and Sweepings

Around lathes, tapping and milling machines, etc., considerable quantities of expensive oils are used, so that the borings and chips are coated with it. This oil is often wasted, and to save it, I devised this oil-recovering can,

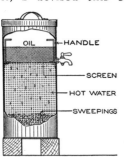

which soon paid for itself. To make the device, get a 5 or 10-gal. can, and provide a cover. Fit in the tray of screen wire, with two handles soldered on, as shown. On one side of the can fit a small drain cock. To use the reservoir take out the tray and fill the can with hot water up to a few inches of the tray. Throw the chips into the water. Put the tray back in place. The oil rises to the top of the water where it can be drawn off. The screen tray is necessary only when wood or sawdust is mixed with the chips, the screen preventing them from rising in the oil.—M. S. Hay, Denver, Colo.

## Whetstone and Strop Kept Handily in Bench Drawer

The disagreeable mess often caused by using a whetstone on a clean bench

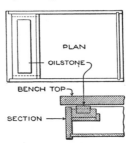

top can be avoided, and the stone made more quickly available, if the latter is placed in a specially constructed drawer in the bench. The drawer consists of a frame 2 in. deep, having a bottom and sliding on two strips in grooves. The oilstone is mounted in a wooden block fitted inside the drawer snugly, and resting on guide strips. It is arranged so that the top of the stone just clears the bench top and extends slightly above the edge of the drawer front. The stone and block may be removed from the drawer if desired, and sharpening accessories, strop, etc., are also kept in the drawer.

## A Nonslipping Ladder End

A large steel mill adopted the nonslipping ladder end shown in the

sketch, to reduce the number of accidents caused by the slipping of ladders. The feet are made of steel and fastened to the ladder ends with rivets. The teeth are filed sharp, and kept well pointed. This type of foot is superior to the common single-prong variety, because at various angles there is always a sharp prong squarely against the floor.—E. B. Hanson, Duluth, Minn.

# Small Power-Plant Tractor Made of Engine and Mower

### By LUTHER STROSNIDER

BY mounting a 1-hp. engine on a heavy plank, supported on driving wheels obtained from an old mower and steering wheels from a light farm machine, I get much more use out of the power plant than when it was set on a portable carrying frame, or on skids. The outfit is rigged so that it runs under its own power, climbing ordinary hills, and making it practically a small tractor, useful in many ways on the farm. It is guided by the lighter wheels, which are pivoted at the center of their axle, and controlled by the hand lever, as shown in Fig. 1. This outfit has been used for the corn sheller, grindstone, sausage mill, feed grinder, pump, washing machine, and wood saw, and I have used it a few times to draw a wagon, instead of going a considerable distance to get a team.

The old mower wheels and driving gear were set so that the pitman shaft is horizontal, as shown in Fig. 1. An 8-in. bevel gear was set on the end of the shaft, to engage a small pinion set on a second shaft which runs across under the plank, and is bracketed from

Fig. 1. This View Shows the Mower Pitman and the Gearing Connecting It with the Engine, and Also the Steering Lever, Gripped by the Driver

it with heavy strap iron, as shown from the opposite side, in Fig. 2. On this end of the second shaft, a clutch device is arranged, two pins fitting into holes in a pulley, which has a rim to prevent

the belt from slipping off when the clutch is released by means of the slanting rod.

The power is belted from the engine

Fig. 2. The Belting of the Power from the Engine Shaft to the Lower Shaft, Which Connects with the Pitman Shaft on the Opposite Side, and the Clutch-Control Rod are Shown in This View

shaft, where a wide pulley is set, to the flange pulley on the lower shaft, as shown in Fig. 2. The lower shaft and pitman shaft are engaged only when moving the power plant. When in use on a saw or other machine, a belt is fitted from the engine pulley to the pulley of the machine being driven. The tools and other equipment for the outfit are kept in the tool box, mounted on the plank.

---

## Liquid Glass Used to Make Asbestos Packing Stick

In setting pipe covering on valves, tanks, and other similar surfaces, it is often difficult to make the covering stick. To overcome this, give the surface a coat of silicate of sodium, known as water glass, and apply dry asbestos by the handful while the surface is wet. The silicate sticks to the metal and retains sufficient asbestos to form a ground for the later coats, applied with a trowel. Wire mesh may also be wrapped around certain forms on which the asbestos will not stick readily, and provides a good foundation.

## A Grade Indicator for Motor Vehicles

The construction of a grade indicator suitable for automobiles, for use on railways, etc., is shown in the sketch.

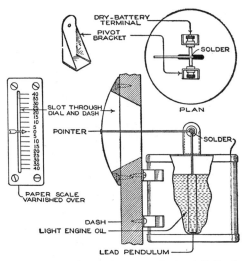

The Pointer Shifts Steadily as the Grade of the Road Changes, Indicating the Percentage

It was made of a baking-powder tin, partly filled with engine oil, in which is suspended a lead pendulum attached to a pivot. Dry-battery terminals form the bearings. The pendulum and pointer arms are of steel wire, soldered to the pivot. The paper scale is glued to a wooden back and is graduated in grade percentages, and not in degrees. The lengths of the arms and dimensions of the parts are omitted as they may be varied. The spacing for the graduations is varied to suit the radius of the pointer. The arm that carries the pointer is of light material and the pendulum reasonably heavy. The liquid steadies the oscillations of the pointer. When attached to an automobile, the device indicates the proper time to change gears, as well as provides a measurement of gradients. An instrument similar in principle is used on aeroplanes to bring the craft on an even keel, when dropping bombs or other explosives.

The scale is determined by using the following degree indications in marking it, the figures being for grades of 0 to 40 per cent, inclusive, at intervals of five per cent: 2° 52′; 5° 43′; 8° 32′; 11° 19′; 14° 3′; 16° 42′; 19° 18′; 21° 48′. This range is satisfactory for all ordinary gradients that a motor vehicle can make.—G. A. Luers, Washington, D. C.

## Steel-Roller Lathe Dog for Making Small Spindles

In turning and grinding small steel shafts it is usually necessary to grip the finished end with a copper dog so as not to mar the work. The steel-roller dog shown in the sketch is superior to this, and for quantity production the making of a set of these dogs was found economical. The dog grips the shaft automatically, and the gripping surface is of sufficient width so as not to mar smooth bearings. The dog is essentially a piece of steel, of the shape and dimensions shown, and having a hole bored through it, the size of the finished shaft on which it is to be used, plus .002 in. A small steel roller fits into an offset at the side of

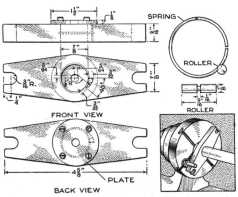

This Lathe Dog was Found Economical for Polishing Steel Shafts in Large Quantities

the hole, and is free to roll about one-eighth of the circumference. When the dog is placed on a shaft and revolved counterclockwise, the roller is forced against the shaft, gripping it firmly. The roller is held in place by a spring ring, fitted into a groove, as detailed. The dog is made of iron, casehardened, and the roller of tool steel, hardened. —Hubert Kann, Pittsburgh, Pa.

## Counting Small Parts by Weighing Them

Purchases of small machine parts, screws, bolts, washers, etc., in large quantities, usually require that they be checked as to number, and counting them is tedious. An ordinary scale, with a scoop pan, was used in counting to great advantage. First the empty scoop was set on the platform, moving the hanging weight along the scale beam until it balanced the weight of the scoop. The parts were poured into the scoop, until a suitable, easily c a l c u l a t e d weight, 10 lb. for example, was registered. The parts weighed were counted, and succeeding batches poured into the scoop until the unit weight was registered. Thus, the total number of parts was recorded in form for easy calculation. If especially accurate results are desired, several tests for the number of parts in a given weight may be made, and the number determined by an average.— C. M. Hall, St. Louis, Mo.

---

## Eyeshade Carried Safely under Shoulder

Frequently it is desired to take an eyeshade from the place where it is

ordinarily used, and those who have t r i e d it know how easily the s h a d e is d a m a g e d. By carrying the eye-shade under the s h o u l d e r, as shown in the il-lustration, t h e shade lies flat, fitting the curve of the body. It is entirely comfortable to the person carrying it and not likely to be broken. —H. Chait, New York, N. Y.

## Sliding Gable-End Hay Doors Easily Operated

Hay doors hinged in the gables of barns are troublesome when the crop

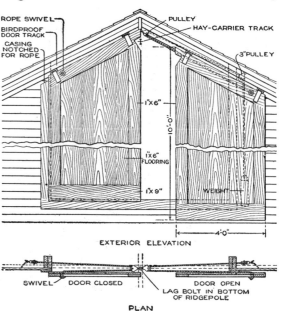

The Doors are Easily Slid into Position on the Inclined Tracks by Reason of the Counterweights

is being hoisted into the mow, and are a constant source of annoyance through damage from the wind or by the weakening of the hinged fastenings. By using sliding doors in the gable, these troubles are easily avoided. Sliding doors, as detailed in the illustration, can be installed easily to operate on the incline of the roof, under the eaves. Provision is made for the usual hay-carrier track, extending under the ridgepole. The doors are strongly framed and suspended on a bird-proof track, from roller hangers, and are counterbalanced by weights suspended on ropes, run over 3-in. pulleys, as shown. This makes it easy to slide the doors into place up the incline. The sectional plan shows the arrangement of the rope counterweight de-vice, and the pulley rigging is also shown in the sketch. By extending the control ropes, the doors can be opened from the barn below.—W. E. Frudden, Charles City, Ia.

## Hollow-Tile Wall Construction Using Metal Bonds

Hollow tile is a sanitary material for building purposes, especially adapted for residences. In the ordinary form of

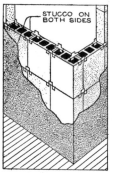
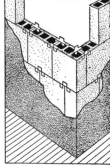

JOINTS MATCHED    JOINTS STAGGERED

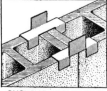

SHOWING APPLICATION OF BOND

GALVANIZED SHEET-METAL NO. 20 GAUGE

A House was Built of Tile at Much Less Expense and Time, by the Use of Metal Bonds, and Proved Substantial, Not a Crack Developing in Four Years

structure, the tile are laid up in mortar, and most building ordinances require them to be 6 to 8 in. thick. This new wall construction, using tile 4 in. thick, provides a very strong, rigid wall. A metal bond is used, and holds together the adjacent tiles, preventing not only lateral displacement at the joints, but deflection in the wall.

The bonds are made of No. 20 gauge galvanized sheet steel. They are 2¾ in. long, and of such size in cross section that the side wings will clasp the web of two abutting tile. The upper side of the bond has an upward projecting wing, to hold the next tile above. Two bonds are used at each joint, as shown.

The tile can be laid with matched or staggered joints. In a building constructed with the bonds four years ago, there is not a single crack. The building was laid up without mortar, and the stucco, or concrete, applied afterward. Partitions can be run from the walls,

the same bond being used. The bonds cost less than the mortar usually employed, and the cost of putting up the tile was less than half that under the usual method. The mortar or cement forced into the cracks between the tile assures a perfect seating of the tile. This bond without mortar assures perfect seating of the tile as they are laid in, and the stucco or concrete finish on both sides is not necessary to make a rigid wall.

---

## Blueprint and Roll-Paper Box with Sheet Cutter

Frequently in drafting rooms the rolls of prepared paper, tracing cloth, etc., are kept in a cupboard or closet. A more convenient plan is to make a long narrow box, with a hinged top. A strip of heavy felt is glued along the top edge and a strip of heavy tin, or galvanized iron, is nailed on the under side of the cover. A small catch at each end keeps the cover against the felt. When paper is required, pull out as much as desired and tear it off against the metal edge. The box has two compartments with independent lids. A yardstick for measuring the

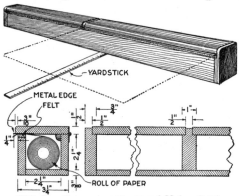

This Box Economizes Paper and Makes Cutting of Neat Sheets Convenient

sheets is pivoted underneath on a screw, and is swung out of sight when not in use.—John D. Adams, Phoenix, Arizona.

---

❡In mixing plaster of Paris, sprinkle the plaster in the water to obtain a smooth mixture.

## Pointers on the Use of Valves

An angle valve is generally more satisfactory than a globe or gate valve and an ell, when a valve is required near a right-angle turn in a pipe line. It demands fewer joints to be kept tight, and makes a better-looking job. Less friction is also caused by water or steam passing through the line. Brass or gun-metal valves should be used on pipe lines that convey superheated steam; never use rubber-disk valves for such duty. In taking down valves, especially those of brass, use a wrench that fits the nut portion closely, so that the corners will not be worn off by the slipping of the wrench.

---

## Old Street-Car Gongs Used as Hardware Trays

An ingenious use of worn-out and cracked street-car gongs is made by a street-railway company in its shops. The old gongs are utilized in making convenient stands to hold small materials, such as washers, screws, nails, nuts, etc., in the storeroom and the shops. A gong weighted with babbitt is used as a base, and the other gongs, inverted, are fastened by pins on an upright, to form receptacles, as shown. Graduated holes in the pipe upright provides for adjusting the receptacles.—Ralph O. McGraw, Chicago, Illinois.

---

## An Emergency Hack-Saw Frame

On a hurry-up bench job in a machine shop, the only available hack-saw frame broke, and it became necessary to provide a substitute or abandon the job. A satisfactory frame, that has proved useful as a regular tool, was made in a few minutes, as detailed in the sketch. The main portion of the

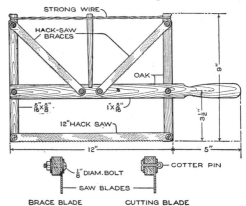

This Emergency Tool Proved so Useful That It was Kept as a Regular Part of the Shop Equipment

frame was made of $\frac{5}{16}$-in. wood and a handle was cut on the crossbar. The saw blade was fitted into place, as shown in the detail, and braces were made of saw blades. A strong wire, tightened with a tourniquet, braced the frame at the top, and made the cutting blade rigid.—J. C. Marsh, Boston, Massachusetts.

---

## Device for Undercutting Mica on Commutators

The mica insulation between the commutator segments of copper, on

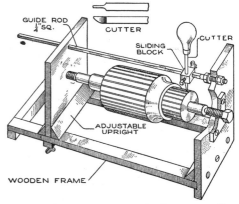

The Mica Insulation between the Commutator Segments is Reduced Uniformly by Means of This Arrangement

motors or similar machines, should be kept below the surface of the segments. Where a number of small motors are to be cared for, a frame for holding the armature conveniently, and a device for cutting the mica are timesavers. In the arrangement shown, the armature is mounted between pointed machine screws set in metal plates, fastened to the ends of the frame. The latter is adjustable, and the cutting device is made of a piece of drill rod suitably ground and handled, for clamping in a sliding block, set on a guide rod.—R. L. Hervey, Baltimore, Md.

## Jig for Piercings on Dies and Machine Parts

A fixture, or jig, for locating piercings can be used to good advantage on follow dies, or dies that blank and

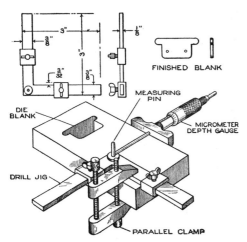

The Piercings on Dies are Located Quickly and Accurately by Means of This Jig

pierce the stock in one revolution of the punch press, in which the die is held. That shown in the illustration consists of a 3-in. right-angle square, made of 1/8-in. flat, cold-rolled steel, or ground stock. Two adjustable sliding stops of machine steel are fastened with thumbscrews. The bushing at the corner of the square is of hardened tool steel and set with a drive fit. The center hole in the bushing can be of various desired sizes. A number of different-sized bushings are convenient. A small pin fits the bushing, and is used

as a measuring point, as shown. The fixture is placed on the die to be drilled, and set so that the center of the bushing is in about the position in which the piercing is to be drilled. The stops are then set, and the fixture is clamped to the die. With a micrometer depth gauge, the fixture is set precisely in position.—William E. Jewett, Jersey City, N. J.

## Economy by Use of Government-Size Letter Paper

While trying to stow away in my files an 8½ by 11-in. sheet of 20-lb. folio bond paper, now selling around 40 cents a pound, I wondered why more persons do not save paper by using the 8 by 10½-in. size, weighing one-fourth less in folio weight, and nine per cent less because of its size. A typical sheet of this size is equivalent in weight to 16-lb. folio stock—17 by 22 in.—but in cutting four sheets out of a paper 16 by 21 in., I get nine per cent more sheets, by weight, for the same money. This size sheet is satisfactory for letters and manuscripts, and often saves postage. The government has used it for years, and many of the government sheets are only half this size.—J. Cecil Alter, Cheyenne, Wyo.

## Grinder as Winch for Hoisting Countershaft

Supporting a piece of machinery against a ceiling while bolting it in place is often a trying and difficult job. Two boys had such a job in the shape of a countershaft and shifter for an emery-wheel grinder, the part being too heavy for them to handle. Two block pulleys were attached to the ceiling timbers. Two pieces of rope were tied to the lower parts of the countershaft, the other ends being attached to the grinder shaft, which was turned by a wrench, making a crude winch. The grinder was bolted to the floor. The countershaft was safely raised, and held in position, while the lag screws were tightened.—E. H. Post, Pittsburgh, Pa.

# A Homemade Hydraulic Ram

### BY B. FRANCIS DASHIELL

THE hydraulic ram is used where considerable flow of water with a moderate fall is available, to raise a small portion of the flow to an elevation. The principle upon which it operates is as follows: An outflow of water falls through a pipe; when the lower end is suddenly closed, the movement is arrested, and the momentum of the current in the pipe forces a small portion of the water, through a check valve, into an air chamber, and out into the delivery pipe. When the momentum is down to normal pressure the outflow valve drops open of its own weight, and the delivery check valve closes, as shown in Fig. 1. The cycle repeats itself about 40 times a minute. Thus, the water is elevated by a succession of impulses.

A hydraulic ram, as detailed in Fig. 2, is easily built. The diagram, Fig. 1, shows the operation of the ram, the water being drawn from a reservoir, or spring, through the inclined drive pipe A to the ram. It overflows through the vertical check valve B. When the velocity of the water through the pipe reaches a certain pressure, the valve is closed. The extreme pressure in the pipe at this moment is great enough to force open the check valve C, and drive some water into the air chamber D, and thence out of the delivery pipe E.

In Fig. 2 the parts are shown assembled. The ram should be set in a

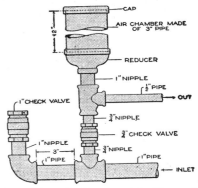

Fig. 2. Assembly Drawing of the Pipes and Fittings of Which the Ram is Made

about 5 ft. below the level of the supply dam, or reservoir, and not over 60 ft. away. The supply should have at least 8 gal. a minute to give good results from the delivery. It will lift water over 20 ft. above the ram, and 200 ft. away, but, of course, the farther away the water is to be delivered, the less will be obtained, owing to the considerable resistance of ½-in. pipe. Fix a strainer over the drive-pipe intake to keep dirt from getting into the ram, and preventing the valves from seating properly.

## Engine Nut Recovered with Pill Box on Stick

I removed a castle nut from my motorboat engine pump, and it dropped from my greasy fingers through several openings to the engine bed. None of the openings near it were large enough to permit inserting pliers or similar devices. Here I was, 50 miles from a good machine shop or other source for obtaining a like nut. I finally used soap, as burglars sometimes do. I tacked a small pill box on a stick, and filled it with soap. I inserted the stick into the engine pit, and there was the castle nut imbedded in the soap.—Egbert A. Clark, Washington, D. C.

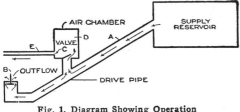

Fig. 1. Diagram Showing Operation of the Hydraulic Ram

vertical position. The supply pipe should be 1 in. inside diameter, and the delivery pipe ½ in. Set the ram

## Stove Lid Used to Repair Forge

The bottom of a portable forge burned out and a thoroughly satis-factory r e p a i r 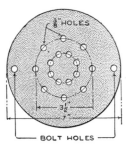 was made by bolting an old 7-in. stove lid into the bottom of the fire pit. Holes were drilled f o r the free passage of the air blast, and similar holes for the fastening bolts, and the lid was bolted into the forge.—Oscar Dzois, Tilbury, Canada.

## Cutting a Glass Tube or Bottle

To break a bottle, or similar glass 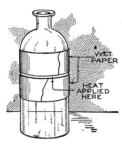 r e c e p t a c l e, smoothly around it, wet two strips of p a p e r and wrap them about the b o t t l e, as shown, a narrow margin interven-ing. Nick t h e g l a s s carefully with a file and apply a hot flame on this line, while turning the bottle.

## Brass Guide Strip for T-Square

Draftsmen know what an annoyance it is to have the working edge of a 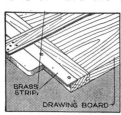 drawing board warp, or wear, so that the head of the T-s q u a r e d o e s n o t fit snugly against it. I have over-come this diffi-culty by fixing a metal edge on the board. I fastened a strip of aluminum—brass will serve —$\frac{3}{32}$ by 1 in., to the working edge of the board with small screws, rab-beting it in flush with the top. The metal projects $\frac{3}{16}$ in., and fits into the groove in the head of the T-square, holding it firmly in place, yet permit-ting it to slide freely.—Guy E. Waite, Ottawa, Ill.

## A Homemade Rabbet Plane

In making skis it was necessary to groove them, and I made a rabbet 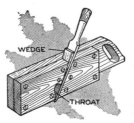 p l a n e for the purpose. T w o pieces of 1 by 4-in. board were cut, 12 and 14 in. long. Two bored holes, and a few cuts with a key-hole saw effected a handle on the longer piece. The short piece was cut in two, at an angle, and the pieces fixed to the longer piece with screws, leav-ing a slot for a $\frac{1}{4}$-in. chisel, and a wedge. A throat was cut, as shown, for the shavings. A slight tap on the chisel at each complete stroke permit-ted the cutting of the groove to the desired depth.—Victor Pare, Glad-stone, Mich.

## Pencil Sharpener with V-Groove Made from Files

An efficient pencil sharpener may be made from two files and a block of  wood, 2 by 3 by 5 in. long. In the top surface cut a 45° groove, as shown. Break the files to two 5-in. lengths, fit t h e m in t h e groove, and glue them in position. The rough sur-face of the files holds the glue nicely. The block is held in the left hand, and the pencil point rubbed, with a twist-ing motion, in the file-lined groove, with the right hand, sharpening the pencil in a few moments. By holding the pencil at different angles, various degrees of fineness of point are ob-tained.

## Revolving File Cabinet on Double Desk Saves Time

A revolving file cabinet, mounted at the center of a large double desk, solved the problem of making the files readily available to two clerks in an office where space was valuable. A cabinet was provided, with short filing drawers, and compactly and lightly built. It was fixed to the center of the desk top by means of an iron pedestal, provided with a center shaft, around which the cabinet turns.

---

## Shop Ladder Made of Pipe and Fittings

In a railroad repair shop where ordinary ladders were found bulky when made strongly enough, ladders built up of pipe and fittings, reinforced, were made and used with satisfaction. They were built of 1½-in. pipe joined with tees, and bolts were passed through the tees and rungs for further strengthening. The ladders being 28 in. wide,

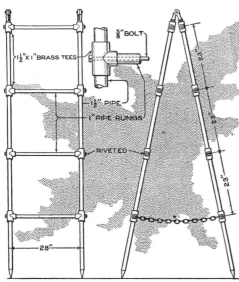

This Strong Ladder was Designed for Use in a Railroad Shop

it is possible to pass planks at any of the rung levels. The ends were pointed to give a secure footing.— Joseph K. Long, Renovo, Pa.

## Reinforcing a Blown-Down Iron Smokestack

One of the guy wires running to the top section of a 60-ft. iron smokestack broke during a high wind, and the

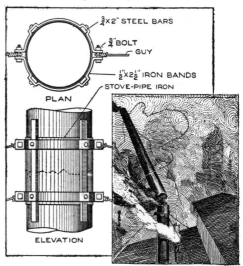

A High Wind Blew Down the Smokestack, and It was Quickly Repaired at Little Expense

stack broke off just above the ring to which the lower guys were fastened. The loss of time to get a new stack would have been great, and the old one was, therefore, patched up and proved satisfactory for continued use. The broken-off section, which remained intact, was hoisted back in place, and kept in line by guys and a set of clamps and bars made for the purpose, as shown in the detail sketch. Guys were run from the clamps on each side of the break, and the stack was made rigid. Around the break, two thicknesses of stovepipe iron were wrapped, before the clamps were put on, to stop leakage.—Donald A. Hampson, Middletown, N. Y.

---

## Wire Mesh for Rough-Surfacing Concrete Walk

Concrete walks can be made with a rough surface, when a regular rough-surfacing roller is not at hand, by applying wire mesh, pressing it firmly on the surface, while the concrete is slightly soft.—H. K. Capps, Stahl, Mo.

## A Shear of Angle Iron for the Vise

A useful piece of apparatus for the workshop is a vise shear, easily made out of two sections of 1½ by 1½-in.

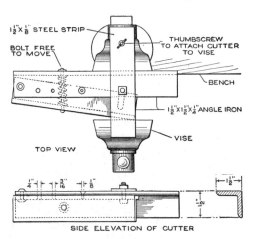

Rivets, Lengths of Small Rod, and Similar Stock can be Cut Quickly with This Homemade Vise Shear

angle iron, riveted together as detailed, and fitted with a stiff spring, on a bolt, which opens the cutter when the vise is released. Holes, the size of the rivets or rods to be cut, are drilled through both pieces of angle iron, when they are in position, as shown in the top view. Both pieces are casehardened around the holes. A metal strap is fastened to the stationary angle iron by bolts, to hold the shears in the vise. A hole is drilled and tapped in the vise to take a thumbscrew, which steadies the shears. The stock to be cut is placed in the hole of the same size diameter, and the vise is tightened to shear the stock. When one requires a number of rivets of a particular length, this device cuts them quickly. By using a slotted plate to hold the rivets, which are fed into the shear steadily, quicker work can be done.—B. E. Dobrée, Battleford, Sask., Canada.

⊂Especial care must be taken in protecting oak from various kinds of oil used on machinery, as this wood is easily spotted black by the combination of the tannin and products from crude oil.

## Pointers on the Care of Auto Tires

Every autoist has his share of tire troubles, which usually start with punctures, and then casing troubles. Half the joys of automobiling can be destroyed if the tires are not properly looked after; so the following hints may be the means of avoiding difficulties and displeasure.

The first rule to be observed is to keep the tires properly pumped up to the pressure specified by the tire manufacturer. A good rule is to make it a point to try the pressure in the tires once a week; a pressure gauge is necessary and should always be carried in the car. Jack up the axle once a week and turn the wheels round and look for cuts, nails, stones, etc., that are likely to injure the casing without causing a puncture. Tacks and nails that have penetrated only the outer rubber may be removed to prevent blow-outs on the road. When a small cut has been made in the casing, it should be vulcanized before dampness or sand has time to work in. Dampness soon rots the fabric, and sand will work in between the fabric and rubber, causing them to separate, and make a boil. Then, undue wear on the rubber is caused and very quick destruction of the tire follows.

There are many gums and fillers sold for filling up cuts in the casings, but vulcanizing is probably the best remedy. Efficient vulcanizers are inexpensive, and convenient for home repairing. If the tire has a bad gash or blow-out, it is best to take it to a vulcanizing shop. The best method to make a temporary repair for a cut or blow-out that has gone through the fabric, is to put an inside blow-out patch inside the casing, being careful to get the edges pinched under the beads of the tire so that the patch will hold in position when the tire is inflated.

Sometimes the fabric of the tire is broken without cutting the rubber. This will cause a blow-out in time, and the only safe way is to take it to the shop and get it repaired; for a blow-out patch inserted will not last long as the continued friction caused at the break in the casing will crack the patch open. Inner linings help a badly worn casing, but they are a poor substitute for a good vulcanizing job.

The only satisfactory way to repair inner tubes is to vulcanize them, and this may be done in the home garage. Cold patches are desirable in emergencies, but when driving for any length of time on macadam, asphalt, or concrete roads, the tires get very warm, and these patches are likely to loosen up, causing a leak. Vulcanizing all punctures at the first opportunity is the best practice in the long run.

When the hole is larger than an ordinary nail hole, the following method of repairing is good: Cut out a regular-shaped hole in the tube, and scrape the inside of the tube, all around the hole, for ¾ in. on each side. Cut a piece of old inner tube, large enough to allow a margin of ¾ in. around the hole. Apply cement to this on one side, previously cleaned, and also on the inside of the tube. When both are tacky slip the patch into the tube, and see that it adheres well all around the inside of the cut. After preparing the outside in the usual way, the patch may be vulcanized. The patch inside will form a good backing for the soft vulcanizing, and when it is clamped up a perfect weld is made.

If there is a slow leak in a tire, before taking the casings off, test out the air valve by holding a drop of water over it; if air bubbles come out, replace the valve. Dirt is blown into the valve seat, causing a slow leak and much trouble; frequently this is the cause of leakage attributed to a supposed puncture. Summing up, the automobile equipment is not complete without a vulcanizer and material for it, an air-pressure gauge, a blow-out patch, extra air valves, and extra tubes. —F. S. Korbel, Detroit, Mich.

---

❡A section cut from a cotter pin is useful for replacing buckle tongues.

## Apple-Packing Table Mounted on Wheels

A table for sorting apples to be packed for shipment was made of odd ends of lumber, and mounted on discarded wheels, as shown, making it

The Table is Moved as Required, and the Culls Placed in the Chute

readily portable. The handiest feature of the rig is a chute from the top, on which the apples are sorted, for culls, leaves, etc., which might get into the barrels. The slats of the table extend lengthwise, and the chute opening is across the top. When the chute opening is wanted wider or narrower, the slats around it are moved.—M. Glen Kirkpatrick, Des Moines, Iowa.

---

## Fitting a Handle to a Pick

A quick and thorough method of fixing handles in the heads of picks is as follows: Put the head on the handle, as shown, and pound the butt on a solid foundation, until the edge of the pick eye cuts its way nearly to the end. Reverse the handle and pound the other end to loosen the pick. Cut off the slivers, insert the handle in the proper way, and pound the butt on the iron or base to a  solid fit. If carefully done, the handles will not loosen even in great changes of weather. — James M. Sherman, Columbia, Mo.

## Charcoal Heating Stove Made of Flowerpots

A small stove that was made originally for taking a chill from winter

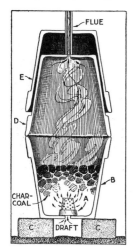

hotbeds, and which can be used for various purposes throughout the year, was made from several clay flowerpots. A small pot, A, was drilled with small holes, as indicated. A 12-in. flowerpot, B, was set on bricks, C, with the small flowerpot inverted over the hole at the bottom. The charcoal fire is made in the flowerpot B, which is covered with a similar pot, D, and over this is another pot, E, which retains the heat. A flue, made of a piece of 1-in. pipe, carries off the smoke and gas. Soft coke may also be used, and the pots will hold heat and fire about 24 hours if pot B is filled three-fourths full.—R. S. Matzen, Fort Collins, Colo.

## Device for Holding Screws While Threading Them

It is often desired to rethread screws which have become burred, and in the

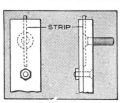

tool room many odd sizes of screws are required. It is difficult to hold a screw in a vise while threading it, and the device shown in the sketch was made to overcome this. The screw is inserted in the hole and the small strip of steel in the slot prevents it from turning. A small bolt holds the two pieces of the device together, so that it may be clamped in a vise.

## Gauge Determines Diametral Pitch of Gears

The simplicity of this gear-pitch kink, that I have worked out, will appeal to a large number of mechanics, and others who have occasion to send a helper to get the pitch of a gear, in a position where it cannot readily be measured or taken down. Obtain a piece of sheet metal, about .008 in. thick, ½ in. wide, and 3.1416 in. long, and bend it to the circumference of the gear on the pitch line. The teeth between these two points will be the diametral pitch. The explanation is that the diametral pitch is the number of teeth to each inch of the diameter of the gear; therefore, if a gear has, for example, four teeth for an inch of diameter, those four teeth cover a space on the pitch line of 1 in. multiplied by 3.1416, and that is the length of the gauge.—Robert D. McElvany, Norfolk, Virginia.

## Rheostat Made from Old Arc-Lamp Carbons

A simple rheostat was made from discarded arc-lamp carbons, as shown

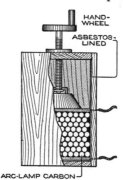

in the sketch. A wooden box, 12 in. high and 6 by 6 in. inside, was used as a container, and lined with asbestos, to guard against overheating. A metal plate was fastened to the bottom of the box, and several dozen arc-lamp carbons laid in. The more carbons used, the greater the range of resistance. A second plate was placed on top of the carbon pile. By employing a hand-screw device the pressure on the carbons between the two plates may be varied. When electrical connection is made to the two plates, the resistance varies inversely with the pressure.

## An Inexpensive Color-Changing Sign

Color-changing signs are effective as advertising devices, and the box sign shown is so simple in construction and operation that it has a wide use. An angle-iron frame is made up to the desired size. The four corner uprights are riveted to the bottom. The top is fastened to the uprights with screws, to permit its being removed for the insertion of the mechanism and glass sides. The front and two sides are of glass, with the desired advertisement painted on one side of each, and the inner side frosted, to obscure the mechanism. The back, top, and bottom are cut from one piece of galvanized sheet iron, A, with a circular opening cut near one end, and a circle of holes near the other. It is then bent to shape and fastened in place.

The inner mechanism consists of a cylinder of celluloid, B, fastened to a revolving air vane, C, which is made of thin metal, preferably aluminum, with the blades bent at an angle of about 25°. This cylinder is large enough to revolve freely around an upright electric-light bulb. A cylinder of sheet metal, D, is next made, slightly larger in diameter than the celluloid one, and serves as the upper part of the air shaft. A strip of metal is fastened across the inside, and supports the revolving member. The bearing is a glass-head pin inserted in the center of the vane and fastened to the cross strip.

The lower air shaft E is made ½ in. smaller at one end than the celluloid cylinder, and extends 1 in. up into the same. The other end flares out to inclose the air holes in the bottom of the sign. The upper and lower air shafts are then fastened in position, at the galvanized sheet iron which forms the top, bottom, and back. A weather-proof electric-light receptacle is mounted within the lower air shaft, so that the electric bulb will be in the center of the sign. The wires, protected, are led from the socket through a hole in the bottom of the sign, and properly insulated in tubing. A hood,

riveted over the circular opening in the top, keeps out the rain. The celluloid cylinder can be painted in broad, vertical stripes with transparent col-

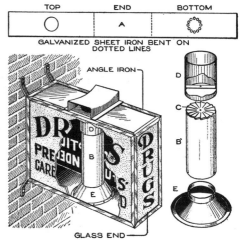

TOP     END     BOTTOM

GALVANIZED SHEET IRON BENT ON DOTTED LINES

ANGLE IRON

GLASS END

The Draft through the Cylinder Operates the Fan. Various Novel Effects can be Devised Readily for This Homemade Sign

ors. The angle-iron frame is given an oxidized-copper finish by sandpapering in spots, and applying a solution of copper sulphate. This will give only a light deposit, and can be protected with a heavy coat of lacquer or shellac.

The expense in operating this sign is for the electricity consumed only, as the motive power is furnished by a draft of air formed through the air shafts.—George Niederhoff, St. Louis, Missouri.

---

## Speed Indicator Counts Turns on Wire Coil

Desiring to rewind a field coil on a form, an electrician placed the form on an arbor and fastened the arbor in the

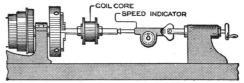

COIL CORE

SPEED INDICATOR

The Number of Turns of Wire Wound on a Coil Core was Recorded by the Use of a Speed Indicator

chuck on a lathe. In order to record the number of turns wound on the form, a speed indicator was rigged up as shown. A taper arbor fitting into the tailstock was notched out to receive the handle of the indicator, and a small pin put through to hold it in place. The tailstock was then run up until the rubber tip of the indicator fitted into the center in the arbor. The number of turns was recorded accurately, and when the wire became crossed, and the form had to be backed up, the indicator automatically subtracted the number of turns unwound. —Earl Pagett, Coffeyville, Kans.

## Rigging for Reboring Engine Cylinder by Hand

A high-pressure cylinder on a steam engine was to be bored out, the casting being of such shape and size as to re-

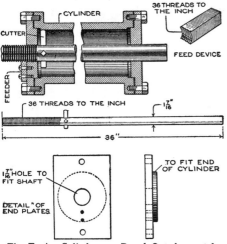

The Engine Cylinder was Bored Out Accurately and Smoothly by Hand

quire much rigging to fasten it in a lathe. I bored the cylinder by hand with the arrangement shown, getting a satisfactory job. The boring bar is a shaft of cold-rolled steel, $1\frac{7}{16}$ in. in diameter, threaded as indicated, and fitted with a $\frac{3}{8}$-in. high-speed steel cutter ground like a finishing tool. A $\frac{1}{2}$-in. square, cold-rolled steel, threaded feed device, on the end of the cylinder, engages the boring bar, causing it to move in or out when turned. Plates of steel, as detailed, provide bearings for the shaft, which is fed in by a crank made of a wrench.—Hermann G. Kroeger, Louisville, Ky.

## Large Wheelbarrow Saves Time in Cleaning Wood Shop

After watching a man cleaning up shavings and hauling them out in an ordinary wheelbarrow that enabled him to take only about one-third as much material at a trip as he should, I had a large hopper made for his barrow, to permit the hauling of a good load each trip. The hopper was supported by a frame of round iron, 36 in. square at the bottom and widening toward the top. The frame was covered with heavy canvas, and the hopper was lifted from the barrow like a basket when emptying it.—M. C. Webster, St. Louis, Mo.

## Wafer Razor-Blade Device for Scraping Paper from Glass

Show windows are often stuck up with posters, playbills, etc., the corners of which are frequently securely pasted to the glass, and removed with difficulty. A tool with which to scrape these off can be made of a wafer razor blade, fastened to a wooden handle. The blade is held by screws, through the holes in the blade, or under the lugs at the end. Kept near the window, this scraper will be found a handy tool.— L. B. Robbins, Attleboro, Mass.

## Device Prevents Loosening of Eyeglass Screws

A defect in many eyeglass frames is that the wings which hold the lenses,

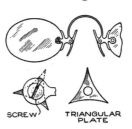

and through which screws pass, are so thin that the screw soon strips the threads, loosening the lens. A thin, flat piece of suitable metal, three-pointed, as shown, provides a remedy. It is placed beneath the wing, and after the screw is driven home, the points are turned over, one of them in the slot in the screw head, preventing the screw from turning. In tightening the screw, the point is raised. This device on a pair of glasses has prevented the slightest turn of the screw for over a year.—J. S. Zerbe, Coytesville, N. J.

## Double-Drive Countershaft Arrangement

On a rush order, floor space was at a premium, and a milling machine had to be set beside a lathe, in constant use. To get the miller going in good time, and with little expense, I put up a double-drive arrangement. After figuring the pulley diameters, for the required speeds, two 14-in. pulleys, one 9 in. and the other 4½ in. wide, with set collars were mounted on the countershaft. Both of these pulleys are loose on the shaft, and held in position by the collars. The drive belt from the line shaft runs on the 4½-in. pulley when the miller is not running, and is shifted over on the 9-in. pulley when

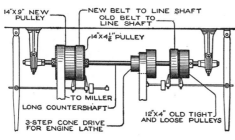

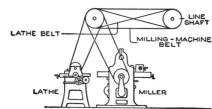

An Old Lathe and the Newly Installed Miller were Driven from the Same Countershaft

the machine is started. This drive has given no trouble, and does not interfere with the running of the lathe.—Joe V. Romig, Allentown, Pa.

❉Circular areas of crosshatching, scratched into triangles near their corners, prevent them from slipping too easily on the drafting board.

## Washing Rack for Blueprints

In using this blueprint-washing rack the prints are spread over the galvanized-iron surface, which is first

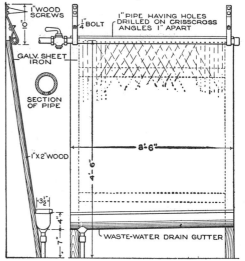

The Blueprints are Spread on the Moistened Surface and Washed Until Developed

sprayed with water, causing the paper to adhere. The water is then turned on as desired, and the paper sprayed until it is thoroughly developed. The water is turned off, the paper is removed, and placed on the drying line. The water-supply pipe is supported by strap-iron brackets, and the washing surface is built over a wooden frame, as indicated. A galvanized-iron drain gutter carries away the excess water.—J. M. Morse, Brooklyn, N. Y.

## Clip Holds Door of Terminal Boxes during Tests

A kink that I have found very handy while working in electrical-terminal and test boxes is the use of a clip for holding the door open, especially in a breeze. It is extremely annoying to have a door of a test box blow shut unexpectedly. This simple holder, which is made somewhat like a large clothespin, slips over the upper or lower edge of the terminal box near the hinge edge of the door, and is set in front of the door, holding it open.—A. Gemmill, Ansonia, Conn.

## Size of Objects Photographed Indicated by Background

When making photographs of small objects for catalogs and similar pur-

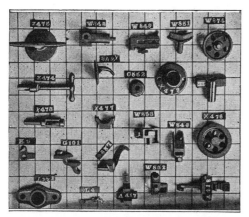

The Sizes of These Patterns can be Estimated by Comparison with the Two-Inch Squares in the Background

poses, divide the background into squares of equal dimensions, and the size of the objects photographed can be estimated readily in the picture. In the photograph of some small patterns, the copy board was divided into 2-in. squares, by means of black strings stretched tightly from brads driven at intervals on the edge of the board.— R. D. Stevens, Lawrence, Mass.

## Raising Shop Desk Increases Its Usefulness

The man in the shop office usually does not care to sit down to write an

occasional order or note, and a desk with a chest-high writing surface saves his time. The photograph reproduced shows a raised desk used by a shipping clerk. The arrangement also enables him to get paper, tags, etc., from any of the drawers without undue stooping.

## Suggestions on Automobile-Tire Economy

In extremely hot weather it is better to start out with automobile tires a trifle slack rather than pumped up too hard. The heat of running will increase the air pressure several pounds. Never run a tire which shows any pronounced "give" when the car is rocked by hand. The moment the car shows an unusual tendency to swerve, or steers hard, stop and make sure that a puncture is not the cause.

## High, Portable Lamp Standard for Shop Lighting

Unless the illumination of a shop is unusually well planned, it will be necessary to employ local lighting at night, and on dark days. The use of the portable lamp standard, shown in the illustration, has been adopted in a large shop. It consists of a gaspipe standard, 12 ft. long, screwed into a heavy cast-iron base. A

high-candlepower, nitrogen-filled lamp is used, providing plenty of light for accurate shop work. The lamp is moved to the work, rather than the work to the light, and suitable electrical connections made.—C. M. Hall, St. Louis, Missouri.

## Preventing Typewriter Platens from Becoming Grooved

By using the variable line spacer frequently on a typewriter, or moving the platen slightly from its previous position, the entire surface of the platen is written over, thus preventing its becoming deeply grooved, as occurs when line after line is written, day after day, over the same point on the platen.— John M. Bonbright, Philadelphia, Pa.

## A Portable Baseball Backstop Built of Pipe and Wire Netting

### By P. P. AVERY

INSTEAD of the common make-shifts, a substantial portable base-ball backstop was installed by a ball club, and proved popular and very practical. It may be wheeled to various positions and even transported to a distant field. By turning the front wheel sideways, the stop is securely anchored in place. Construct the frame of 1¼-in. galvanized-iron water pipe, with elbows and fittings, as shown. The wheels are cast-iron pulleys of 3-

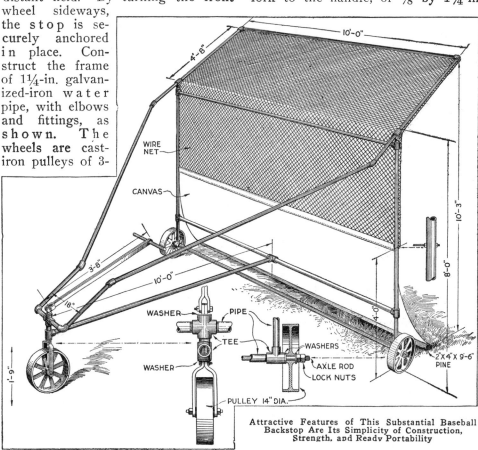

WIRE NET

CANVAS

WASHER — PIPE

TEE

WASHER

WASHERS

AXLE ROD

LOCK NUTS

PULLEY 14" DIA.

2 X 4" X 9'-6" PINE

10'-0"

4'-8"

3'-8"

8"

10'-0"

1'-6"

10'-3"

8'-0"

4'-0"

Attractive Features of This Substantial Baseball Backstop Are Its Simplicity of Construction, Strength, and Ready Portability

1½-in. band iron, bent to shape, as shown, and for a bearing use a heavy washer. The top part of the fork is rounded and riveted together to pass through the pipe connections. Drill a ½-in. hole at the top and fasten the fork to the handle, of ⅜ by 1¼-in.

in. face, secured to the bottom cross member, as detailed. Secure the steering wheel by a fork made of ½ by

iron, 3 ft. 8 in. long, arranged to be swung back when not in use.

A net of heavy galvanized-wire mesh

is stretched over the main frame, and heavy duck, or canvas, is fitted over the lower section. Secure the wire mesh by heavy galvanized-iron wire wrapped around the pipe. The canvas is secured by lapping it over and sewing it. A basket may be slung under the lower front rod, in which baseballs, bats, gloves, etc., may be carried.

## Canvas-Covered Wardrobe Protects Workmen's Clothes

Considerable dust collects on the clothes of workmen and employes in

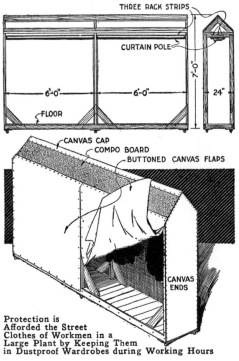

THREE RACK STRIPS
CURTAIN POLE
6'-0"     6'-0"     24"
7'-0"
FLOOR
CANVAS CAP
COMPO BOARD
BUTTONED CANVAS FLAPS
CANVAS ENDS

Protection is Afforded the Street Clothes of Workmen in a Large Plant by Keeping Them in Dustproof Wardrobes during Working Hours

shops and workrooms in spite of precautions unless a covered inclosure is provided for them. In a large manufacturing establishment, wardrobes like that shown in the illustration are provided for this purpose. Each employe has a numbered clothes hanger and a portion of a hat rack above its place on the curtain pole, as shown. The clothes are placed in the wardrobe as the employes report for work, and are ordinarily not removed until the lunch hour. The framework for the

wardrobe is built up of 2 by 4-in. stuff, strongly braced. The hat rack is made of three strips set under the gable. The curtain pole is supported by wooden blocks, bolted into place. The dimensions shown may be varied to suit special needs. The frame is set on casters and can be moved handily. The gable is covered with compo board and the sides and ends with canvas. The side curtains are buttoned securely into place when the clothes are placed in the wardrobe.—Charles M. Petersen, Buffalo, N. Y.

## Typewriting on Tracing Paper for Blueprint Reproduction

In making duplicate copies of manuscripts having inset illustrations, or in reproducing specifications, the blueprint process is often the most convenient. To letter a considerable quantity of text is tedious, and, if properly done on a typewriter, the result will be more satisfactory. Tracing cloth, or tracing paper, preferably of the unglazed onion-skin variety, may be used. In writing the text on the typewriter, reverse a piece of carbon paper under the tracing paper, so that the impression is made on both sides of the sheet. This will give density, and make the blueprints sharp. If white prints with dark lines are desired, a new sheet of carbon paper should be used, and this taken as the negative in making the prints.

## Enlarging Cylinder Fins Aids in Cooling Engine

Repeated overheating of the cylinders of an air-cooled gasoline motor led to experimenting in an effort to prevent this trouble. The result was the fitting of disks, or split rings, of sheet copper, around the cylinder, between the smaller fins cast on the cylinder. The rings were bolted into place, becoming practically a unit with the cylinder. The heat is radiated rapidly, and the cylinder is kept cool in spite of heavy running of the motor.

# A Traveling Crane for the Farm

On a large farm, operated with heavy traction engines and other machinery, a method of moving or lifting heavy weights is often necessary. This traveling crane is on a farm at Williams, Calif., and pays for its cost every year in time saved in making repairs or doing other heavy work. The construction can be simplified greatly, to fit the needs of smaller farms, where only a small range is necessary.

The supporting structure is of heavy timber, made in standard braced construction, with posts securely set into the ground. The horizontal beams carry steel rails, on which the carriage rides. It is drawn along by a rope arrangement, which extends, through pulleys, to both ends of the framework, making it easy to move the carriage and load by drawing on the proper rope. The ends of the rails are guarded to prevent the carriage from rolling

When the Farmer or an Employe Is a Trained Mechanic, Even Heavy Machine Work can be Done on the Farm with the Aid of a Crane

off. The carriage consists of a cross I-beam, braced to two wooden supports, in each of which two flanged wheels are mounted. These engage the steel rails. The load is supported from the I-beam by a differential pulley, or other tackle. The tackle should be suspended from a trolley, which rides along the I-beam.

---

## A Truck for a Canoe or Small Boat

A canoe must frequently be carried over a trail, or other place, and this work is made convenient by the use of a small truck made of two rubber-tired baby-carriage wheels, suitably mounted. A piece of ½-in. iron rod is used for the axle, as shown. An old trunk strap, two iron clamps, two small wooden brackets, and a carrying handle of ¼ by 1¼-in. band iron are the fittings used.

To make the truck, cut the main piece of 1¼-in. oak, and outline the lower section of the canoe on it, as shown. Make the

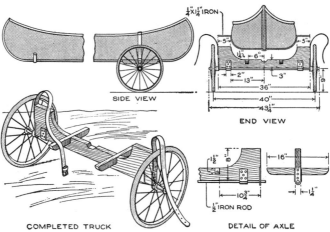

COMPLETED TRUCK                    DETAIL OF AXLE
**This Canoe Truck, Made of Baby-Carriage Wheels, can be Knocked Down and Carried Handily in the Craft**

as shown. Secure the wheels with washers and cotter pins. Attach heavy trunk straps at the ends. To use the truck, set the canoe in place, and buckle the strap around it, as shown. The

cross brackets, used to keep the truck steady, and fasten them with screws. Fit the axle into a groove under the main piece, and attach it by clamps, iron carrying handle is placed under the opposite end. The entire outfit can be carried, knocked down, in the canoe.
—J. A. Downs, San Francisco, Calif.

## Gong Warning System for Freight Elevator

A simple mechanical safety device that will give returns in the way of immunity from freight-elevator accidents can be rigged out quickly. Gongs are fitted to the frame of the elevator, at each floor, 6 ft. above it, with the handles below the bells. On the top floor, a coil spring is arranged which pulls the connecting rods

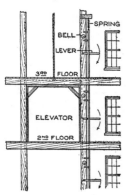

back to the original position after use. A conspicuous card near each handle reads: "Ring Bell before Using Elevator." The bells are the usual trip-gong pattern. The pull rods and handles are of flat stock, iron or soft steel, 3/16 by 3/4 in. Round stock can also be used, but requires more work to make the proper connecting joints. The use of jam nuts makes a better job.—S. A. Seipel, Indianapolis, Ind.

## Cutting Floor Openings with Hand Circular Saw

In removing a few sections of flooring to install pipe or wiring, a handy

way of cutting the boards, especially across the grain, is to use a small circular saw. This can be mounted on the spindle of a hand emery grinder, as shown. A handle should be fitted to the frame of the grinder, to steady it, and a projection added to rest on the floor and aid in gauging the depth of the cut. An old plane blade is useful in cutting the tongue from the flooring.—E. C. Galbreath, Denver, Colo.

## Wire across Lamp Relights Acetylene Flame

Thin piano wire placed slightly above and at right angles to the acetylene flame of an automobile tail lamp has been found efficient in preventing the light from going out without the knowledge of the driver. The wire becomes incandescent, and reignites the gas when the flame is jolted or blown out. The wire should be drawn taut, so that it is continually in the flame.

## Roofing Paper as Emergency Pipe Connection

A quick, cheap, and satisfactory connection for pipes, to carry liquids not

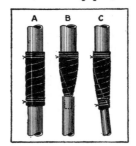

under pressure, can be made from a piece of one-ply roofing paper. Roll the paper into a tube of double thickness, as indicated at A, and tie it into place with wire or cord. Pipes of different sizes can be joined in this way by the methods suggested at B and C. Pipes that are out of line can thus be connected, as shown at C, and by using heavy paper, and more thicknesses, a connection can be made that will stand being left underground for some time. —Henry Simon, Laguna Beach, Calif.

## A Tough Cement for Pipe Joints

A cement which has stood the action of 60 lb. of steam, in a pipe connection where rubber glands and white lead had failed, is made of 10 parts of fine iron filings, and 3 parts of chloride of lime, with water added to form a paste. So tough is this cement, that when two joints of 3-in. cast-iron pipe, which had been secured with it and left one night, were broken apart, the cement scaled off a portion of the iron flange of one of them. The cement is applied in the usual manner.—W. S. Standiford, Youngstown, Ohio.

# Equipping Buildings with Lightning Protection

## by Terrell Croft

L IGHTNING destroys about $10,-000,000 worth of property annually in the United States, largely on farms. The United States Bureau of Standards estimates that the yearly loss is about $8,000,000, but it is probable that this is a conservative valuation. Now, it can be shown from unbiased statistics that buildings properly and scientifically equipped with lightning protection are seldom, if ever, damaged. Reliable statistics indicate that lightning rods, even as they are ordinarily installed—and they are not always arranged most effectively—prevent at least 90 per cent of the possible lightning damage. Lightning rods, so the Bureau of Standards report asserts, reduce fire hazard from lightning as much as 99 per cent, in the case of barns. Every individual who owns, or expects to own, property, will find some practical knowledge on this subject valuable, as set forth briefly in this article.

Contrary to general impression, to install lightning rodding so that it will be most effective requires special knowledge, and experience. Any lightning rodding placed on a structure, provided one end is connected with the ground, affords some protection, but the aim is to obtain maximum protection with material purchased at reasonable expense.

Modern lightning-rod practice is largely the result of practical experience, because it is seemingly impossible to duplicate in the laboratory the actual conditions of, and the enormous electrical quantities involved in, a lightning flash. In the appliances for, and in the arrangement of, a lightning-rod installation, simplicity is desirable, and mechanical considerations are almost, if not quite, as important as the electrical features.

Some of the terms used are indicated graphically in Figs. 1 and 2. An aerial terminal, a point constituting the upper extremity of an aerial terminal; the conductor, usually a cable or rod interconnecting the aerial terminals and joining them with the earth connections; the earth connections, and other parts, are shown.

Whether iron or copper should be used in the conducting portions of a lightning-rod installation has been a

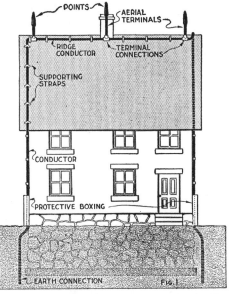

Installation of Lightning Protection on a Small Cottage, the Various Essential Features being Designated

much-debated question, and both sides are partly right. In the light of experience to date, the situation sizes up as follows: Electrically, one may be as good as the other. With either metal, there must be sufficient material in the lightning conductor—and in the other components of the system that may carry current at the instant of a

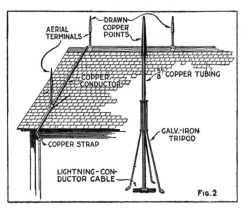

Details of a Roof Installation with Short Aerial Terminals, and a Typical Larger Aerial Terminal

flash—to insure that they will not melt. Because of the fact that iron is a poorer conductor of electricity than copper, it is necessary, from an electrical standpoint, to use a heavier conductor if it is made of iron than if it is of copper. Copper withstands the action of the weather much better than does commercial iron or steel, and has, under practically all conditions, an almost indefinite life. Commercial iron and steel have, relatively speaking, short lives. In certain instances, where iron lightning rods have been installed in dry climates, or where the air is pure, or where they have been kept painted, they have often lasted for many years. From the standpoint of temporary protection it makes little difference which metal is used for the rodding, provided there is enough of it. An iron-rod installation, correctly disposed, will afford much more effective protection while it lasts than will a copper-rod installation applied without regard to the physical facts. Furthermore, flimsy, light-weight, copper-cable conductor comprising very small diameter wires is probably not as good as a heavy-wire conductor because the frail copper is likely to be broken mechanically. It is possible that, with these conditions, the iron would last longer than the copper.

Copperplated or copper-sheathed iron lightning rods and fittings can be distinguished easily from solid copper, but unless one is familiar with the characteristics of metals, the deception may be difficult to detect by superficial inspection. Test the material by its attraction for a small permanent magnet, which will not attract any of the common metals except iron and steel. If the magnet tends to stick to the metal, which appears to be copper or brass, it is evidence that a copper or brass coating is concealing an iron core. The magnet will attract through the deceptive plated-copper, or sheet-copper sheath.

Should or should not the lightning rodding be insulated from a building is answered fairly by this fact: Only a few of the manufacturers of lightning-rod material now recommend and furnish insulators for the rodding. From a physical standpoint, it is undesirable to insulate the rodding from a building, and a great majority of the reliable lightning-rod manufacturers discontinued the use of insulators long ago. However, it is probable that the diminutive insulators, as installed, are almost ineffective as insulators, particularly when they are dirty or moist. These are in certain cases the cause of inductive "side flashes," because they

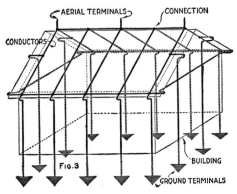

An Ideal Lightning-Conductor Installation, the Structure being Completely Caged

may prevent all parts and the contents of the building from rapidly attaining the same electrical potential as that of the lightning-rod system.

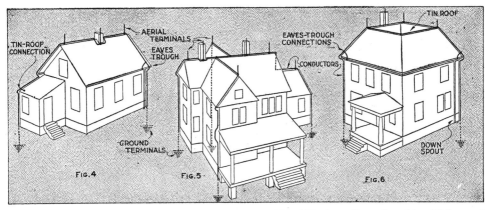

Typical Installation on Various Residential Buildings, the Aim of Maximum Protection with a Minimum of Material being Carried Out Reasonably

The ideal lightning-rod installation would be a metallic cage surrounding the structure. The cage should be electrically connected to the earth and surmounted with metallic points, as shown in Fig. 3. In practice, installations are not made in this way, except where powder magazines, oil tanks, and similar structures, are to be protected. Cheaper methods provide protection which, though possibly not quite so effective, experience has shown to be adequate. The practical problem in arranging protection for a building is so to dispose the minimum amount of material that maximum protection will be afforded by it, and so that it will approximate the ideal grounded-cage arrangement of Fig. 3. Figures 4, 5, and 6 illustrate examples of typical installations.

The conductor should preferably be of copper. It may be round, flat, tubular, or of star section, and solid or woven from wire strands, provided it possesses sufficient mechanical strength, and conductivity. Since stranded cable is mechanically more desirable than a tubular arrangement, it probably presents the best form of lightning conductor. There is no valid practical objection to a solid conductor, except that it is difficult to handle and to install. It must ordinarily be manufactured and shipped in relatively short lengths, which are joined on the job to form the complete conductor. Joints are undesirable, if they can be avoided.

If a stranded conductor is used, no strands should be smaller than .04 in. in diameter. If the strand wires are too small, they will be mechanically weak. There is no reason to believe that "lightning travels in a spiral"; hence, twisted conductors have no advantages, on this ground, over untwisted ones.

In attaching the conductor to the building it should preferably be held thereto with clips of the same metal as that of the conductor. If dissimilar metals are permitted in contact, this may, under certain conditions, cause an electrolytic action between them, which will eat away one of the metals, at the point of their contact. Copper straps, similar to pipe straps, are ordinarily utilized for supporting round-cable conductors. Specially designed fasteners are used where the conductor is not of circular cross section. As a general proposition, the conductor should be supported at least every 5 ft. in vertical runs, and every 2½ ft. in horizontal runs. A conductor should never be supported with nails driven through it, or driven in at one side and bent over, particularly if it is of cable form. Such treatment will certainly sever some of the strands.

---

❡The tendency of varnish to "crawl" on the second coat, in cold weather, may be overcome by applying benzine on the first coat, permitting it to dry before applying the second coat.

## A Novel Footbridge of Woven Wire

Spanning a small stream on a farm in Missouri is a novel footbridge which a farmer constructed out of woven

A Practical Bridge for a Small Stream on a Farm was Made by Supporting the Footboards on Woven-Wire Fencing

wire supported on heavy fence posts. The bridge will support a load of several persons, but is ordinarily used only for one person at a time. Strong woven-wire fencing was stretched across the stream on posts, set 3 ft. apart and strongly braced with anchored wires. Six-inch boards, 1 in. thick, were fastened on the second horizontal strand of the fencing, and the boards further supported by lacing wire around them, and attaching it at the same time to the several lower horizontal strands of wire, as a safety feature.—George M. Petersen, Buffalo, New York.

## Spark Plugs Cleaned with Bag of Shot

A small cloth bag filled with fine lead shot can be carried in the tool chest of an auto without trouble and is of great assistance in cleaning spark plugs. After placing a few drops of gasoline on the plug, the mouth of the bag is tied around the plug body by means of the tie strings. By taking the plug between the fingers and shaking it up and down

a few moments the carbon deposit is removed. The shot does not scratch the glaze on the porcelain, or injure its insulating properties. It may be used repeatedly.—Thomas W. Benson, Philadelphia, Pa.

## Rigging for Grinding Screw Threads

Grinding of hardened screws, worms, etc., such as are used in talking machines, sewing machines, and ordnance work, was done by cutting the thread, hardening the work, and straightening it on centers. This method was slow, costly, and inaccurate. The method shown is now in daily use in a large shop, and is very satisfactory.

Of the two spring centers, C and D, the tail center D has a helical spring of about one-half the strength of the spring in the headstock C, and the function of this weaker spring is to keep the centers in place, while the spring in C holds the thread against the flat spring A. These centers and springs fit accurately in the bores of the head and tailstocks, with no lateral play.

The indexing attachment is clamped to the head of the grinder, and the flat spring, at A, is set so that when a point in the thread being ground passes the emery wheel, it reaches the flat spring as soon as possible. The screw to be ground is turned by hand, and as it is turned in the direction of the arrow B, the screw is moved in the

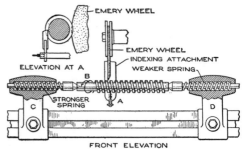

The Emery Wheel Grinds the Threads as the Screw is Turned by Hand

direction of the tailstock, the stronger spring in C compressing the weaker spring in D, and the cut of the emery wheel is regulated by the flat spring at A.

This method has many applications in taper and spiral dividing-head work, and in some cases where a dividing head is useless, the work may be readily done.—J. B. Murphy, Plainfield, N. J.

## Sanitary Shields for Shop Cuspidors

In a large shop, where numerous cuspidors were provided, the floors and walls around them soon became insanitary, and it was decided to provide a standard type of cuspidor and a shield that would overcome this objectionable feature. Enameled basins filled with sand were used, and a shield of sheet metal to fit over the basin was devised. One hundred of these were made cheaply and distributed about the shop. They are easily cleaned with water

Sanitation was Promoted in a Large Shop by the Use of Many Cuspidors Provided with Metal Shields

from a hose, and the results were much better from a sanitary as well as a practical standpoint.—Alfred J. Bell, Detroit, Mich.

## Mystery Sailing Ship as Window Display

Devices which excite the curiosity of spectators are often useful as window displays, and it is on this basis that the mystery sailing ship keeps a crowd before a window in which it is displayed. A small wooden ship with sails is placed in a tank, which has rounded ends and is partly filled with water. The ship D sails around the tank A, as indicated in the diagram, because of the draft from two fans, B, hidden

behind screens C. When the ship is forced to the end of the tank, the draft from the fan at that end strikes the

The Ship Sails around the Tank and the Onlookers Are Curious to Learn What Keeps It Moving

sails, shifting them, and driving the craft to the opposite end, where this process is repeated.—R. S. Matzen, Fort Collins, Colo.

## Gas-Mantle Fixture Used as a Blowtorch

The portion of a gas-mantle fixture having an air shutter can easily be made into a Bunsen burner, or a blowtorch of considerable force, by flattening the round end A into the form shown at B. The fixture is attached to a gas hose, and the air shutter regulated to produce a sharp blue flame with the desired pressure. This simple arrangement is often useful where a

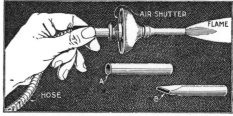

The Mantle Fixture was Quickly Converted into an Effective Bunsen Burner, with a Blowtorch Action, by Flattening the End of the Tube

Bunsen burner of the ordinary type, having a base, is not practical.—M. J. Doyle, Cleveland, Ohio.

## Blast for Forge from Stream of Water

For use with a forge, where running water is available, the arrangement shown in the sketch provides a satisfactory blast at small cost. A strong barrel is made water-tight and fitted with a 1½-in. pipe through the top. The water pipe, in which a valve

is set, is passed into the larger pipe, and when the water flows into the barrel, air is drawn in between the pipes, causing a compression in the upper end of the barrel. The compressed air is conducted to the forge by means of a tube. An overflow pipe provides for the excess water.—L. R. Williamson, Astoria, Ore.

## Wedge-Shaped Marking Stakes Prove Superior

In the making of marking stakes used by surveyors, builders, and others,

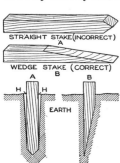

a wedge stake, formed as at B, is preferable to one of the straight type, shown at A. The wedge stake is more difficult of withdrawal, and is more likely to remain at the point where it was driven into the earth, a feature of considerable importance because much time and money may be sacrificed when stakes must be relocated. When a straight stake is driven, the hole which it makes in the earth is larger, as shown at H, at the surface of the earth, than it is at the lower end of the stake, and there is not much adhesion between the stick and the soil. If the stake is cut to form a long wedge, as shown at B, then all of the surface of the two sides will be in firm contact with the earth, and the resistance to withdrawal will be increased. To determine the relative advantages of the two types, 100 straight stakes were driven in a certain job, and also 100 wedge stakes, under identical conditions. Thirteen of the straight stakes, and only three of the wedge stakes, were lost.

## Replacing Broken Foot on Iron Lawn Bench

A bench with metal supports, in a school playground, was broken as in-

dicated, and the foot part was lost. A neat repair was effected by students in the machine shop. Two pieces of ¼ by 1-in. strap iron were riveted to the broken end, and to these strips a rounded piece of ½-in. iron was riveted as a fastening plate, like those on the other legs.—A. L. Braun, New York, N. Y.

## Repairing a Hole in a Small Water Tank

A special outlet in a kitchen-range boiler was no longer needed, and, since the locknuts in it were rusted badly, it was necessary to plug the hole by other means. A rubber disk was fitted closely into the hole,

and ⅛-in. lead washers were placed on each side of it. Iron washers were slipped over these and the entire set was bolted together very firmly, with a ⅜-in. bolt. The lead washers were forced into the opening, compressing the rubber, and forming a tight packing.—Fred W. Page, Winfield, Kans.

## Compression Coil Spring with Double-Action Case

An arrangement of a coil spring in a case so that the spring will be compressed both when the points of fastening, A and B, are brought farther apart and closer together is useful on doors and on many mechanical devices. A typical housing of a coil spring in a case, such as would be suitable for a door, is shown in the illustration, which is a longitudinal sectional view. When the points A and B are brought closer together, the collar C acts on the spring, compressing it against the collar D, and the bolt head slides in its pocket. When they are brought farther apart, the collar D compresses the

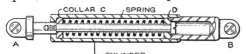

The Feature of This Device Is That the Spring is Compressed When the Distance between the Points of Fastening is Extended or Shortened

spring against the collar C, bearing on the end of the cylinder.—George M. McGinley, Woonsocket, R. I.

---

## Chuck on Emery Grinder Used for Washing Bottles

In a shop and laboratory, an emery grinder was rigged to provide a handy power bottle-washing machine, by mounting a chuck from an old drill on one end of the grinder spindle. The chuck was set on a ½-in. rod, and this was threaded into the spindle. The bottle brush was gripped in the chuck

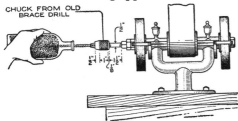

Bottles were Washed Quickly and Thoroughly by the Use of This Improvised Washing Machine Attached to the Emery Grinder

and the bottles slipped over it, and held in the hand as shown.—P. F. Jamison, Chicago, Ill.

## Pockets on Switchboards for Memos of Special Calls

The traffic manager of a telephone exchange handling a large number of

Telephone Service was Improved by Providing a Code File for Delayed Toll Calls

long-distance messages found that his operators lost considerable time in keeping track of their ticket records of toll calls that could not be completed immediately. To keep the "delayed" tickets constantly before the operators, pockets were constructed along the top face of the switchboard, each pocket marked with the code letters showing the reason for the delay in handling the message, as UDLW: "Party called for is out; left word for him to call." The pockets were made of light tin, painted dull black, and lettered in white. The scheme is very successful in speeding up the service, keeping delayed call tickets in sight of both the operators and the chief operator in charge.—E. C. Blomeyer, Waco, Tex.

---

## Soldering Wrought-Iron Rings by Dipping Saves Time

Certain kinds of machinery require the use of wrought-iron rings, made of cylindrical bar iron of small diameter. It is common practice to solder together the ends of these rings by the use of a soldering iron. When a large quantity of these rings were made at one time, it was found more economical to substitute a dipping process. After the ring is formed, the ends are dipped into a pan of molten solder. This method reduced the soldering time 50 per cent.—Joseph Plogmann, Cincinnati, Ohio.

## A Swine Cafeteria in a Barrel

To make this "help yourself" eating house for swine, which was built at the Minnesota Agricultural College at a

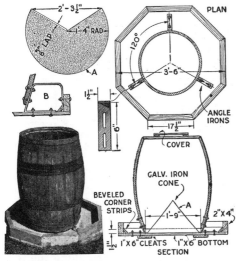

The Construction Is Simple, and the Barrel can be Adjusted Quickly to Increase the Quantity Fed

cost of $6.50, including labor, obtain an empty barrel, some boards, nails, a piece of sheet iron, and some strap-iron angles. The barrel is supported slightly above the platform, and the grain, or tankage, feeds out around the lower end, from the sheet-iron cone A. Angle irons, as detailed, keep the barrel in position. Two slots permit

Twelve Shoats or Six Full-Grown Hogs are Accommodated by This Self-Feeder

the supports to be slipped out far enough to clear the bolts in the barrel, for easy adjustment of the latter. The trough and platform are made of 1-in. lumber, and the rim is of 2 by 4-in. pieces. Guards may be attached to keep the pigs from rooting out the feed, as detailed at B. This outfit accommodates 12 shoats or six full-grown animals, at a time. The barrel feeder is cheap and simple in construction, and its durability is limited only by the material used for the trough.—E. R. McIntyre, Madison, Wis.

## Builder's Survey Level with Sights from Old Rifle

This homemade arrangement provides a means of ascertaining true levels on buildings, floors, stone foundations, etc., and is made of materials easily obtainable. Make a tripod, using the top plate and the attaching wing nut from an old camera, if possible. Band iron is bent, as shown, and on the top arms an old

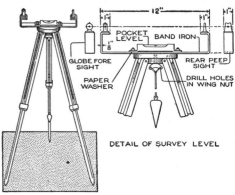

DETAIL OF SURVEY LEVEL

A Serviceable Survey Level, Made at Small Cost, Which Gives Accurate Results

pair of rifle sights are soldered in place, taking care to get them very accurate. Fix a pocket glass level, about 4 in. long, on the direct center of the iron bracket, by the use of two ordinary carpenter's squares. The level in its level position must be absolutely parallel with a line through the peep-sight centers. Insert small paper washers under the pocket-level clamps, and after the sights are soldered to the top ends of the bracket, it will be easy to obtain an accurate parallel. Three holes are drilled in the iron level bracket, the center one tapped for the camera-tripod thumbscrew, by which the tripod is fastened to the level bracket. The other holes are for securing the pocket level. Old rifle sights are easily obtainable at a locksmith's shop. The plumb bob is suspended as shown.

## A Wire-Gauze Stencil

A good background stencil can be made by attaching letters and figures to wire gauze, the color being applied over the lettering, producing a background of the desired color. This stencil is flexible, making it useful on irregular surfaces.

## A Tipping Cradle for Carboys

Large bottles or carboys cannot be handled safely while pouring out the contents by tipping, because of their weight and shape. The arrangement shown is built of wood, and makes the handling of carboys safe and convenient. The carboy is placed on the two rockers; the frame of the carboy is gripped by small nails, which protrude ¼ in. from the upper edges of the rockers. A strip nailed to the sides of the rockers holds the carboy from slip-

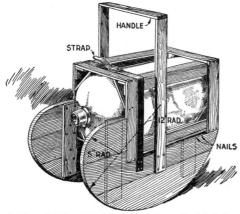

*Acids and Other Liquids may be Poured with Safety by the Use of This Carboy Rocker*

ping from the cradle. The handle gives a good hold in tipping the device.—John E. Cahill, Jr., New York, N. Y.

## Torch for Burning Off Old Paint

A device for burning old paint, or enamel, from automobiles, carriages, passenger cars, locomotive cabs, etc.,

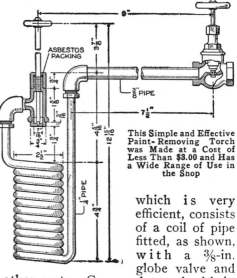

*This Simple and Effective Paint-Removing Torch was Made at a Cost of Less Than $3.00 and Has a Wide Range of Use in the Shop*

which is very efficient, consists of a coil of pipe fitted, as shown, with a ⅜-in. globe valve and other parts. Gas can be used with it, or a reservoir filled with oil and connected by hose to an air line, which forces the oil out through another hose connected to the ⅜-in. globe valve, can be utilized. The globe valve regulates mainly the flow of the oil, and the needle valve controls the size of the flame.

The user holds the device in one hand, and goes over the painted surface, keeping the torch moving slowly, and then holding the burner away, while he removes the burnt paint with a scraper held in the other hand. In using oil, the coil serves a twofold purpose, helping confine the flame to a proper area, and the flame passing inside the coil heats the oil being forced through it to a high temperature by the time it gets to the burner, thus preparing it for combustion.—Joseph K. Long, Renovo, Pa.

❡Concrete that collects on a mixing machine can be removed easily if a heavy coat of grease is applied to the surfaces where the concrete collects before the mixer is put into operation.

## Safety Mirror Attached to Automobile Mudguard

A novel way of mounting traffic mirrors on automobiles, instead of the usual position at the side of the windshield, is on the mudguard of the front wheel, facing the driver, using only ordinary pipe fittings. A crowfoot, or flange, is attached to the back of the mirror, into which is fastened an ell and straight piece of 1/4-in. pipe, long enough to extend a few inches below the mirror. A crowfoot is also fastened to the mudguard. The mirror frame and fittings are painted the same color as the car. A better view of what is going on back of the machine is obtained by the mirror in this position.—Harry Slosower, Pittsburgh, Pa.

## Old Steel Columns Reinforced by Concrete Casing

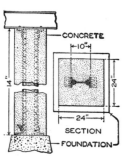

Structural-steel columns, that are rusted to such an extent that further painting is both inadvisable and ineffective, may be kept in a good state of preservation and be strengthened as well by incasing them in concrete, as shown. This system is applicable to many types of columns, and if the concrete is carried to the top, it really becomes a reinforced-concrete column, the steel furnishing the reinforcing for the concrete. Such work has the further advantage of being possible to construct without removing the column from the load it is supporting.—H. P. Roy, Kansas City, Mo.

## White Opal Glass Useful for Headlights

An excellent headlight lens that eliminates the glare, gives an ample amount of light when the lights are dimmed, causes no perceptible loss of light on the road in front, while giving more light on the sides of the road and being easy to keep clean, can be provided by using panes of white opal glass cut to the required size. It costs a little more than paper dimmers, but much less than patented lenses. This glass gives a pleasing cream-colored light.—Horace M. Fulton, Washington, D. C.

## Ripsaw Cuts Large Nail without Injury

A nail-cutting trick which has many practical uses, and which will interest

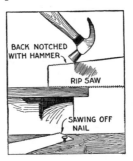

users of handsaws, is performed as follows: The performer announces that he will cut off a tenpenny nail with a ripsaw without injuring the saw. He then notches the back edge of the saw with a hammer, as shown, and, driving the nail into the bench or into a block, cuts it off squarely with the notched edge. This will not deface the saw if the notches are made small, and even adds to the tool's usefulness.—E. Ward, Detroit, Mich.

## Pipe Cutter Marks Round Stock for Sawing

Careful work is necessary to saw off round stock with a square end, and the sharp edge resulting is undesirable in many instances. By marking a V-groove in the round bar at the line where it is to be sawed off, a guide is provided for the sawing, and the edge is neatly beveled off, when the cut is finished. Use a pipe cutter for the groove.

## Babbitting Mountings for Ball Bearings

When a ball bearing is used in assembling machines, the housing, or mounting, should be finished to close dimensions. This work is expensive. A quicker and cheaper method is to make a dummy of iron, exactly the same size and shape as the inside of the housing. It should be polished, so that no babbitt can stick to it, as shown. The mountings are made in halves. When ready for pouring the babbitt, the dummy is put in one of the halves of the housing so that the shafts of the dummy are resting on the proper bearings in the housing. In order to prevent the hot babbitt from running out at the ends, fire clay, or whiting mixed with asbestos fiber, is used to seal up the ends. The dummy

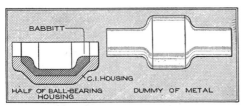

Housings for Ball Bearings can be made Quickly by the Use of a Metal Dummy

is removed when the babbitt has cooled, and the other half of the housing is babbitted similarly.—Joseph Limbrunner, Shelton, Conn.

## Wire Protective Screen Increases Usefulness of Vacuum Cleaner

In the cleaning of trays containing small screws, and similar fittings used in shops, it is inconvenient to remove the articles in order to get at the dirt. Especially when the parts are small, such as metal type, the use of a powerful vacuum cleaner is not practical, and blowing out of the dust is not satisfactory. By covering the trays, or other places to be cleaned, with wire screening, and rattling the contents, the dust may be effectively and quickly removed with a vacuum cleaner.—John Robinson, Hillsdale, Mich.

## Barrel Truck Made of Pipe and Fittings

Adjustability to various sizes of loads and great strength are features of a truck made of pipe and fittings. To make this truck, obtain two ¾-in. pipe crosses, A; two tees, D; a union, F, and suitable

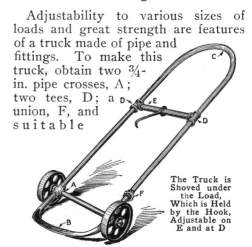

The Truck is Shoved under the Load, Which is Held by the Hook, Adjustable on E and at D

lengths of ¾-in. pipe for the other parts. Bend a section of pipe, 26 in. long, as shown at B, so that the "U" is 18 in. wide. Thread each of the ends and flatten the central portion at B. Join the crosses on this piece, as shown. Thread and shape the piece C, which is 5½ ft. long, to the same width. Slide the tees D, fixed to the pipe E, on pipe C, setting the hook in place. The latter is made of ⅜-in. round iron, to slide on pipe E. The hook and the bar and tees D may be moved as desired. Fit the union and a suitable nipple at F. Run an axle through the crosses A, and put on the wheels. To use the truck, run end B under the barrel, or crate, and place the hook over the top, holding the load securely.—S. N. Miller, Denver, Colo.

## Emergency Fuse Circuit for Motion-Picture Lanterns

To save time in exchanging fuses in a motion-picture-show lantern room, I devised the plan of wiring shown in

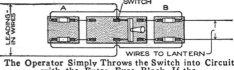

The Operator Simply Throws the Switch into Circuit with the Extra Fuse Block, If the First Set Blows Out

the diagram, consisting simply of a double-throw knife switch connected with two fuse blocks, so as to throw either of them into use at will. Thus, if a fuse burns out, it is only necessary to throw the switch over, and go ahead with a new set of fuses, while the burnt-out one may be replaced at leisure.—Fred Kuhlmann, Peru, Neb.

## Hinged Tread Covers Puddle at Worn Doorstep

Often it is desirable to lay a board over a spot where water is apt to lodge just outside the doorstep. An im-

The Wooden Tread Bridges a Worn Place in the Doorstep, Where Puddles Form

provement on this method is shown in the sketch, being a riser and a tread hinged, by means of two bent iron straps, to the door frame. The hinges hold the step in place and permit its being raised when sweeping.—Albert O'Brien, Buffalo, N. Y.

## Stereotyping without Special Apparatus

Frequently it happens, in small newspaper or printing offices not pro-

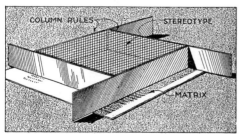

By This Method Small Cuts can be Cast from a Matrix with No Special Apparatus

vided with stereotyping equipment, that some advertiser wants a cut made from a paper matrix, and it can be done with very little trouble, as follows: The mat is warmed, and laid on a previously warmed stone, or other flat surface. A dam of column rule is built around it, and held in position by weights against the outside. The dam is filled with metal, and, after cooling, the casting is cut down to size, and made type-high by pasting paper or Bristol board to the bottom of the cut. —J. S. Hagans, Toledo, O.

## Device for Unrolling and Measuring Wire Mesh Handily

Screen wire, when being unwound, has a tendency to roll toward the part that is being unwound, and will not remain still. To remedy this, a hardware man made an arrangement as shown. A counter, about 12 ft. long, was used, on which to unwind the wire. On one end of the counter, two rollers, 2 in. in diameter, were placed, about 4 or 5 in. apart. The rollers were set so that the roll of wire can be placed on them, and then be unwound. The weight of the wire holds it on the two rollers. Rolls of screen

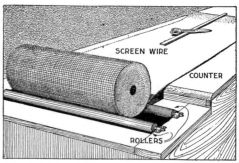

The Awkward Handling of Screen Wire in Rolls is Overcome by This Arrangement

wire can be kept handily under the counter on special shelves.—Lee M. Delzell, Maroa, Ill.

¶By slitting the point of a pen-filling quill on an ink-bottle stopper and bending it into a cuplike form, ink can be transferred to the ruling pen more handily.

## A Folding Cabinet for Drafting Equipment

Provision is made for the storage of a great variety of drawing equipment —instruments, pens, brushes, inks, etc. —in small space, by the cabinet described, and the contents are readily accessible when needed, or in use. It can be placed on a stand or drafting table, but a better arrangement is to mount it on a swinging wall bracket, of such radius that the contents can be swung to the most convenient position. When not in use, the materials are packed into their places, and the cabinet closed up and swung out of the way. No dimensions are given, as these will be governed by the equipment to be housed, and the space accommodations.

The outfit, as shown, consists of three trays and an outer case, the upper and lower trays C and A being movable, while the center tray B is stationary. The various kinds of materials and tools suitable for the compartments are suggested in the photograph. The construction and operation of the trays are shown in the sectional view. When the case is closed the compartment C slides back into its original place. The compartment A folds down as indicated by the dotted line, and the cover D folds forward to its dotted position. The brace E, which is held in place by the clip F when supporting the raised tray A, is released and folds into the cover section D, when the

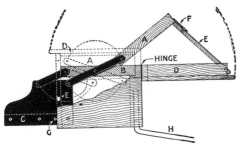

Diagram Showing the Method of Folding the Various Sections into the Cabinet

cover is closed. The compartment C is locked into place by a metal strip engaging the round-head screw G, and

the arm H is set into a hole bored in a block, glued in one corner of the lower

When the Cabinet is Folded Open, the Drafting Equipment is Compactly Arranged, Yet Easily Accessible

section.—T. T. Sturgeon, Los Angeles, California.

## Tool for Fitting Piston Rings

When assembling the pistons and cylinders of gasoline motors, trouble is usually experienced in inserting the

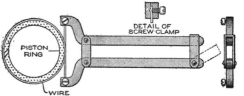

Piston Rings can be Fitted Handily with This Homemade Tool

piston rings. An effective tool for this purpose is shown in the sketch. A piece of music wire, $\frac{1}{16}$ in. in diameter, is given a turn around the piston ring, and the two ends are fastened in the proper ends of the levers, as shown, by means of the clamping screws, with the handles wide apart. When the handles are brought together and clamped in the loop, the wire is tightened up and the piston ring compressed, so that it will readily enter the cylinder. The tool can be made to suit the pistons, and should be made of $\frac{1}{16}$ by $\frac{5}{8}$-in. strap iron, and about 9 in. long over all.—W. B. Burr, Boston, Mass.

⟨A good working surface is provided on a drafting table by covering it with smooth, heavy paper.

## Cutting Thin Metal Washers by Hand

When washers are needed, heavy metal or tools with which to make them are sometimes not at hand. Washers made of thinner metal may be substituted, several being used to build up the proper thickness. An easy method of cutting these is to mark them on the sheet metal, trim them off on the outside, and cut the centers out with a cold chisel. Turn the washer as the cut progresses, guiding the chisel on the vise.—Hugo Kretschmar, West Nyack, N. Y.

## Setting a Rivet Handily in an Awkward Place

To get a rivet into an awkward hole so that it can be riveted from the outside, put soft laundry soap on the end of the finger, press the rivet in firmly, and put the finger at the rivet hole. With the other hand, put the nail in as

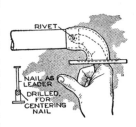

a leader, and work the rivet into the hole. A small countersunk hole in the end of the rivet makes it easy for the nail to engage the rivet.—Arthur F. Stern, Milwaukee, Wis.

## Measuring the Velocity of a Stream

To measure the velocity of a stream, step off or measure 120 ft. along the bank, where a straight course may be found. Throw several floats—tightly corked bottles will do—into midstream, and time them over the 120-ft. course. The average time of all floats divided into 100 is the average rate per minute. Water flows faster at the top of the stream than at the bottom and sides; the ratio of 100 to 120 is about the proper one to correct for this fact, giving the average velocity at a given cross section. By using the 120-ft. course, the calculation is simplified.— R. Z. Kirkpatrick, Washington, D. C.

## Gas Engine Transported by Rolling It on Flywheels

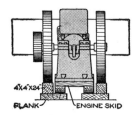

To obtain the maximum hours of daily service from a gas engine, I was obliged to move it from place to place. By using squared pieces of timber under the flywheels on which to roll the engine on the wheels, this work was made easy for one man. By turning the wheels the engine can be moved readily considerable distances, the timber being moved forward as required. The water tank should be empty. Timbers 4 ft. long are handiest, especially in turning corners. Unless in a dusty place, it is well to open the compression-relief cock when moving the engine in this way.—J. E. McCormack, Haliburton, Ont., Can.

## Handy Wrench with Drift-Pin Handle

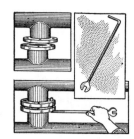

When erecting or installing machinery where cast-iron flanges, with bolts, connect the parts, it is often necessary to draw one of the flanges into place, to get the bolt holes to match. When there is not sufficient clearance to use a mandrel or drift pin, a rod bent to a short right angle is handy. An angle of this kind forged on the handle of a wrench, as shown, combines two useful tools, and has proved quite popular, as indicated by frequent borrowing of it.

# Cable Trolley Rides over Guy Wires in Its Path

By J. S. ZERBE

THERE are many places where it is impossible to run cables for the transmission of carriers for ore or other products around mountain sides, or across gorges, without using guy wires laterally from one or both sides of the cable. The suspension of the buckets, below such a winding and stayed cable, is accomplished by a contrivance in which the trolley wheel, which supports the carrier on the cable, is rigged with two spider wheels and a special carrier frame, as detailed. The pivot pin of the trolley wheel extends out, to receive, at each end, a spider, the arms of which project beyond the periphery of the trolley wheel, as shown in the side view. The ends of these arms, or spokes, are each provided, on their outer sides, with an antifriction wheel. The carrier frame is grooved to ride on these wheels. This frame is built up of two sidepieces, generally triangular. The upper rim of these plates is curved and grooved to ride on the antifriction wheels. These pieces are joined together below the spider by bolts, as shown in the end view. The load is carried on the load bar of this frame. The spiders turn independently of the trolley wheel.

When the trolley wheel moves in either direction, the spider wheels do not turn until one of the arms strikes a cross wire. The cross wire then passes up between the arm which strikes it and the next arm ahead. The action is a stepping over the guy, or cross wire. The carrier passes beneath

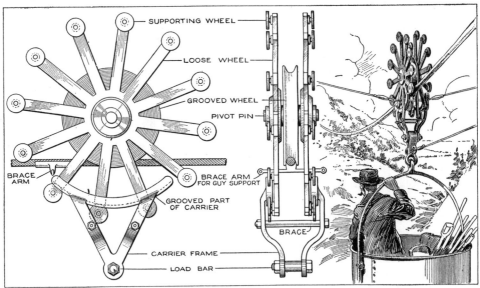

When a Guy Wire is Encountered, the Trolley Wheel Rides on the Cable, Passing over the Wire, and the Load is Carried under the Wire, by Means of the Spider-Wheel Device, Which Supports the Load Carrier

the cross wire, riding along on the anti-friction wheels, as the spiders revolve. The spiders again remain stationary until the next cross wire is reached. The propulsive force can be applied to the pivot pin of the trolley wheel, or to the carrier; in either case the spider will ride over, and the carrier beneath, the guy wires. This arrangement can also be used for a large variety of suspension cable lines for amusement devices, as the lines can be run in many directions in a comparatively small area, and can be laterally supported so as to prevent a swinging motion. Two of these wheels can be used to support motive power, the trolleys being connected by a frame. The carriers are thus self-contained, and useful for transporting products by cable where the usual motive cables are not practical, or economical.

### Hinged Insulator Brackets Prevent Breakage of Wires by Swaying

Municipalities with electrolier street lighting often find trouble in keeping the overhead wires from rubbing on trees. The swaying of the trees wears the insulation from the feeder wire, and on wet days produces a partial ground and leakage of current. Steel pins driven into the trees, or wooden brackets spiked on, with the feeder securely tied to the glass, or porcelain, insulator, are unsatisfactory, in many cases causing an almost perfect ground. A simple remedy was devised by attaching a wooden wire bracket to a large hinge, spiked to the tree trunk. The swaying in the direction of the line is provided for in the hinge and the cross swaying in the slack in the feeder wire.—J. F. Bront, Denver, Colo.

### Air Pumped through Water Jacket Cools Gasoline Motor

A four-cycle, water-cooled gasoline engine was installed in a small shop and used only intermittently for small jobs. When the weather became cold, the danger from frost and the job of filling and emptying the tank and jacket caused the operator to devise an air-cooling system for it. Into a collar of suitable size he put a projecting pin, in such a manner that when the collar was put on the end of the crank shaft, the pin served as a crank pin. From this improvised crank pin he operated bellows attached to the floor below. By means of hose, he connected the nozzle of the bellows with the lower water connection of the water jacket. This caused air to circulate through the jacket while the engine was in motion. Frost did not injure it, and it required practically no attention. The method is, of course, hardly feasible on an engine running for long periods.—J. E. McCormack, Haliburton, Ont., Canada.

### Weight of Goggles Relieved by Rubber Band

In steel foundries, or shops, where the eyes of the workmen are endangered by flying particles of steel or sand, many of the men do not keep their goggles on as much as they should, because the goggles are heavy, and unless a man is used to wearing glasses continually, the weight on the bridge of the nose is annoying. A light rubber band looped over the bridge of the goggles and slipped into a small hook of a hook and eye, sewed on the edge of the cap or hat band, as shown, relieves the pressure. The adjustment desired can be obtained by moving the cap.—J. A. Fitzpatrick, Altoona, Pa.

HOOK SEWED IN CAP

RUBBER BAND

## Roughening Slippery Iron-Floor Plates

When iron-floor plates become worn smooth, they are dangerous under foot, especially when wet. A method of roughening them slightly is as follows: Mix a small quantity of powdered sal ammoniac thoroughly with fine sand. Sprinkle the mixture over the iron floor, covering it with a thin layer. Dampen the surface with a sprinkling can and permit the material to remain over night, or preferably over a holiday. Sweep up the sand, and it will be found that a rough coating has been formed, which will last several weeks. The process may be repeated until the desired roughness is obtained.

## Raised Letters and Designs Painted with Roller

A quick and effective way of painting raised letters, with flat faces like type, or other designs, is to roll over them with a small roller such as printers use in inking type when they pull a proof. The paint is carried on a board, and the roller is covered with paint by running it across the board. In some cities the names of streets, on lamp-posts at the corners, are written in flat-faced white letters, raised, on a background of green, and this method was used with success to paint the letters after the post had been painted green.—Alfred J. Miller, Albuquerque, New Mexico.

Much Time was Saved in Painting Street Signs by This Method

## Pedal Controls for Washbasin Faucets

A physician has an ingenious device in his operating room by which he can turn on the water in the lavatory with-

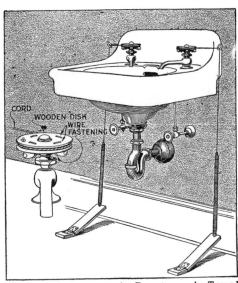

With This Arrangement the Faucets can be Turned On with the Foot, the Hands Not Soiling the Handles

out gripping the handles of the faucets at the washbowl. This is a sanitary feature of importance in his surgical work. The arrangement consists of two pedals fastened to the floor beneath the washstand, and rigged as shown. They are hinged to the floor, and the free ends are held slightly elevated by cords. These cords run through screw eyes in the wall, and are connected to pulleys set on the faucets, as detailed. By treading on either pedal, the corresponding faucet is turned on; when the pressure is released, the spring in the faucets shuts off the water.—John D. Gilbert, Eugene, Ore.

## Gate Adjustable to Heavy Snowfall

In regions where the snowfall is heavy, especially on the farm or in suburban places, considerable labor is involved in shoveling away the snow so that gates can be opened at their usual level. By arranging the gates so that they can be raised above the level of the snow as it accumulates, much of this labor becomes unnecessary. In the arrangement shown, a heavy iron

Instead of Shoveling a Path for the Gate at Its Usual Level, It is Raised and Supported on Pins Set in the Long Pipe

pipe, 3 ft. higher than the usual height of the gate, was set in a concrete base and supported by bolts through the fence posts, at the hinged end of the gate. The gate was arranged to slide vertically on this pipe, which supported it from large eyes, or loops around the pipe. Holes bored through the pipe at intervals were fitted with adjusting pins, one for each hinge support of the gate. The gate was quickly raised to the proper level, and the pins set into place.—Ethel S. Platt, Traverse City, Michigan.

## Guide for Cutting Triangular Strips on Circular Saw

In reinforced-concrete construction the inner corners of the beam and column forms are filled with triangular

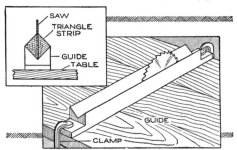

The Guide is Clamped on the Saw Table and the Squared Stock Ripped Diagonally

wood strips, known as fillets. The contractor's circular saw usually is not equipped with a tilting table, and some sort of a jig is required for ripping the fillet strips from the square stock. The sketch shows such an arrangement. A trough-shaped guide, with a slot to accommodate the saw, is clamped to the saw table, and the square stick is pushed along this guide.—J. J. O'Brien, Buffalo, N. Y.

## A Homemade Low-Pressure Angle Valve

A low and medium-pressure valve, that is valuable as an emergency device, and which also gives good service as a fitting for the home workshop, was made of materials easily obtained. This valve possesses points of superiority over some commercial valves, for when the valve is open, the water, etc., passing through the pipes, has an

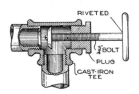

unobstructed flow, and because of its simple construction will appeal to the home mechanic. It is made of a tee in which is fitted at one end a pipe, beveled to form a seat for the valve. In the other end of the tee is a common plug, drilled and tapped centrally for a ¾-in. bolt used as a valve stem. The handwheel is a makeshift, and a plain metal or fiber disk, beveled to fit the valve seat, is fastened to it with a screw. The valve was designed especially for a low-priced tree-spraying and painting machine.—J. B. Murphy, Plainfield, N. J.

## Scraping Dirt from Piston-Ring Grooves

I put in many piston rings in automobile-repair work, and as it is quite a job to scrape carbon from ring grooves, I use a section of a broken piston ring as a scraper. It is fitted in a file handle, and scrapes both the sides and bottoms of the grooves.—Irl R. Hicks, Centralia, Mo.

# A Sanitary Drinking Fountain of Concrete

By GEORGE E. TONNEY

**B**UBBLING drinking fountains are being installed on the sidewalks by many cities throughout the country, but because of the expense fewer than needed are often provided. By making forms for a substantial, artistic fountain of standard design in concrete, like that shown in the illustration, these public conveniences can be built at small cost. The mold, as detailed, is adaptable to a large variety of designs. It is built up of wood, joined together at the four corners in a miter joint, and the sections are held together, while the form is in use, by a top and a bottom plate, and wires twisted around the shaft portion of the mold. The concrete is poured in through an opening in the upper frame, or plate. For quantity production, several duplicate forms may be made. The water-feed pipe is incased in a 1½-in. drain pipe, cast into the mold when the concrete is poured in.

The construction of the fountain, detailed briefly, is as follows: Lay out a full-size sketch of the fountain, as shown in the sectional view of the working drawings. This can be done handily on a wide board, or on a long strip of wrapping paper. Indicate both the front and top views, and then lay out the parts of the wooden form, as detailed in the top view and the vertical section of the mold ready for the concrete. The wood used is ⅞ in. thick. Care must be taken in laying out this drawing carefully, especially as to the joining of the pieces, which are arranged to be nailed handily. In shaping the pieces make all the light

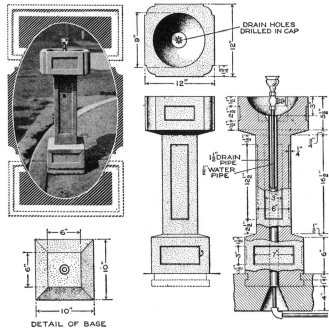

DETAIL OF BASE

This Substantial and Artistic Sidewalk Bubbling Drinking Fountain was Made in a Simple Wooden Form, Which can be Adapted to a Large Variety of Designs

strips at the same time, cutting a board long enough for all the shorter sections of each variety. Fit the pieces to the full-size drawing, and cut them, for the corner joints, in a miter box. Smooth the inner surfaces of the pieces carefully before nailing them together.

When the outer ⅞-in. boards are shaped and fitted for the four sides, nail them together, driving the nails part way in, and fit the sides together. Then make the top and bottom frames to hold the sides in place. If the joints fit snugly, drive the nails in and set their heads slightly below the surface.

Before putting the panel blocks into place, smooth off the inner surface of the mold and sandpaper away all the sharp corners. Then make the panels, which are ¼ in. thick. Nail them into place, centering them carefully on the sides of the sections. The panels should be beveled slightly, so as to withdraw readily from the concrete. Fill all of the nail holes smoothly with plaster of Paris. Make a wooden block for the basin at the top of the fountain, and arrange it to be set on top of the pipe, which is adjusted carefully in the center of the mold and held in place by nails driven into blocks set in the ends. A tin pan may also be used to form the

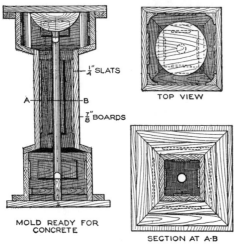

MOLD READY FOR CONCRETE

TOP VIEW

SECTION AT A-B

In Making the Forms, a Full-Sized Diagram is Laid Out and the Pieces of Wood Fitted Accurately to the Drawing

basin. Apply two coats of shellac, sanding them lightly when dry, on all surfaces of the mold which come into contact with the concrete. If the mold is to be used repeatedly, it will pay to use extra-good wood, preferably pine, and to soak the wood in oil.

If the form is properly made, little difficulty should be experienced in setting it up and pouring the concrete. Apply a uniform coat of linseed oil to the inside of the form. Bind the center portion of the form tightly with heavy wire, and set the top and bottom frames securely into place, tacking them with light wire nails. Mix a 1:3 mixture—one part Portland cement to three parts coarse clean sand—making it quite wet. Pour in the mixture, and jar the mold slightly to insure that the concrete runs into all the corners. Permit the fountain to dry at least 48 hours, in a cool, dry place. Remove the form carefully, tapping it slightly to prevent any of the corners from breaking. Repair any breakage or holes by filling the spots with the mixture. Wet the fountain for several

days, while it is permitted to dry thoroughly. If desired, the surfaces may be tooled smooth by applying a paste of cement.

Provision is made in the mold for locking the fountain securely into the concrete sidewalk, as shown in the sectional view. The fountain is set in a recess in the sidewalk, 2 in. deep, and concrete surfaced around it to the lower edge of the paneled base.

---

## An Improved Mixing Box for Mortar or Grouting

In repairing a roadway, the varying levels and the crown from the curb to the center made it awkward to use a box of the ordinary construction, mounted on wheels, for mixing the grouting and moving it from place to place. When the box was nearly full, the varying level of the material caused splashing and spilling. A special mixing box was therefore constructed, the principle of which can be adapted to mixing boxes for various uses. The mixing trough was constructed so that the mixture flowed to one corner, which was the deepest. The top of the box was so arranged, by varying the height at the four corners, that it was level

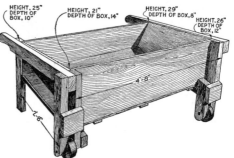

The Varying Height of the Supports for This Mixing Box Made Possible the Transporting of a Large Load without Spilling

in spite of the curve of the roadway when the box was transported, the back end being raised.—J. E. Cahill, Jr., New York, N. Y.

---

◖Do not force a tap that binds, but remove it and determine what is the cause, or a broken tap may result.

## Cutting Grooves in the Edges of Thin Disks

Having to make slots, $\frac{1}{32}$ in. wide by $\frac{1}{32}$ in. deep, in the edges of a number of 5-in. disks of aluminum, $\frac{5}{64}$ in. thick, to carry fine steel wire, we used the following method: First, in the tool post was fitted a piece of boxwood with a slot, $\frac{5}{64}$ in. wide and $\frac{1}{4}$ in. long. Over this was placed the special cutter which had a point, $\frac{1}{32}$ in. wide and $\frac{1}{32}$ in. long, projecting beyond a shoulder, which acted as a gauge for depth. The slot in the boxwood guide was just a snug fit for the thickness of the disks. As the holes in the disks and their hubs were but $\frac{5}{32}$ in., and there must be no vibration, such a method became necessary. When all was ready, a very slight turn of the end screw on the lathe moved the carriage slightly toward the chuck. This

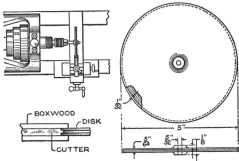

BOXWOOD — DISK
CUTTER
DETAIL OF CUTTER — ALUMINUM DISK

These Aluminum Disks were Grooved on Their Circumference by Rigging a Special Tool, as Shown

kept the disk absolutely true. We drove the disks 3,000 revolutions per minute, and as the cutter fed slowly forward, a hairlike thread of aluminum came almost unbroken up to the full depth. Under a magnifier, the slot showed a polished surface.—L. M. Drake, Daytona, Fla.

## Roller-Skate Truck Saves Carrying Doors and Sash

In a sash-and-door factory, much time and labor was saved in moving doors, and similar products, by the use of a small truck made of a roller skate. The four wheels, with the two axles, from an old roller skate were removed, and the distance between them lengthened by a strip of strap steel, about 4

Doors and Sashes were Handled Singly, Quickly, and without Damage, on This Small Truck

SKATE ROLLERS
HEAVY STRAP IRON
STOVE BOLT
4'-0"

ft. long. This was bolted to the center of the two axles, as shown. The doors were quickly shifted singly, in spaces where a large truck could not be used. —Dale R. Van Horn, Milton, Wis.

## Stock Racks for Rods and Pipes Quickly Devised

On a large machine job, where a great quantity of steel rods had to be handled quickly, it was found that the necessary racks were not available in the shop. As the work was only temporary, it was not desirable to make additional racks, and a makeshift was devised. Steel kegs, or drums, used in the shop were set up in pairs, and lengths of iron pipe, or rod, set in them to form a rack, as shown in the sketch.

This Method of Storing Pipes or Rods Temporarily can be Adapted Widely, Using Wooden Kegs or Boxes if Necessary

The arrangement proved very efficient, it being easy to transport the pipes and kegs from place to place, as needed. —Charles Doescher, Waterbury, Conn.

## Leather Wrench for Tightening Screw Clamps

Many workmen, especially those who make use of the common wood clamps

only occasionally, blister their hands in attempting to tighten up the screws on hand clamps of the cabinetmaker's type. In order to avoid this, a handy tool can be used, that is made of a strip of leather belting fastened to a handle with screws, as shown. The leather loop acts as a wrench, and the clamp screws can be tightened as securely as desired by the use of this tool.—Henry Wedde, Chicago, Ill.

## Band-Sawing Cabriole or Curved Furniture Legs

Among the many pieces of work brought into a job shop, or undertaken by the ambitious home cabinetmaker,

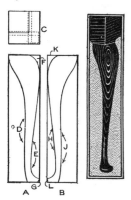

one which is perplexing to the workman who undertakes it for the first time, is the band-sawing of a Dutch or cabriole leg. A pattern for the work is desirable. The outline is marked upon two adjoining sides of the stick from which the leg is to be sawed, as indicated at A and B, C being a top view. The cuts D, E, F, G, should be sawed first. Cut each piece whole, and lay it back in the place from which it came, to provide a true surface upon which the stick may rest while the other sides are being sawed. Each piece may be held in place by hand, by fastening with small brads so

the saw will clear them, or by gluing them lightly. The latter is the best method if time permits. Next saw through H, J, K, and L.

After band-sawing the leg, it will be square in section, and often a leg of this sort is finished this way. If finished round, as in the sketch, careful work is necessary to make the sweeping curves without destroying the proportions and outlines of the leg.—Charles A. King, East Kingston, N. H.

## Changing Grinder to Left-Hand Drive

A hand grinder which I used in my home shop was arranged so that the

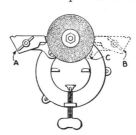

grinding was done with the left hand, while turning a crank with the right hand, in using the tool rest. I drilled a hole and tapped it, as indicated at C, so that the tool rest may be used either at A or at B. The grinding may thus be done with either hand, as is convenient.—Hugo Kretschmar, West Nyack, N. Y.

## An Improved Charcoal Soldering Furnace

This soldering furnace, which I made and have used for some time, is quite

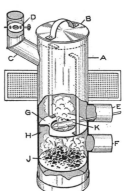

an improvement over the old kind. To make it, obtain a can, A, 6 or 8 in. in diameter and 18 in. tall, with a lid, B. Rivet on a piece of 2-in. sheet-iron pipe, C, having a damper, D, as shown. Next rivet on two pieces of pipe, 2 in. in diameter and 3 in. long, E and F. Fit a piece of sheet iron, G, inside of the pot, providing lugs, H, for riveting it to the can at three places. Cut a 4-in. opening in this, and rivet it just below pipe E. Put a charcoal fire in the bottom J, and it is ready for use. The soldering iron K is inserted through the pipe E. As considerable air goes in at E, the handle of the iron will not heat easily or burn. The draft for the fire goes in at pipe F. The copper itself will heat more quickly, owing to the intensity of the heat through the hole H.—R. S. Matzen, Fort Collins, Colo.

## One-Man Method of Adjusting Auto Foot Brakes

Many automobile owners neglect the close adjustment of foot brakes, causing needless expense and possible danger. The principal reason for such neglect is that it usually takes two men to adjust the brakes successfully. One presses the pedal, while the other tests the wheels to insure even breaking power. One man may easily and  successfully adjust the brakes with the use of a jack, as shown in the illustration. The jack A, with a block, B, to protect the seat, is placed between the seat and the brake pedal C. The jack is applied to the desired pressure on the brake pedal, and the proper adjustments made.—Koerner Rombauer, Prescott, Ariz.

## Repair for Air-Pump Stuffing Box

When the fine threads of the brass stuffing box on an air pump became so worn that they no longer held, the following method of repairing it was used: The stuffing-box cap was removed and its threads filed down until they cleared the inner threads. Two hose connections were procured, and one soldered into place, as shown in the sketch. The other was screwed

into place with a metal washer between it and the stuffing-box cap, so as to distribute the pressure evenly on the cap

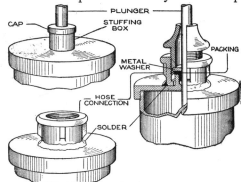

Hose Connections were Used to Repair the Stuffing Box, Making It Quite Serviceable

head. The repair proved even stronger than the original arrangement.—James M. Kane, Doylestown, Pa.

## Handcart for Railway Tracks

For use in repair work on tracks and other railway equipment the handcart shown in the illustration was found convenient. It is strongly built of oak and mounted on an axle fitted to a set of flange wheels. The frame is supported on the axle by means of two bearings of strap iron, formed as

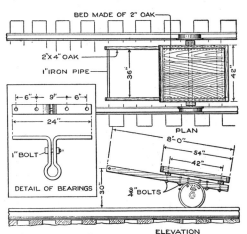

Heavy Loads are Carried on This Cart for Railway Repair Work

shown in the detail, and bolted to the frame.—Roy H. Poston, Flat River, Missouri.

## Stopping a Hole in a Hollow-Metal Float

A simple and effective method of repairing a leak in a float is as follows:

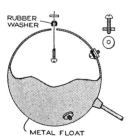

Ream out the hole in the float to the size of the head of the 3/16 by 1/2-in. stove bolt used. Tie a piece of string to the bolt, as shown; push the bolt into the ball, and place the washer over the string. Double the washer and force it through the hole in the float. Pull up the bolt through the hole in the washer, and screw on the nut. The bolt will not turn, and considerable pressure can be put on the nut without pulling the washer through the hole.—James E. Noble, Portsmouth, Ont., Can.

## Fire or Warning Whistle Operated by Electric Release Weight

A reliable electric trip for a fire whistle, suitable for small towns or villages, was constructed as shown in the diagram. The weight fastened to the whistle cord is hung on a lever, D. This lever is held in place by a hook, C. Both the lever and the hook pivot on bolts. A magnet coil, A, is placed directly above the hook,

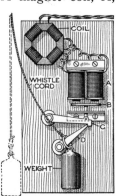

and its armature, B, is attached to it by a short connecting rod. When the current is turned on, the magnetic action in the coil lifts the hook, allowing the lower lever to drop. The whistle weight then slides off the lever, opening the steam valve, and blowing the whistle. The controlling switch may be located at the local telephone exchange or city hall. When an alarm of fire is telephoned in, the telephone operator turns on the switch and immediately the whistle sounds the alarm. When the weight is replaced, the device is in readiness for the next alarm. The device may be arranged on the ordinary 110-volt circuit with suitable fixtures. Various kinds of warning whistles may be similarly controlled.—P. E. Bertram, Crystal Lake, Illinois.

## Drill-Press Table Supports Tool Tray

Many times when using a drill press, the job takes nearly all of the table, and there is no room for calipers, gauges,

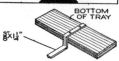

etc., without danger of losing them. I have found a little table, made as shown in the sketch, very useful. A bar of iron or steel, to fit the slot, is bent with an offset so that the top of the tray set on it will be below the top of the drill-press table. A wood tray is fastened to it by two round-head bolts. The tray can be used on the table where most convenient, and laid aside quickly when not needed.—Alfred E. Carter, Providence, R. I.

## A Starting Handle for Small Gas Engine.

A neighbor who had a 4-hp. pumping engine, was often away when water was needed, and, as his wife could not turn the flywheel over to start the engine, he rigged up a device for starting the engine and the pump without any undue effort. A hardwood lever, A, of a length twice the diameter of the flywheel, was fitted as shown. The lever is wider at the bottom, and through the center is sawed a slot as detailed. The pivot plate B was made by a blacksmith. It just clears the rim of the flywheel. A coil spring is fitted between the pivot bolt and the bottom of the slot, at C.

To install the device, turn the engine until the compression point is reached, and one spoke of the wheel is slightly raised above the horizontal. Then fasten a pin, E, to the spoke, about 2 in. in from the rim, and a bolt, D, to the lever to engage the pin at this point. The operation is simple. Turn the wheel to compression, engage the bolt D over E, on the under side of the spoke, and pull sharply forward by the handle. As the rim rises in its revolution, the bolt follows it by means of the slot and spring regulation in the lower end of the lever. The bolt D is forced out from its place at the pin E by the action of a second coil spring at the bottom of the lever, eliminating any danger if the grip on the lever is re-

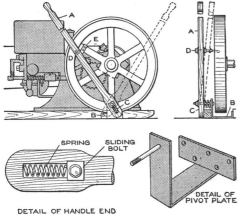

DETAIL OF HANDLE END

An Engine, Too Heavy to be Started Handily Except by a Strong Person, was Rigged with a Starting Lever That a Woman can Use

leased too soon. When not in use the lever is laid on the floor beside the motor.—L. B. Robbins, Harwich, Massachusetts.

## Large Wheel Refaced on Lathe Rigged as Grinder

Machinists in small communities, where there is not sufficient work to install machinery for many kinds of jobs, often have their ingenuity tested. The photograph shows how a job, which many machinists, without spe-

cial equipment, would have given up as impossible, was done. The wheel on the framework is one of two used for a band saw to run on. The ma-

By This Simple Yet Ingenious Arrangement a Special Machine Job was Accomplished in Spite of Very Limited Equipment

chine had been left out in the weather until the surface was rough and uneven. It was necessary to dress the face, and the shop had no equipment for handling work of that size. The job was accomplished by fitting a shaft into the wheel, fitting a drive pulley onto the same shaft, and squaring the arrangement up in front of the lathe. A belt was run from the revolving shaft of the lathe to the drive pulley, thus putting the large wheel in motion. An emery wheel, operated by an individual motor, was then fastened on the lathe, on an adjustable shelf, and put in contact with the moving wheel. By this method a perfect face was put on the two wheels.—Elbert Bede, Cottage Grove, Ore.

## Safety Gas Cock with Ball Valve

A simple appliance can be made from any ordinary gas cock insuring a more nearly safe connection with a rubber hose, when the latter is accidentally pulled from a gas heater, or stove, unnoticed. A coil spring and a small rubber ball, with retaining collar, are fitted, as shown. When the hose is removed from this gas cock

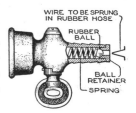

the rubber ball springs in place, stopping the flow of gas. The wire set in the end of the hose pushes the ball from the opening when the hose is attached. —A. H. Hale, Brooklyn, N. Y.

## Hood Confines Forge Fire for Intermittent Use

Having trouble with the fire going out in a portable forge, as soon as I left the blower, I overcame the trouble by fitting a 100-lb. sheet-steel, white-lead drum over the fire. A 2-in. hole was cut in one side close to the bottom. To hold the fire for some time, I heap the coals in the middle of the forge, place the drum over it, and press the rim firmly into the ashes around the fire. The fire inside is protected from drafts, and will keep for a long time.—Dennis L. Wilson, Orr's Island, Me.

## Foot-Rest Locker Built into Auto Tonneau

A locker set crosswise in the tonneau floor of an automobile, just behind the front seats, and fitted with hinged covers, inclined at the correct angle to make them serve as comfortable foot rests, is a practical feature that the autoist, himself, may install. The covers and the top of the locker are bound in brass and carpeted with the same material used on the floor of the tonneau. Each lid is fitted with a lock, and the compartment is subdivided as desired. It extends to a depth of 3 or 4 in. below the floor level. Robes

can be locked up to prevent theft when the car is left unguarded, and one of the chambers can be used for carrying the pump, jack, and other frequently used tools, which, if stored under the back seat, cause considerable inconvenience to the passengers. Where the drive shaft interferes, a space can be left for it.—Winsor R. Davis, New York, N. Y.

## Attaching a Hose Coupling with a Vulcanized Joint

A good method of fastening a metal splicer in rubber hose is one by which the coupling is, in effect, vulcanized

into the end of the hose. Support the end of the hose securely, as shown, clamping a block of wood over it with nails. The hose can also be held in a vise. Hold the coupling with a pair of pliers, and heat it in a flame to a dull red. Then the hot coupling is thrust into the end of the hose, where it will stick, and immediately the hose end, with the coupling, is soused in cold water. The rubber has, after a fashion, been vulcanized to the metal. Then, after the usual wire, or spring, clamps have been applied, on the outside of the hose around the coupling, the metal will, under ordinary conditions, give no further trouble from coming out.—R. A. Talbot, Omaha, Neb.

## Refacing Jaws of Wooden Clamps

When the jaws of wooden clamps become "chewed up" from heavy use, new life can be given to the clamp by cutting away the inner faces of the jaws along the whole length, deep enough to remove the marred parts. Another way is to cut out about 1/4 in. in the front end of each jaw, and fasten in pieces of fiber, or wood.

# Combination Turning, Sawing, and Grinding Machine

By HENRY L. COOLIDGE

SIX different kinds of machine work can be done on a combination jobshop machine, which I rigged up from an old high-wheeler bicycle: a circular-saw table rips lumber up to 1¼ in. thick and crosscuts stock nearly as thick; a molding-cutting attachment on the saw spindle cuts various kinds of wood moldings; the emery wheel does general grinding, and the lathe, and scroll saw perform the usual work done on these machines, within the range of these features. The photograph shows the machine in operation, and the sketch shows the arrangement of several of the working parts. While the machine cannot readily be duplicated, it offers suggestions for the building of other novel combination machines of pickup materials. The lathe and emery wheel are shown in the foreground of the photograph; the scroll-saw table is tilted upward, back of the emery wheel, and the circular-saw table is shown in the background. The large wheel of the bicycle was mounted in

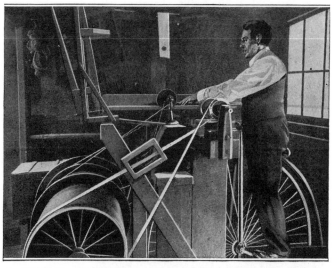

An Old-Fashioned High-Wheeler Bicycle was Rigged Up to Provide the Driving Gear for This Combination Machine; the Operator is Ripping Stock on the Circular-Saw Attachment

the frame, and supported on the floor by hangers at the pedal shaft and pipe connections at the rear brace, as shown in the sketch. The lower part of the wheel runs in a pit in the floor. The power is transmitted from the pedal shaft to a countershaft, by means of a round rope belt, running in the tire groove of the large wheel, over an idler, and engaging a 9-in. grooved

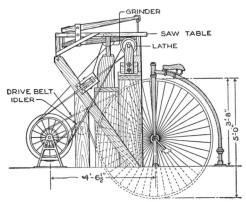

Side Elevation of the Machine, Showing Several of the Working Features, and the Driving Mechanism

pulley, set on the middle of the countershaft. Two of the small rear wheels used on this type of bicycle are mounted on the ends of the countershaft, and drums built over them, to carry the necessary belts for the lathe, emery wheel, and other tools.

The lathe bed is mounted on a wooden platform, and carries the wooden headstock, in which the bearings and spindle are mounted, as indicated. These were made from the bearings and shaft of the bicycle. The tailstock of the lathe is not shown, as it is moved back on the bed, behind the circular-saw table, when the latter is in use. The emery wheel is mounted on an iron stand, which is hinged to fold back toward the countershaft, when the scroll saw is in use.

The scroll saw is mounted in the usual type of wooden arms, and the saw table for it, together with these arms, folds upward, as shown in the photograph. When in use, the front end rests on the lathe bed, and power is transmitted to the arms from the lathe spindle, a lever giving a stroke of 2 in. The circular-saw table is shown at the farther end of the lathe bed, and is folded upward, similar to the scroll-saw table, when not in use. The free end of the table rests on the lathe bed, and is supported firmly. The rip and crosscut saws, and the molding cutters, are mounted on the circular-saw spindle, which is driven directly from the farther end of the countershaft by a pulley and belt.

## Motor Commutator Turned Up True in Position

The commutator of a motor became badly worn, requiring truing up. In making the repair, the brush yoke was removed, slipped over the bearing, and laid down, as shown. A piece of timber, fitted with another piece which

The Commutator was Turned True Quickly with This Arrangement, and the Motor was Out of Commission Only a Short Time, Because It Was Not Necessary to Take Down the Machine

acted as a knee, on which was fastened a tool rest, was bolted to the motor. The tool rest and slide fixture used were taken from a small speed lathe. This provided a movement for the feed of the tool and the depth of

cut. The rigging was fastened firmly, to prevent vibration and consequent roughening of the surface cut. The armature was driven by another motor connected to it by a belt. One side of the commutator may be harder than the other, and so care must be taken when moving the tool across the soft parts to prevent it from digging in.—Harvey Mead, Scranton, Pa.

## Rubber Goods Kept Pliable by Oil

Soft-rubber apparatus deteriorates comparatively rapidly, and a method of preserving it sometimes used by surgeons is to inclose the rubber articles in a tight receptacle, in the bottom of which a small quantity of kerosene oil is permitted to evaporate. A large tin box, or can, with a close-fitting lid makes a good container. Perforated trays are fitted into it to hold the rubber goods. The bottom tray should be several inches above the oil, about two teaspoonfuls of oil being required. The oil must not come in contact with the rubber, which must, of course, be given a thorough washing before use, if sanitation is a requirement.

## Automatic Feed-Water Pan for Furnaces

Most hot-air furnaces are equipped with a water pan placed usually at the front, or side, in the narrow space between the outside casing and the fire chamber. Such a pan is commonly filled only when the overbaked smell from the dry pan gives tardy notice of the need of attention. The following description of a thoroughly satisfactory, automatically filled pan devised for a hot-air furnace is suggestive as to further means of accomplishing the same purpose.

The pan A, which need not be large, was placed where a sufficient volume of water could be evaporated, on top of the fire box. The heat might melt soldered joints, so a seamless drum, a container of white lead, was used. A hole was punched through the side, near the bottom and fitted with a horizontal length of ½-in. pipe, B, long enough to extend through the sheet-iron casing of the furnace, a distance of about 2 ft., to a wooden post, as shown. On this post, a shelf was placed to hold a paint can, D, to which the other end of the 1-in. pipe was attached, also near the bottom. Within this can, a float, F, was devised, in the form of an inverted cup, open at the bottom, and guided by a central tube, G, fitted over a vertical wire, H, soldered to the bottom of the can. To the top of the float was attached a needle stem, I, about 2 in. long, serving as a valve stem for the control of the water supply.

A water connection was made by a short length of garden hose, L, as shown. The valve J consisted of a thin sheet of copper soldered over the

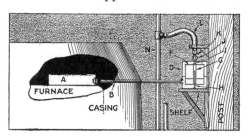

This Arrangement Automatically Keeps the Humidifying Water Tank of the Furnace Filled to the Proper Level, and Insures Healthful Moisture in the Rooms Heated

end of a hose coupling, connected to a nipple, K. A small hole was made in the copper disk, and the needle point entering this hole made a self-guiding valve. The evaporation of the water in the hot-air chamber of the furnace lowers the water level, causing the float to descend and let in water from the hose until the float is raised again, and the water shut off. The regulation of the water supply thus becomes automatic.—B. H. G., Chicago, Ill.

❡A careful operator will not carry developer over to the fixing bath on his hands, or bring them into contact with the developer, until after washing them thoroughly, if any of the fixing bath has come into contact with them.

## Back Rest for Supporting Wood in Lathe

In turning a long piece upon an ordinary wood-turning lathe, one or more back rests, or supports, may be necessary to control the vibration. The device shown in the sketch was found efficient, and can be made easily. The piece B passes between the shears A of the lathe, and is held in place by a wedge, C, space being left to allow the

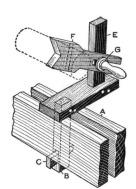

wedge to pull. The top end of the piece B is mortised and pinned into the base, and the standard E, mortised and pinned. The front end of the arm F is V-shaped. The other end of the arm is slotted to permit lateral adjustment. The screw G, and the hole in the upright E, are threaded, and arranged to hold the arm in place. In use, the V of the arm should be kept waxed with paraffin, so that the spindle will turn easily without scratching, and the rest should be centered over the stock carefully.

## Renewing Wooden Posts with Concrete

Wooden posts, supporting fences, signs, or buildings generally, decay at the ground line. It is not always possible to renew them without disturbing the structure they support, and besides, if the timber is sound except at the one point, there is a needless waste of lumber if they are discarded. To renew the life of such a post it is only necessary to remove the dirt for 6 in.

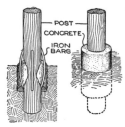

around the post. Next a wooden or sheet-metal form is made, and concrete poured in the form around the post, reinforced with iron bars, to a level with the top of the form. After the concrete has set, the post is stronger and less likely to decay farther than before the treatment.—K. M. Cogge-shall, Webster Groves, Mo.

### Safety Circular-Saw Guard Prevents Back Thrust

The old saying "never monkey with a buzz saw" is as sound as ever, and the careful mechanic will provide his circu-lar saw with a guard which can be homemade, as shown. Make two steel plates, as detailed, and grind or file teeth into them on the curved edge. Drill the plates for screws and fasten them to a wooden core, permitting the toothed edge to project slightly. Various ways of clamping the guard on the saw-table fence can be devised. The dangerous back thrust of stock being cut is overcome by this guard.—L. J. Young, Cape Porpoise, Maine.

### Revolution Counter Rigged to Determine Lineal Travel on Machinery

It is often desirable to know the speed a belt is traveling, or the rate of surface travel of a piece of metal being cut in a machine tool. These speeds can be easily calculated if the diameter of the surfaces and the revolutions per minute are known, but often it is inconvenient to measure one or both of them. Most machine shops and engine rooms possess a revolution counter of the type shown. A wheel,

exactly $1\frac{15}{16}$ in. in outside diameter, with a rubber rim, was made as shown, to slip onto the counter in place of the pointer. This diameter is calculated so closely that it gives very accurate results. The revolutions per minute, as indicated by the counter, are timed by a watch. To obtain the distance travel of the surface in feet per minute, divide the revolutions per minute of the counter wheel by 2, which gives the number of feet per minute of surface travel, the circumference of the counter wheel being very close to 6 inches.—R. L. Hervey, Washington, D. C.

### Tool for Applying Hose Clamps Handily in Vise

The operation of putting a clamp on a rubber hose at a connection is sometimes difficult, especially if it is an 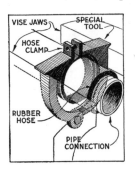extra-tight fit and the bolt accompanying the clamp is a trifle short. In a shop where the application of clamps on hose, for the purpose of splicing, is part of the daily routine, a tool was made which simplifies the operation. The device, as shown in the illustration, is U-shaped, hinged at the bottom, and large enough to accommodate hose from 1 to 4 in. in diameter. It may be forged with but little trouble. In applying a clamp to the hose, the tool is applied so that its jaws grip the ends of the clamps, and the whole is placed in a vise. By gradually closing the vise jaws, the ends of the clamp are brought together, and a connection made easily and quickly.—L. School-craft, Chicago, Ill.

¶In stenciling around the corner of the wall, use two stencils, one for straight work and the other to bend around the corner, as the bending injures the stencil.

## Clothes Drier Attached to Kitchen Boiler

Men in the household usually object to the stringing of wash lines across the kitchen, and the home mechanic who is willing to do a little work to do away with this nuisance, can provide for a considerable quantity of clothes to be dried by arranging a drier around the kitchen boiler. The heat from the boiler reduces considerably the time necessary to dry the clothes. The device should be set near the top of the tank, as shown. It consists of a band-iron ring, which is split at one side and drawn tightly around the boiler by means of a bolt. Small angles, bent from similar band iron, hold the wooden strips on which the clothes are hung. A novel feature of these supports is the spring-clip device, shown in detail, which supports the strips when used. When not in use, the strips can be folded down, out of the way, against the side of the tank. The spring clips are bolted beside the left

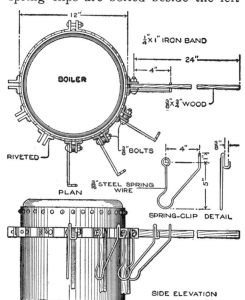

Quick Drying of Clothes in the Kitchen is Provided For by This Practical Arrangement, Which Permits the Wooden Strips to be Folded Down When Not in Use

angle of each pair of angles, which support the wooden strips bolted between them.—P. P. Avery, Garfield, N. J.

## Folding Table, Robe Rack, and Extra Compartment in Automobile

An ingenious method of construction and manner of stowing a folding table, and other details of luncheon equip-

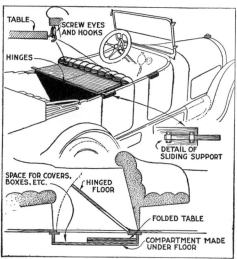

The Table Is a Handy Feature, and When Folded is Stowed Away with Other Articles in the Floor Compartment

ment, is used by the owner of a light five-passenger car. The table consists of two nearly square boards, secured together by two strap hinges on the under side. Two metal slides and two screw hooks are provided for setting it up in the rear of the car, as shown. At the rear of the upper edge of the front seat, two screw eyes are secured. A leather strap through them serves as a robe rack. The hooks on the edge of the table are placed through these screw eyes, and the slides are extended, resting on the doors. The slides are wooden strips set in sheet-metal straps, fastened to the under side of the table. Under the rear floor of the car is a shallow container, and the floor boards have been cut out and fastened together to form a cover. The compartment accommodates the table when folded, and also other materials. The preference for eating in the car arose because of insects and other annoyances, when the luncheon is spread upon the ground.—G. A. Luers, Washington, D. C.

## A Farm Feed and Water Heater of Concrete

An ingenious farmer made a handy cooker for cooking feed for stock and poultry. The forms for pouring the concrete were set up with rough boards. The food is cooked in an old iron kettle, under which is

This Concrete Outdoor Farm Cooking Stove can be Made Handily with Simple Forms

provided a place for a fire connecting with the chimney. The water is supplied by the pipe shown at the left. The device is thoroughly practical, and one that any farmer can build in spare time at small cost, as a permanent farm improvement.

## Adaptable Tool for Machining Circular Curves on Lathe

Considerable lathe work involving circular corners and grooves was done

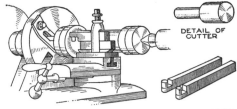

DETAIL OF CUTTER

RADIUS CUTTERS

Smooth, Circular Curves were Cut in Turned Work on the Lathe by Means of Adaptable Cutters Made in Several Standard Sizes

in a machine shop, and this made it worth while to design and make a set of radius cutters of standard sizes, by which the curves could be cut quickly and uniformly. The cutters were turned up in various sizes, ranging upward from $\frac{3}{32}$ in., made of tool steel, as shown in the detailed sketch. They were set in shanks of steel to fit the tool post. In use, the cutters were set in the tool post upside down, as shown; the drive belt was reversed, and plenty of oil was applied to the cutter. An accurate, smooth job resulted when the feed was carefully regulated.—Ben Frantzreb, Indianapolis, Ind.

## Fitting Gasoline-Motor Piston Rings Accurately

One of the most common causes of a lack in power of an engine is poor compression, the result of poorly fitting valves or leaky piston rings. First, there is much difference between fitting in and putting in piston rings. A method of fitting the rings, that has been found highly satisfactory, is here described.

The ring, as it comes from the factory, should be a trifle oversize. First fit the ring to the cylinder, and then to the piston. A wooden piston is made, slightly smaller than the cylinder. To the end of this wooden plug, the piston ring is fastened by a strip of wood held in place by a screw. The ring should be held loosely. The inside of the cylinder is next coated with Prussian blue, then the wooden piston and ring are inserted, and moved back and forth a few times. Upon removing the ring, the high spots on the ring are bright, while the low spots are colored. The high spots on the ring should be filed down carefully, or polished off with emery cloth. After a few trials, the ring can usually be made to fit the cylinder all the way around. Attention must be given to the joint in the ring. A very small clearance, $\frac{1}{64}$ in. often being sufficient, should be left at the joint to allow for expansion from the heat.

The ring is then ready to be fitted to

the piston. The ring should be turned around in the groove, and if it binds, it should be smoothed off. To smooth off the sides of the ring it should be rubbed across emery cloth laid flat on a board, shifting it during the process. It frequently happens that an engine does not have as good compression after new rings have been put in without proper care. Proper fitting of the rings will make a surprising difference in the efficiency and power of a motor.—B. F. Bell, Waverly, Neb.

## Emery-Wheel Dresser Made of Old Emery Wheel

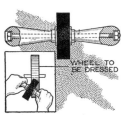

For dressing down emery wheels, a small worn-out emery wheel is useful, when properly mounted. Set the small wheel on a large bolt, provided with two handles, as shown. Place two large washers between the wheel proper and the handles, which are held by nuts, with washers, at the ends to give slight play. In use, the small wheel is held against the wheel to be dressed, at an angle, and the handles are forced together to slow up the dressing wheel, and produce a grinding effect.—Thomas W. Benson, Hastings-upon-Hudson, N. Y.

## Pulley Lever That does Not Damage Rims

In the maintenance of machinery and mechanical power-transmission equipment, it is frequently necessary to turn a pulley, which is mounted on a shaft or machine, through a revolution or fraction thereof, to reset it. When a lever is required, monkey wrenches are often used, with a piece of pipe slipped over the handle. This method sometimes breaks pieces from the rims of the pulleys. A pulley-starting lever, which will not break the rims, can be

made as detailed in Fig. 1. With this lever the stress on the pulley rim is distributed over a wide area. For best

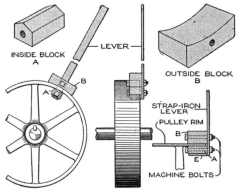

By the Use of This Lever Arrangement the Rims are Not Nicked in Resetting Pulleys

results, a different-size outside block, B, should be made for pulleys varying considerably in diameter. The blocks A and B may be made of cast or wrought iron, or even of hard wood. The lever is of strap iron, and the blocks are held to it with machine bolts.—R. C. Farrell, Chicago, Ill.

## Device for Centering Work on Boring Mills

The centering of round work on a vertical boring mill is easily accomplished with the use of the roller centering device shown in the sketch. The casting is placed on the table, not bolted down, and the table run slowly, and, as the wheel on the

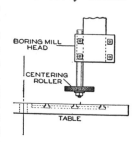

centering device is loose, the casting is centered by moving the head horizontally until the wheel runs against the casting all the way around. Centering work on a boring mill is usually done with the aid of the cutting tool, which often results in damage to the work, but with the use of the roller there is no liability of damage from this source.—J. R. Minter, Washington, Ind.

## Ventilating Door on Roof Opened from Ground

A novel door made for the roof of a silo, in place of the usual type of ventilating door, and which can be opened from the ground by means of a rope threaded through pulleys, has numerous other applications. The door is hinged in the usual manner, and a wooden bracket built on its inner

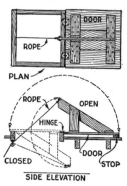

side, as shown. The rope is tied at the upper corner of the bracket, when the door is opened and resting on its stop on the roof. By drawing on the rope, the door is raised sufficiently so that its weight acts as a counterbalance, closing it. To open the door, the rope is also pulled, until the door is carried past the point of balance, when it again carries itself to the open position by its own weight. If the door is a heavy one, counterweights and bumping pads should be arranged for it.—L. A. Knutsen, Everett, Wash.

## Simple Method of Making Core Prints without Lathe

It is customary with patternmakers to turn core prints integral with the patterns themselves. At times, however, the separate print is preferred. Also, some patternmakers have no power tools be

sides a saw and a sand wheel. Then prints can be easily and as quickly made as in a lathe by rough-sawing the block, as shown, and sanding it down to the scribed circle. A scribed circle on the pattern locates the print.— Donald A. Hampson, Middletown, New York.

## Pile of Rods Protected by Painted Stripe

A practical method of detecting if pieces have been taken from a pile of pipe, tubing, or bar stock, as often is the case especially where the material is stored in vacant lots or in shop yards, is to paint a bright-colored stripe over the pile. If pieces are taken from the pile, there will be a break in the colored stripe. This aids in placing the responsibility quickly, and cuts down the unauthorized use or theft of stock. —C. C. Spreen, Flint, Mich.

## Block for Starting Flow of Ink in Ruling Pen

The ink in a ruling pen often refuses to flow, and in order to avoid the com

mon practice of touching the point on the finger, I made a block that does the work nicely. To make it, drill a ½-in. hole in the end of a 1¾ by 1½-in. block of wood, as shown. Cut a curved slot from the top into the hole, rounding off the corners smoothly. Glue pieces of cardboard over the ends and provide a base. When the pen is contrary, push the point through the slot, and the ink is released. The block can easily be cut to fit pens of various sizes.—Walter Whitley, Lawrence, Mass.

## Cleaning Glass Chemical Containers

Graduates, reagent bottles, and similar vessels used for chemicals, should be cleaned thoroughly before refilling them, especially if a new liquid is used. A good cleansing agent is vinegar into which a quantity of coal dust has been poured. Fill the vessel about one-third full and shake it vigorously until the interior is polished clean. Wash the vessel in clear water, preferably distilled.

# Shop Notes

## Fertilizing and Irrigating a Farm with Muck from Lake Bed

By E. R. McINTYRE

AN original and successful scheme for using lake water and its muck deposits for irrigating and fertilizing an adjoining farm was used by a Minnesota farmer. There being no complete outfits on the market for such projects, he worked out his own methods which have a wide application for similar projects. The pumping outfit transfers 90 tons of muck-laden water an hour from a small lake to the farm land. Of this solution nine tons an hour is muck. The lake has about 5 ft. of water at its deepest point. The muck is from 8 to 35 ft. deep, of loose formation, and easily pumped.

sionally with a long-handled rake, to stir up the muck.

Engine and pump are fastened to a small barge, as shown in the lower photograph. Connecting with the pump are two lines of pipe. One draws the muck and water into the pump, and

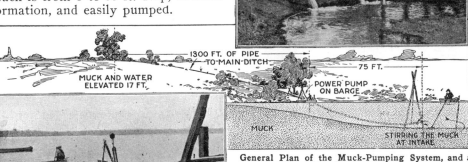

General Plan of the Muck-Pumping System, and a View of the Discharge Pipes at the Main Irrigation Ditch

The Barge is Anchored near the Shore and Carries the Pump and Engine

The equipment consists of one 7-hp. kerosene engine, a 3½-in. centrifugal pump, intake pipe, and a pipe used to carry the water from the pump to the highest point of land whence the distribution is through open ditches and furrows. While the pump is in operation, a man in a boat about 100 ft. off shore agitates the lake bottom occa-

the other transfers it in turn to the land. The intake pipe of wood is kept at the bottom of the lake by means of weights. A 6-in. pipe is fastened to the wooden pipe and may be swung in various directions. With added pipe the supply of muck is readily extended.

To keep out stones and sand a special device is used. A box, measuring 3 by 3 by 5 ft., is placed between the pump and the intake pipe. This catches the extra large particles and keeps them out of the pump. The water and muck are taken to the highest point on the farm, 650 ft. distant, with a rise of 17 ft., by two lines of 4-in. pipe. These are fastened to the exhaust openings of the pump on the barge. Old boiler flues are used for these pipes. Instead of piping outward from the highest point on the farm, ditches were dug, and the strawberry beds and orchard irrigated in this way. On kerosene, the cost of operation is about 10 cents an hour, the muck thus being deposited on the land at a cost of 10 cents a ton, exclusive of labor and repairs to machinery and the initial cost of $250 for the equipment.

### Cutting Threads Accurately on Small or Thin Pipe

In cutting threads on thin or small pipe it is often troublesome, especially on short pieces, to get the threads square with the length of the pipe. There is also trouble in getting a suitable grip on the pipe so as not to bruise or scratch it if plated. A good method is to put the die holder in a bench vise, and reverse

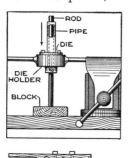

the dies, that is, turn them upside down. This will make a piece of pipe thread in the direction of the arrow. Select a piece of steel rod of a size to just slide through the pipe. Run this down between the dies into a block so fastened as to make the rod vertical. Slide the pipe down over the rod and it will be threaded straight and true. The best grip I have found is shown in the smaller sketch. Select a piece of hard wood, 1⅛ in. thick and 15 in. long. Shape it as shown, and bore a series of holes along a center line, of sizes to take the outside diameters of the pipes. Then bore two ¼-in. holes for bolts. With a thin saw, cut along between the pieces. When clamped on the pipe, this device will not slip or bruise it.—L. M. Drake, Daytona, Fla.

### Portable Stand for Janitor's Cleaning Equipment

A stand, on casters, and built to accommodate the various articles that a janitor uses in cleaning rooms and

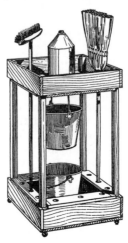

halls in large buildings, is a time and labor saver. It is made to fit a hall closet, and can be kept out of sight easily when not in use. Painting it with white enamel gives a neat appearance. When needed, the janitor rolls the stand to the room he intends to clean, leaving the stand just outside. The casters should be of the pivoted roller type, and for use on highly finished floors larger, rubber-covered caster wheels are desirable.—Thomas O'Dea, New Haven, Conn.

### Tool for Grasping Small Machine Parts

Four pieces of steel wire and a file handle are all that is needed for the construction of a handy tool useful for

setting bolts, nuts, screws, etc., in places difficult of access. It is also convenient for recovering coins, rings, washers, etc., from plumbing fittings. The tool is made by driving into the file handle three steel wires, in prong fashion. A wire is made ring-shaped, to slide over the prongs and compress them about the piece to be handled. The length of the prongs will vary to suit the needs of the individual user.

## Shaft Hangers and Fittings
## for the Small Shop

When it was found too expensive to buy hangers for a shaft in a small shop, they were improvised, and proved so serviceable that they were left in place as permanent equipment. Six of these hangers carry a 1-in. line shaft, 34 ft. long. The method of construction is simple, and the parts used can be obtained in most small shops.

Cold-rolled steel is used for the shaft. The bearings are made of short sections of gas pipe, into which babbitt is poured. The bearings require a 1¼-in. pipe, cut from 4 to 6 in. long, depending on the load to be carried.

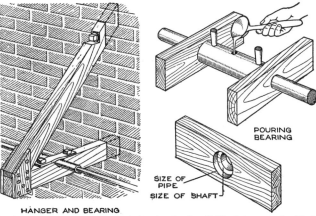

HANGER AND BEARING

POURING BEARING

SIZE OF PIPE

SIZE OF SHAFT

Equipment for Power Transmission in the Small Workshop can be Made Cheaply by Using Babbitted Pipe Bearings and Hangers Built Up of Wood

After the pipe is cut with a hacksaw to give a square end against which collars can be fitted, the sections are bored with three holes, as shown in the sketch. Two of the holes are oil holes, and the center one is for the pouring of the babbitt.

The pouring of the babbitt is accomplished by means of two wooden supports, bored, as shown, to fit the shaft, and shouldered for the pipe. The arrangement is set up as indicated, the oil holes being plugged, and the babbitt is poured into the bearings. The bearings are smoothed and cleaned in the usual manner. If the shaft and pipe are warmed slightly, a better job will result.

The method of hanging the bearings can be arranged to suit conditions. In this instance the shaft is run along the wall, and the hangers are made of wood, strongly braced, and set into the wall, as shown. The bearing is clamped into a V-groove by means of a metal plate.

The wood pulleys to transmit the power from the shaft are made by building them up of alternate layers of ⅞-in. wood, which are cross-banded, and fastened with glue and bolts. The pulleys can be turned true by mounting them on the shaft, and rigging up a suitable rest for the turning chisels. Collars for holding the pulleys and other fittings on the shaft, can be made up of short sections of pipe, drilled and tapped for setscrews. To guard the setscrews, they should be short, and the threaded collar covered with a second collar, bored so that the head of the setscrew is recessed in a socket, and the covering collar cut to form a split ring. Suitable setscrews may be made by cutting off the threaded end of a bolt, and slotting the upper end to engage a heavy screwdriver.—Ray F. Kuns, Cincinnati, Ohio.

## Small Wire Scratchbrush
## Handy in Soldering

In soldering teakettles, pans, etc., it is often difficult to clean the surface to be soldered, especially on the inside of the vessel. This trouble can be overcome by using a file cleaner with long steel-wire bristles. If the cleaner is too large, cut some fine steel wires, form them around a small brass rod, bind them securely with a piece of brass or copper wire, and then sweat a little solder in around them. Such a scratchbrush will give good service for cleaning small areas.—A. Gemmell, Ansonia, Conn.

## Window Lamp with Revolving Shade Attracts Attention

The animated window display described is automatic and requires no driving mechanism. To make the re-

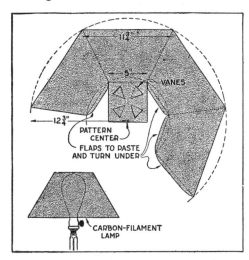

The Heat Generated by the Lamp Turns the Shade, Which is Pivoted on the Tip of the Globe

volving shade, cut from light, strong cardboard, a form, as shown. The sides may be cut with stenciled letters or designs, backed with translucent paper, or may be left solid. Four triangles are cut in the top, and the resulting vanes are bent downward at right angles. A small paper disk is then pasted in the exact center of the under side of the top, and a small hole centered in it. Mount a large carbon-filament lamp on a suitable pedestal, pivot the shade on the tip of the lamp, and turn on the current. The heat generated will flow up between the vanes and slowly turn the shade as long as the current is turned on.—B. L. Dobbins, Boston, Mass.

## Cutting Hard Sheet Rubber with Scissors

Hard sheet rubber is difficult to cut, and the average experimenter has few facilities for doing such work. An easy way to cut this material, up to $\frac{3}{16}$ in. thick, is as follows: Mark the outline to be cut on the rubber with

a scriber. Plunge the sheet into hot water; take it out and cut on the outline with a pair of heavy scissors. The rubber will become soft like leather and will cut easily. As it becomes cooler, it will cut harder. If any more cutting is to be done, plunge it into hot water again, and continue until the cutting is finished. The sheet will probably be somewhat out of flat. To remedy this, dip the rubber in hot water, place it on a sheet of plate glass, or metal, and put another sheet of glass over the rubber, with a weight on it. Permit it to cool, and it will be flattened.—W. S. Standiford, Youngstown, Ohio.

## Device for Opening Stove Damper Handily

It is often inconvenient to get near enough to a damper in a stove or furnace to open and close it. To overcome this difficulty I arranged a simple device, as shown in the sketch. I first made four pieces of wood, $\frac{7}{8}$ by $\frac{1}{2}$ by 6 in., and two of them were halved together in the form of a "T," as detailed. On the ends of the crossbar I inserted screw eyes. The other two pieces I fastened on the handle of the damper with two screws, and also put screw eyes in the ends of one of these pieces. To the floor joist I nailed a brace long enough to be within easy reach of a person standing in front of the furnace. On this brace I pivoted

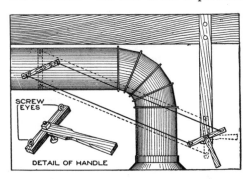

This Arrangement Made in Half an Hour Is a Great Convenience at the Furnace

the T-shaped piece, as shown. Parallel wires connected to the eyes, as indicated, completed the arrangement. By means of the T-shaped piece I can move the damper readily from the front of the furnace.—Walter S. Jennings, Buffalo, N. Y.

## Chipped Grooves Drain Rainwater from Walk Depressions

After several years, stone and various composition walks begin to wear away on the surface. Depressions form near the center of each square of walk, and after a rain pools of water settle in these depressions. A remedy is to chip a small groove from the low spot to the side of the walk, to afford drainage for the water.

## Variable "Will Be Back" Sign Quickly Made

To save time in answering telephone calls for men who are out of the office, a clerk in a large organization devised an inexpensive device to tell when each man expects to be back at his desk. Across the top of a 3 by 5-in. filing card is lettered "Will Be Back at," and below this is the name of the man for whose use the card is intended. Two horizontal slits, 1½ in. long, are cut in the middle of the card about ½ in. apart, as shown. A fairly stiff piece of paper about 8 in. long is slid through these slits. On this strip the office hours, divided into half-hour periods, are indicated. The ends of the strip are pasted together forming a support for the sign. When John Smith intends to leave his desk at 10:00 a. m. for an hour, he simply slides the stiff paper through the two slits until "11:00 a. m." appears on the face of the card. This device makes it unnecessary to bother several people to ascertain when he will be back.

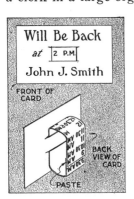

## Devices That Add Comfort to Winter Touring

Winter automobile touring or driving, without special preparation, subjects the tires of the car and its occu-

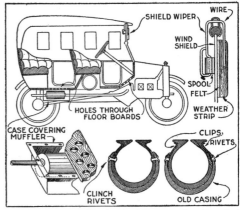

These Homemade Devices and Features Are Practical for Winter Touring or Driving. The Car is Warmed, the Tires Protected, and the Windshield Kept Clean

pants to unusual severities. With comparatively slight labor, protection may be provided that will also decrease expenditures for tires. Excess heat, usually lost in radiation, can be diverted to portions of the car to the comfort of the occupants. The method shown in the sketch is effective. Construct a boxlike case for the muffler, and fasten this to the under side of the floor. The casing may be of sheet metal or wood. Through the floor, directly above the deflector, a number of holes should be bored, which will not materially weaken it, yet will permit the heat from around the muffler to escape into the car. The floor boards in the front compartment may be drilled in a similar manner for the heat from the radiator and engine.

Tires should be protected from the frozen roadbeds. Discarded casings will render efficient service as covers, taking most of the punishment of the winter roads, and also increasing the tire diameter and bearing surface, thus making progress through the snow less difficult. The heads of the casings are removed. Coppered clinch rivets hold the casings securely in place, as detailed.

Another convenience, when driving through snow, rain, or mist, is a home-made windshield wiper. One made of a piece of felt-edged weather stripping, mounted on a bent rod of spring wire, as shown, is practical. The clip is made of sheet metal, fastened by means of a small bolt, and, on the other end of the wire, a spool, with flanges removed, is mounted. If the felt edge is occasionally saturated in equal parts of glycerin and alcohol, it will coat the glass with an oily film, which tends to shed water and makes necessary only occasional use of the cleaner.—G. A. Luers, Washington, D. C.

---

## Fitting Angle-Shaft Bearing Brackets to a Machine

A shaft to be placed at an angle on a machine in bearing brackets, as shown, requires considerable fitting to get the

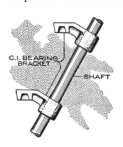

brackets in line, so that the shaft does not bind. To avoid this trouble, the bearing brackets should be bored out ½ in. larger than the diameter of the shaft. The brackets are secured to the machine; small collars, ⅛ in. wide, are provided to slip over the shaft, their outside diameter being the same as the bore in the bearing brackets. These collars are placed in position to enter the holes in the bracket, centering the shaft. Babbitt is poured through a hole drilled in the hubs of the bearing brackets. The babbitt will run around the shaft, locating it easily. It is only necessary, after removing the shaft, to scrape the inside of the bearings and drill an oil hole.—Jos. Limbrunner, Shelton, Conn.

---

❡In clamping smooth work on machine-shop machines, the slipping of the metal on the surface of the machines can be overcome by inserting a sheet of paper between the work and the machine bed.

## Replacing a Strong Coil Spring

Great difficulty is often encountered in replacing the clutch spring on an

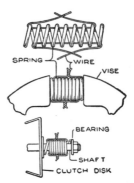

automobile, or other strong coil springs, which must be compressed. The operation is frequently dangerous, especially for one man. By binding the spring with wire, as shown in the sketch, and clamping it in a vise, one man can replace the spring quickly and safely. Two pieces of wire are inserted in the spring, which is then clamped in the vise. The wires are twisted and drawn up tightly. Then the spring is set into place, and, when the wires are cut, springs to its proper position.—Ralph M. Brown, Ithaca, N. Y.

---

## Channel Bars Mitered in Power Hacksaw

In making a large frame out of channel iron, the ends had to be cut at an angle. The rigging, shown in the dia-

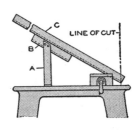

gram, was made to line up the channel irons for cutting. The upright A is fastened to the bed of the hacksaw, its lower end being bent at a right angle. The strip B is fastened to the upright A at such an angle that, when the channel iron rests against it, the end will be cut off at the required angle. The channel iron C is held against the strip B with a wooden clamp. The rigging should be in line with the vise so that the lower end of the work may be clamped in the vise. This method saved much time as against doing the work by hand.—C. Anderson, Worcester, Mass.

## A Quickly Made Shaft Coupling

Two old gears from the shop scrap box were used to make a shaft coupling, which proved quite satisfactory. It was used to con- nect an electric motor to a small water pump for experimental work. The gears were pinned to

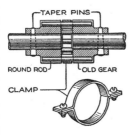

the shafts by means of standard taper pins, as shown, after which a series of round steel pins were placed in the spaces between the teeth. These pins were of such diameter as to allow them to fit in the spaces snugly. A clamping collar, made in two sections as de- tailed, was slipped over the pins, hold- ing the latter firmly in place. The coupling has proved efficient, and also has the advantage of being readily dis- assembled.—A. L. Snell, Minneapolis, Minn.

## Wall Pockets for Storing Rivets and Small Hardware

A method of storing rivets, used by a tinsmith, has many practical adapta- tions for the home workshop, as well as for the shop or hardware store. The tinsmith made a series of sheet-metal poc- kets, as shown in the sketch, 6 in. wide and 8 in. long, with an eye at one end to be hung on a nail, or shoulder hook, set in a large board or in the wall. On the front of each

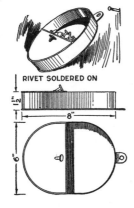

pocket, he soldered a rivet, or sample of whatever small article was contained in the particular pocket. When used on a workbench, the pockets are laid flat, exposing the contents.

## Thawing Out a Fire Plug Quickly

When the fire department was called out one night to a serious fire, the street fire plug was frozen, and ordi- nary remedies failed to open it promptly. While some of the firemen attacked the blaze with chemicals and what water was available, others poured gasoline, from the tank of the fire truck, over the frozen plug and set fire to it. The plug was soon thawed out, and the fire brought un- der control.

## Novel Display Wheel for Show Window

A window advertising novelty which attracted considerable attention, was homemade of inexpensive materials, and driven by a small motor, the whole arrange- ment being com- pactly inclosed, as shown in the illustration. A good size for the case is 15 in. high, 3½ in. deep, and 12 in. wide, with a disk about 10 in. in diameter made of two ¼-in. boards. The smaller disk is used as a pulley, and is belted to the motor by small round

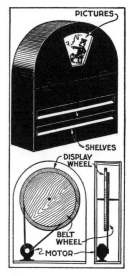

belts, or cords. Cartoons, or similar devices, with advertisements between them, are mounted on the face of the disk, which can be covered with velvet or other attractive material. The wheel is driven around making the onlooker curious to see the various figures that appear in the opening. Two narrow shelves may be set into the front of the box, as shown, for displaying rings or other small articles. The front of the case is hinged as indicated, so that the disk can be re-covered as desired.

## Combined Hinge and Stop for Cellar Doors

Strips of flat iron, ¼ by 1 in. wide, were used to make serviceable hinges

_¼"X1" FLAT IRON_

These Combined Hinges and Spring Doorstops Strengthen the Doors, and Keep Persons from Walking on Them

for cellar doors, and a strip was attached to each hinge, curled in the form of a spring, as shown, providing also a practical stop. The usual difficulty with such doors is that the hinges are soon torn loose and the doors racked to pieces. These hinges act as braces across the doors as well as stops. —M. E. Duggan, Kenosha, Wis.

## Proof on Letter-Printing Machine Made with Carbon Sheet

A simple way to obtain a proof sheet of a letter that has been set up for running on a letter-printing machine, without going to the trouble of attaching and detaching the ribbon and getting the fingers full of ink, is to lay a piece of carbon paper on top of the letterhead with the carbon face in contact with the letter, and then feed the two sheets through the machine together. The result will be a legible carbon copy in which all errors are readily found. On account of the extra thickness of paper, the lever regulating the impression should be properly adjusted.—Alfred J. Miller, Albuquerque, N. M.

## Broken Motorcycle Nut Repaired on Road

While on a motorcycle trip, far from a repair shop, one of the main nuts on the rear axle of my machine broke in two. It was an odd size, and I could not get another. Finally I clipped a loose end of heavy wire from a near-by fence, filed a V-groove around the edge of the nut on the six corners, and twisted the wire tightly around the nut in the groove. When screwed into place on the axle, the nut held satisfactorily until I arrived home.—W. H. Thies, Washington, District of Columbia.

## Hook for Removing Cap Rings from Piling or Posts

In driving posts or piling, a steel ring is usually set over the top to prevent damage to the post from the blows of the hammer, or pile-driver head. Where a number of stakes are driven, it is also convenient to use a ring which may be removed and used repeatedly. The device shown in the sketch can be

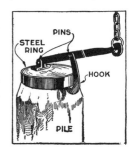

STEEL RING — PINS — HOOK — PILE

made in various sizes for removing these rings quickly. On large jobs, power may be applied to the drawbar, and on smaller posts a lever may be hooked to the chain, or the bar may be made long enough to give good leverage.

## Surfacing Typewriter Platens with Sandpaper

When rubber typewriter platens become hard and uneven they can be made soft and smooth by turning them with coarse sandpaper, and then smoothing them with fine emery cloth. They will then be almost like new, thus avoiding the poor writing caused by hard and uneven platens.

# An Electric Spot-Welding Machine

By K. M. COGGESHALL

ELECTRIC spot welding is rapidly replacing riveting as a means of permanently holding together two or more sheets of metal for many kinds of work. The electric weld is more quickly made than the riveted joint; it will not loosen, and is nearly as strong and durable as the material itself, if properly made. For this work a special machine is necessary. The sheets to be welded together are placed between two copper electrodes, as shown in the heading illustration and detailed in the assembly sketch and working drawings. A large current, at low voltage, is then made to flow from one electrode to the other, passing through the intervening metal sheets. As these sheets, which are generally of iron, have a much higher electrical resistance than the copper electrodes, they instantly become hot at the points where the electrodes touch them. The hotter

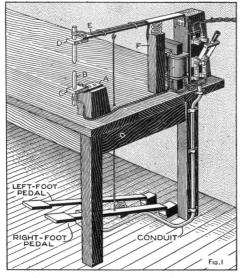

**A Large Range of Spot-Welding Work can be Done with This Homemade Outfit, the Current for Which is Taken from the Ordinary 110-Volt Lighting Circuit**

the metal becomes, the greater is the resistance. Finally, the iron sheets are brought to a welding temperature, and a very slight pressure forces the molten metal together, forming a perfect weld at the point of application of the pressure.

The constructional features of a modern spot-welding machine for high-speed factory work are quite complicated, but a simple, homemade machine may be built for the small shop at slight expense and without the use of special tools. A machine of this type is shown in Fig. 1. There is no danger of getting an electric shock in operating this machine, the pressure being only three volts, or little more than that of a dry battery. The transformer will stand an instantaneous overload of 400 or 500 amperes on the secondary, which is plenty for small work.

A heavy table, or workbench, serves as the support for the welding apparatus. Near the edge of the table is fastened a wooden block, about 6 in. high and 4 in. square. This forms the support for the bottom electrode, which is held in position by an iron holder fastened to the block by screws, as shown in Fig. 2. The flat bar A is only $\frac{1}{4}$ in. in thickness, and cannot provide sufficient holding surface for the electrode B. Accordingly an iron block, C, $\frac{1}{2}$ by 2 by 3 in. long, is bolted to A, the electrode being set through it and held by means of a setscrew.

The upper electrode is adjustable up

3027

and down only, with no lateral movement. This is accomplished by bolting the electrode holder D to a flat iron bar, E, as shown. The electrodes must never be permitted to come together while the machine is operating, and as a safeguard a block, F, is provided with a coil spring inserted between it and the bar E. This spring holds the electrodes 4 in. apart.

For the mechanical control of the machine, a right-foot pedal is used. This pedal is connected to the bar E by a wire controlling the position of the upper electrode. The construction of the transformer is next undertaken. A direct-current supply is seldom used for welding, and the alternating current used requires a suitable transformer. It is assumed that the lighting-circuit supply is 110 volts and the frequency 60 cycles, which is the form of current in general use. The transformer consists of two windings on an iron core, as detailed in Fig. 4.

The first winding, connected to the supply circuit, is called the primary, while the other winding, which in this instance is connected to the electrodes, is the secondary. Current flowing in the primary winding will induce a voltage in the secondary directly proportional to the number of turns of wire in each winding. For the making of the core several thin sheets of iron are cut into strips, 7½ in. long and 1½ in. wide, as shown. A sufficient number should be prepared to give two piles, each 1½ in. high. Cut the same quantity of 1½-in. strips, 3½ in. long. These strips are then annealed. Using the longer strips, proceed to build up the pile. The second strip is laid on the first so that it overlaps it at one end by 1½ in. The third strip is then placed on the second, directly over the first one, as shown. The fourth strip laps the third, lying directly over the second, and so on, to complete the pile. It is then bound temporarily with tape. Two such piles are required. The same procedure is carried out with the 3½-in. strips.

From thin fiber or strong wood, cut four end pieces, 3 in. square, with holes through the centers, 1½ in. square, as shown. Slip two of these end pieces on each of the long piles of strips, and secure them in position. Between these ends several layers of linen, or friction tape, are wound on the core for insulating purposes. A coat of shellac is then applied. When the shellac is dry, neatly wind on each of these two bobbins two layers of 63 turns each No. 14 gauge, double cotton-covered wire. This forms the primary winding. After giving the primary winding several coats of shellac, wind on three layers of tape, taking care that the work is neatly done as this insulation must be perfect. Again apply shellac.

Upon this insulation is wound the secondary, for which heavy wire is used. On each bobbin wind two coils of seven turns each of No. 6 gauge, double cotton-covered wire. An outside covering of tape is put on to give the coils a finished appearance. With the two wound bobbins lying side by side, sandwich the other two packs of laminated strips into the ends of their cores, so that a continuous core in the shape of a hollow square is formed.

In making connections great care must be exercised. Reference to the winding and wiring diagrams, Figs. 5 and 6, should be made, noting that the two coils on the primary are connected in series, while all four secondary coils are in parallel. The outside connections are quite simple. Two heavy cables carry the current from the secondary to the electrodes to which they are soldered, as shown in Fig. 2. The primary winding connects, through a pedal-control switch, to the 110-volt lighting circuit. A knife switch and fuses may also be inserted in this circuit if desired.

The pedal-control switch arrangement, shown in Fig. 3, is similar to the mechanical control pedal, except that, when the pedal is depressed, electrical connection is made in a quick make-and-break switch with snap action. The switch is inclosed in a metal case and set in a wooden block fixed to the floor. A heavy coil spring raises the hinged pedal when it is not held down

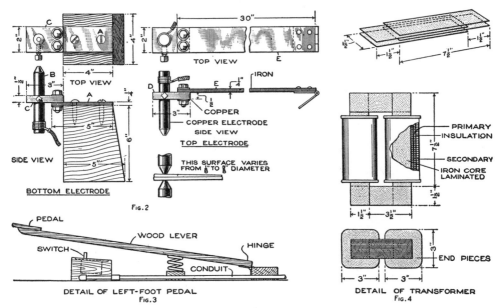

Details of Construction: Fig. 2 Shows the Details of the Electrodes and Their Fittings; Fig. 3, the Arrangement of the Pedal Control of the Switch, and Fig. 4, the Details of the Transformer

by the foot. Copper rods are used for electrodes, their diameter being about ⅝ in. The welding end is tapered to a surface varying from ⅛ in. to ⅜ in. in diameter, depending on the work to be done.

Several trials are necessary before successful results are obtained in the use of the machine. The operator should sit down to work the machine so that both feet may be used to control the pedals. After fitting the two sheets together in the exact position desired, they are placed between the electrodes. With the right-foot pedal depressed, the electrodes are brought in contact with the material, and a slight pressure applied. The left-foot

pedal is then depressed, allowing the current to flow for several seconds. The localized current heats the metal sheets to a welding temperature, and with a further pressure on the right pedal, the sheets are forced into close contact and the weld is made.

In conclusion, several kinds of metal can be satisfactorily spot-welded. Copper and aluminum are exceedingly difficult to weld, as they offer low resistance to the flow of an electric current. Galvanized iron may be welded satisfactorily, although the zinc will be burned off at the point of the weld. Tin can be welded to tin, or to sheet iron, as may also brass. Sheet iron to sheet iron gives the best weld.

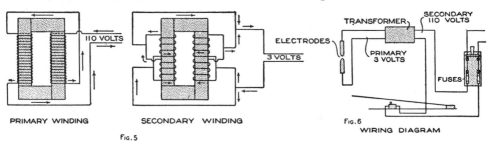

The Winding and Wiring Diagrams should be Studied Carefully, so That No Mistake is Made in the Making of the Transformer and the Hooking-Up of the Wiring Connections

## Quick Method of Making Small Doors

Small doors made of several pieces of board, extending vertically, usually require cleats on the back to keep them from warping. A panel door for the purpose is often too expensive, or too troublesome, to make. An attractive 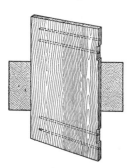 and substantial small door can be made by taking two, three, or more pieces and stringing them on dowels, seated in holes bored through the several pieces, as shown. This method is practical in making doors up to 18 in. wide. Match the boards together and nail strips on, to keep them straight. Put the rough door in the vise, mark the places where the hinges will go, and with a long ⅜ or ½-in. bit, bore through the pieces successively, to within 1 in. of the edge of the end piece. Cover the dowels with glue, and drive them home. The bit must be sharp, and the grain must be observed in order to avoid boring through the side.—Henry Simon, Laguna Beach, Calif.

## A Perforator for Loose-Leaf Book Fillers

Having a set of loose-leaf books, I made the perforator shown, instead of punching the holes with a plier-type hand punch. It perforates 10 sheets of ordinary paper at one time. To make the device, cut two pieces of ¼ by 1-in. strap iron, A, and drill ³⁄₁₆-in. holes, B, in them. Drill holes, D, suitably spaced, for the punch rods F. Bolt pieces, A, together, as shown, with ¼-in. strips, C, between them, at the ends. Make the piece E as detailed, and drill holes to match those at D and also holes for the bolts at the end. Fit strips under the ends of the piece E. Thread the steel pins F at one end. Cut and drill the strip G as shown. Thread holes in strip G, and set the threaded pins in place. Fit a wood or metal handle, H, to the piece G. Assemble the parts as shown, and fit open coil springs, ½ in. long, between the plates G and E. Grind off the lower ends of the pins F, so they just come through the top plate A, grinding them at a slight angle to give a shearing effect. The sheets of paper are placed between the plates A, and a sharp blow with the hand on the handle H drives the pins through, cutting neat holes.—Bert Waychoff, Fort Collins, Colo.

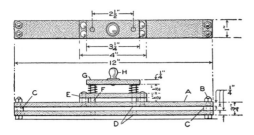

A Homemade Perforating Punch of This Type can be Made Easily, and Is Useful Especially for Loose-Leaf Sheets

## Shingles Set by Gauge on Shingling Hatchet

It is desirable when working on a roof, or other similar place, that as few tools as possible be required for the work. In shingling, this is especially necessary, in order to make speed. A kink that will save much time is the fitting of a small gauge on the front edge of the shingling hatchet, as shown in the sketch, to measure the weather exposure of the  shingles. The gauge is a small U-shaped strip of iron, with a setscrew in one side of it, by means of which it is clamped at various positions on the hatchet.—C. J. Shields, Indianapolis, Ind.

## A Round Storage Cellar
### for the Farm

A round storage cellar has attractive features as to practicability, inexpensive construction, and the securing of maximum storage space. That shown was built of brick, but various kinds of masonry materials, or concrete, could also be used. The inside diameter is 12 ft., and the height from the floor to the ceiling line is 10 ft., giving a good-sized cellar for the average farm. The cellar is built largely underground, and the area surrounding it is graded up, after the wall is completed. The floor, the wall foundations, and the steps are of concrete, made of a mixture of one part cement, three of sand, and five of gravel. The footing is heavy, and the floor is 4 in. thick, with a 2-in. bed of cinders or fine gravel. The walls are 12 in. thick, and can be made satis-

factorily of 8-in. hollow clay tile, faced with common brick. This gives a desirable double air space in the walls. The door should be 3 ft. wide and 7 ft. high, made in double thickness of matched lumber, with heavy roofing felt between the boards to provide in-

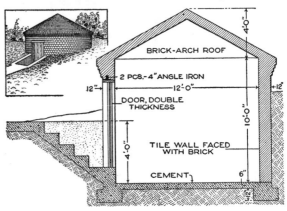

A Good Storage Cellar Is a Worth-While Investment for the Farmer, or Even for the Home Gardener and Fruit Grower

sulation against heat and cold.—W. E. Frudden, Charles City, Iowa.

---

## Cement-Bandage Repair on Large
### Pipes or Cylinders

For mending leaks in irrigating pipes, cracked pumps or cylinders, steam-heating pipes, etc., a bandage of cement and cloth makes a good job. Mix Portland cement and water to a paste; next take a long strip of loose-woven cloth, burlap, or cheesecloth, 3 in. wide, and roll it into a roll like a surgeon's bandage. Work the loose end full of the mortar, and wind it around the leak, taking a handful of the cement mortar and working it well into the cloth, at each round. Continue until the bandage is 1 in. thick; then finish over the surface with the mortar, and let it stand for 48 hours, well protected from wind and sun. It will then be ready for use. If there is a heavy pressure in the pipes, wrap wire mesh around to reinforce it. I have mended leaks in 8-in. irrigating pipe with a 20-ft. pressure, both wooden and iron, by this method.—D. H. Snowberger, Payette, Ida.

## Leather Angle Washers Stop
### Oil Leakage in Crank Case

It frequently happens that the oil in the crank case of a gasoline engine leaks out through the ends. This was

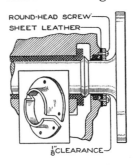

the case on the engine of my automobile, and I eliminated the trouble in the following manner: I took a piece of 1/8-in. leather and made a tube of it, the inside diameter being equal to that of the bearings and its length 7/8 in. It was then placed on an arbor, swedged back to the shape shown in the illustration, and cut into halves. Both halves were placed into position, as shown, and two small semicircular segments of a flat ring were screwed on, holding the leather in position.— A. K. Rudolph, New York, N. Y.

## Counterbore Ground Quickly from Round Stock

Often the mechanic in the machine shop requires a special size of counterbore and does not find it in his stock of

A Counterbore of This Type can be Ground Quickly from a Piece of Tool Steel, Which is Then Properly Tempered

tools. A quick method of supplying such a bore is to take a piece of tool steel and turn it to a shoulder pivot, as shown in the sketch, and then grind it to the proper cutting edges. The grinding can be done readily on an ordinary emery wheel, and care should be taken to provide the necessary relief at the cutting edges. The pivot, of course, must be made of the proper size for the center hole, and the lower cutting edges of the counterbore should also be given a relief toward the back.

## Simple Devices for Lubricating Automobile Springs

A simple method of supplying oil to the transverse, or cross, springs on automobiles, is employed by an expert mechanic. On both the front and rear springs, where these are fastened to the

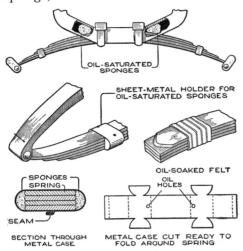

These Devices for Lubricating Automobile Springs can be Easily Installed and Give Good Service

channel frame, forming pockets, he placed small sponges soaked with oil, as shown. When the springs are deflected, the oil flows onto the springs, keeping them lubricated and free from rust. Occasionally the sponges are removed and the oil supply replenished.

Another good method for elliptical, or semielliptical springs, is to use strips of felt, or other porous material, binding this neatly around the spring with twine, and pouring oil over it. The felt is covered with waterproofed cloth or leather. A lubricator, as shown, can also be made, of tin or sheet brass, for inclosing small sponges, which are held to the edges of the blades, on springs of these types. This attachment, as detailed in the pattern, can be either folded over at the under side, into a seam, or flanges may be left to fasten with a screw and nut.—G. A. L., Washington, D. C.

## Adjustable Roller Stand for Pipes, Bars, and Rods

In handling long pipes, bars, rods, and similar pieces, a stand, having a roller at the top, is a great convenience, both in the saving of time and of heavy labor. Several of these can be arranged in a row where workmen are shunting the pieces a considerable distance. The stand shown in the sketch is of cheap and simple construction, yet quite substantial. A section of pipe is mounted on iron

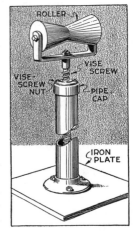

plates and into the top of it is fitted a screw arrangement. This may be a vise screw and nut, as shown, or a large bolt. The roller is set in a bracket, which is bolted to the vertical adjusting screw.—R. B. Sands, Detroit, Michigan.

## Aluminum Salt Shaker Made into Lens Holder

When the hard-rubber holder of an eyeglass lens, used considerably on fine shop work, was broken, it became necessary to re-

place it promptly. A novel method of replacing the parts was used, the upper end of an aluminum salt shaker being cut and shaped for the purpose. The end was cut as indicated, after the salt shaker had been mounted in a lathe chuck, and the upper end was spun out to fit the lens. The larger end was also spun out to give the proper curve to the holder. The blunt-nose spinning tools used were ground from steel rods and mounted in the tool post.—Ben Frantzreb, Indianapolis, Ind.

## Proper Method of Folding Blueprints

When folding large blueprints for mailing, filing, or other purposes, they should be folded with the blue, or printed, side out, and with the title, or description, in the lower right-hand corner of the folded print. This facilitates handling and filing, and saves the useless unfolding of the print, which wears it unnecessarily.

## Old Saws Provide Good Stock for Tools

Various kinds of tools made of flat pieces of steel can be cut from old saw blades, ordinary handsaws being used for the thinner stock, and heavier circular saws for heavier material. The steel must be annealed to make it easily workable, and the tools may be hardened if desired. Some of the tools that can be made in this way are squares, calipers, gauges, and various types of measuring and marking tools, shaped from flat steel.

## Metal Case with External Control for Knife Switch

It is dangerous to have an unprotected knife switch so placed that it may be unwarily touched by some one with the bare hand. A good plan is to inclose the switch in a homemade metal case, so that the electric arcs made on opening and closing the switch are properly guarded. A V-shaped box several inches longer than the switch should be constructed from sheet iron, as detailed in the layout. Screw the box to the switch panel, as shown, and make a suitable cover, hinged at the top. The box and cover can be painted black, or the cover painted red to locate the switch box easily. To make a control operated from the outside of the box, as detailed, bore two ¼-in. holes through the front of the box. A staple is driven into the panel near the switch

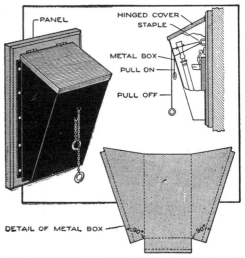

The Switch is Properly Guarded, and can be Opened or Closed Handily by Means of the Chains

handle. A small chain or cord is passed through the holes and thence through the staple, and to it is fastened the switch handle. Rings are attached to the ends of the chain, and by pulling the correct end the switch will open or close, as desired.—C. M. Hall, St. Louis, Mo.

⟪A small boat being towed may be steadied by dragging a bucket behind it.

# A Homemade Paper-Baling Press

### By CLIFFORD A. BUTTERWORTH

HOME mechanics fairly handy with tools can make this baling press at a comparatively small cost, depending on whether or not old material is used. It will soon pay for itself through the sale of scrap paper that would not be accepted in loose form. To operate the press, push the lever D back to the position shown by the dotted lines, lift the ram as far as it will go, and put in the paper. Then lift the lever J about 2 ft., pull the lever D forward so the bolt K will slip into one of the notches, and pull down. Repeat until the paper is well compressed. To make a good bale, a piece of heavy cardboard should be placed on the top and at the bottom. Iron wire of No. 18 gauge is used for tying. When sufficient paper has been used to make a good-sized bale, take three 6-ft. lengths of wire and without removing the pressure insert them in the slots. Run the ends through spaces between the strips, at the top and bottom of the bale, and bring them together in front, fastening them tightly by twisting. Then release the ram and take out the bale. The press should be screwed to the floor with heavy angle irons.

First construct the box of matched 7/8-in. boards. Fasten them together with cleats long enough to project 7/8 in. on each side, and 1 1/2-in. screws. Make the sides 15 in. by 36 in., and the back 21 3/4 in. by 36 in. In making the back, do not put a cleat at the lower edge. Before screwing on the cleat A, cut the three slots shown in the side section, making them 3/4 in. wide. Fasten the sides to the back with angle irons, and then screw in the bottom, which is 15 in. by 20 in. long. Nail the eight 15-in. strips across it, spacing them about 1/2 in. apart.

Make the frame next, as detailed in the working drawings. In the plan above the end view, the lever arrangement is omitted, to show the frame construction clearly. The lock must also be put in place. Fasten a piece of sheet metal over the beveled end to keep the bolts from wearing the wood, as shown in the lock detail. Lining the slot with metal will make the lock slide easier. A heavy spring, B, is attached to pull the lock forward, so it will engage the notches as the ram goes down, and keep it from springing up. A lever, C, 14 in. long,

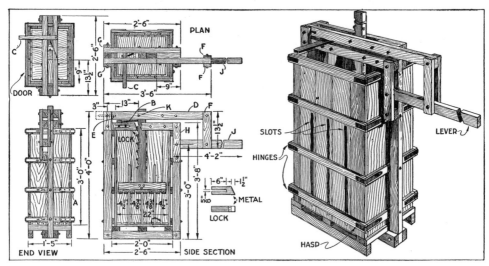

A Substantial Paper-Baling Press can be Made at Small Cost of Used Lumber, and will Soon Repay the Labor and Expense from the Sale of the Baled Paper Not Otherwise Salable

is arranged to force back the lock when it is desired to release the ram.

The main lever D is built up as detailed. Cut a slot, E, in the two main upper pieces of lever D, making it ⅝ in. wide. The two 13½-in. pieces F connect the levers as shown. These, as well as the pieces G and H, should be of ash, or other hard wood. The piece H is 15 by 3 by 1 in., bolted at the upper end with an 8-in. bolt, which also holds the frame together.

To make the ram, take a 2-ft. 6-in. piece, and beginning 9 in. from the end, bore seven ½-in. holes, 3 in. apart, from center to center, and insert 4-in. bolts. Then, just above each bolt and as close to it as possible, cut a notch, shaped as shown, 1½ in. wide and 1 in. deep. The other details can be easily observed from the working drawings and the perspective sketch.

---

## Novel Illuminated Flag Made of Christmas-Tree Ornaments

The owner of a drug store wanted to display our national emblem in a novel way, and asked me to help him make up a flag, about 12 by 18 in. in size, of small electric lights, for his window. After figuring the cost, I made up a flag that answered the purpose of electric lights at night, and which has the advantage of being plainly visible in the daytime. It was made as follows: A picture frame was procured, and painted a dead black. A piece of black velvet was stretched and tacked over the back of it. An equal number of small red and silver glass balls, ¾ in. in diameter, used for Christmas-tree decorating, were obtained, and also some blue ones, ½ in. in diameter, for the blue field, and ½-in. silver balls for the stars. The stem of each ball was dipped in thick glue, and the balls set in position on the velvet, to make the stripes, the blue field, and the stars. When dry, the framed flag was hung in the show window, and an electric light, inclosed in a reflector, was directed upon it from in front. The colored balls each reflected the electric-light bulb in miniature, giving

the appearance of the glowing filament in small electric lamps, and the flag proved very attractive.—G. H. Niederhoff, St. Louis, Mo.

---

## Blowtorch Homemade from Strong Can

A blowtorch is easily made of an old maple-sirup can of heavy tinned

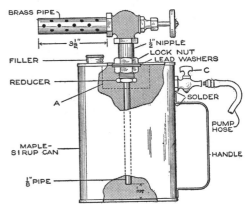

This Homemade Blowtorch Is Inexpensive and Has a Wide Range of Use for the Mechanic and in the Home Workshop

sheet iron, as shown. A ½-in. brass nipple is soldered to the can, and an old globe valve fitted on. Into this is screwed a 3½-in. piece of thin brass pipe with holes bored in it, ⅜ in. apart and staggered. An old bicycle pump, with a ball check valve is provided. A small brass cock supplements the ball check valve, which is opened to force air into the tank. On one side of the can, solder a handle. Remove the cork insert in the filler cap, and in its place put an asbestos washer. Fill the can half full of gasoline and pump in air.

To start the torch in operation, after the proper pressure is obtained, fill a baking-powder can cover half full of gasoline, set it under the torch pipe, and light the gasoline, which heats the valve and nipple. When it is hot, open the valve slightly by the handwheel, and by igniting the spray, a hot flame is produced, which is intensified by the increase of the air pressure.—P. P. Avery, Garfield, N. J.

## Tackle for Hoisting Heavy Barrels

Instead of using grabhooks or improvised rope slings for handling heavy barrels on a derrick or with other hoist-

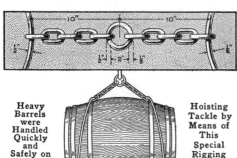

Heavy Barrels were Handled Quickly and Safely on     Hoisting Tackle by Means of This Special Rigging

ing apparatus, the shop blacksmith was ordered to make a set of rings with suitable chains to fit the barrels so that they could be hoisted quickly and safely. The rings were made of ½-in. round steel rods, welded. They should be of a size to fit the barrels snugly and to cramp in the positions shown in the illustration.—C. C. Spreen, Flint, Michigan.

## Combination Doorstop and Coat Hook

A homemade device which is used as a combined doorstop and coat hook, singly or in series, is practical where space is limited and the walls behind doors are available for the hanging up of clothes in shops or similar places. It consists of a ½-in. pipe nipple, about 4 in. long, one end screwed into a coupling, in which a rubber stopper is pressed, acting as a buffer, so as not to

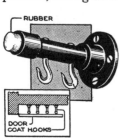

injure the wall. The other end is screwed into a flange which is fastened to the wall. The hooks are riveted in the pipe. The device is inexpensive, and if bronzed, nickel-plated, or painted, makes a neat fitting. —Ernest Schwartz, Brooklyn, N. Y.

## Hot-Air Heater Protects Water Pipes from Cold

In many buildings that have more or less exposed water pipes, considerable trouble is met with in thawing out pipes during a cold wave. This is a tedious, tiresome job, especially where the pipes are hard to get at. This was the case in an oblong three-story building with a large light court running up the center. The water pipes run up along the wall of the light court and are inclosed in a box. The owner avoided frequently frozen pipes by rigging up a stove to heat the pipes in winter, the box carrying the pipes acting as a chimney for heat. There was a natural-gas jet close to the pipe box. A shelf was put on the wall, and an old stove was connected up as shown. The top was made solid so that most of the heat is carried up into a larger pipe with closed top. To avoid danger of fire, the larger pipe has V-shaped

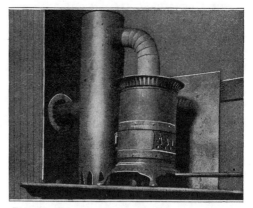

This Heating Arrangement Overcame Troublesome Freezing of Water Pipes in Cold Weather, and was Cheaply Installed

openings cut around the bottom edge to take in air, and the pipe conducting the heat into the box has a large galvanized-iron ventilating collar so as not to scorch the wood. A gas flame, ½ in. high, does the work and uses about 1,000 ft. a month.—Arthur L. Burgess, Columbus, Ohio.

Shellac is suitable for varnishing carburetor floats used with gasoline, but is not satisfactory if alcohol is used.

## Winding a Roll of Several Layers at Once

To wind a stock roll of several layers of paper, tin foil, etc., in one operation, first have as many small boxes as strips to roll, each one a little lower than the one back of it, arranging them in a row as shown. Cut pieces of ½-in. dowel rod a little shorter than the width of the boxes, and make a roller of each dowel piece. Have the roller just above the front of the box. The rollers are necessary to protect the paper. Have the strips wound, placing them in their proper order in the suc-

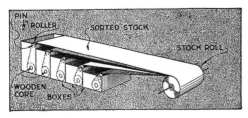

A Stock Roll of Several Layers can be Made Easily with an Arrangement of Bobbins

cessive boxes. Bringing out their ends, roll or fold them together as desired. Strips 100 ft. long can be nicely handled in this manner. This method can be used for many purposes, where long strips of different materials are to be rolled together, and kept free from air currents and dirt.—L. M. Drake, Daytona, Fla.

## Small Magnet Useful in Woodshop

An ordinary magnet is a great help in picking out small tools, nails, and other iron objects, from shavings and sawdust. By running it through the shavings collected on top of a workbench, it will collect every small iron article and save many a loss. It can also be employed in locating the position of covered nails before sawing through old work. The magnet should be hung up with a "keeper" across its ends when not in use. An electromagnet, used similarly, will prove still more useful than a common magnet for the purposes mentioned.—Henry Simon, Laguna Beach, Calif.

## Deflector for Bottom of Rock or Gravel Chute

The sketch shows a method of building a crushed rock or gravel drop, or catch, box to be placed at the lower end of an inclined chute. The continued action of rock or gravel falling from a chute on a bare wooden deflector, or even a deflector lined with sheet iron, soon wears it out, and it must be replaced. By the method shown, the gravel forms its own wearing surface, and the wooden box does not require frequent renewal. This method can be applied to a large variety of work where building materials, coal, etc., are handled in wooden troughs, or in various gravity conveyors.—Roy H. Poston, Flat River, Mo.

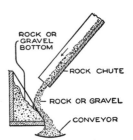

## Pivoted Rear Caster Improves Barrow Truck

Many hand trucks for carrying heavy loads have only two casters or wheels, and when a considerable weight is being moved the workman finds it hard to handle the outfit. In a large shop it was found that the work was made much easier by fitting the trucks with an extra double-roller caster pivoted under the rear support of the truck, as shown in the sketch. This enables the

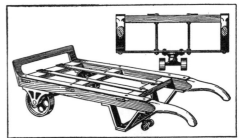

The Pivoted Rear Caster Makes It Possible to Handle Heavy Loads without Lifting Them Clear in Transit

workman to rest the load and shift it along the floor on its bearings.

## Sanitary Shop-Refuse Can with Pedal-Control Lid

To promote sanitation, and the keeping down of possible contagion from

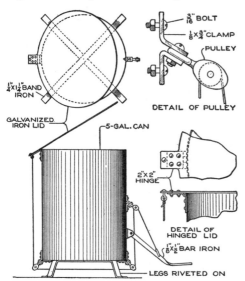

Sanitation was Promoted in a Large Shop by Providing a Strong Pedal-Control Covered Receptacle for Refuse

flies and other pests, a strong and practical refuse can was designed as the standard for a large plant, and the various shops were fitted out with these receptacles. Five-gallon cans were used for the containers, and the lids, of heavy galvanized iron, were fitted to them by means of a hinge, as shown in detail. The legs, of band iron, were arranged to support the bottom, and the cover was controlled by a pedal, rigged with a heavy cord and suitable pulley. A detail of the upper pulley is shown in the sketch. The interior of the can was suitably painted, with a black asphaltum paint, and the exterior painted with a lead paint.—A. P. Midland, New York, N. Y.

## Concrete Liners Overcome Wear at Turns in Flumes or Troughs

In wooden flumes used for transporting material in water, such as cinders, gravel, and other materials that have a tendency to cut out the sides

of the flume, especially at bends, repairs or renewals are often needed, causing a great deal of annoyance and expense. Concrete liners, fitted into the flumes, or troughs, at the points of wear, greatly increase the durability of the flumes, especially at the bends. Nails are driven in the side of the flume before the concrete is set to hold the liner in position.—H. P. Roy, Omaha, Neb.

## An Adaptable Socket Wrench

A design for a strong, light-weight, adaptable socket wrench, especially useful for the motorist's tool kit, is shown in the sketch. It is for use on nuts up to 5/8 in. across flats, and its best feature is that new inserts can be quickly and cheaply made for it to fit various sizes or shapes of nuts within its range. These interchangeable inserts are driven by a key in the end of the shank, at the bottom of the socket. The insert is retained in the socket by a spring snap which engages a nick on one side of the insert, as detailed. The inserts are made of tool steel, hardened. Machine steel, casehardened, can also be used. The shank is made of steel tubing. The sleeve is also a piece of steel tubing, and is brazed or pinned in place. The spring snap is made by cutting two saw kerfs, about 3/8 in. apart, as shown, and upsetting the end of the

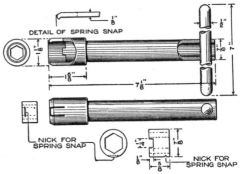

An Adaptable Socket Wrench with a Set of Inserts to Fit Various Nuts Is a Handy Tool for the Motorist or General Mechanic

metal between them so as to engage the nick in the socket.—W. B. Burr, Bridgeport, Conn.

## Substantial Power Drill Press Made of Pipes and Fittings

By RAY F. KUNS

PRACTICAL mechanics who build small machines for use in their workshops, often make use of pipes and fittings and usually get fair results. By carefully working out a design for a drill press, which is suitable for construction with these standard parts, and giving special attention to the machining and joining of the various members, the drill press shown in the photograph and detailed in the working drawings, was made. It gives very satisfactory service, and compares favorably with standard machines of its size, though the cost was comparatively slight. It has stood up well under very hard service in a school machine shop. The design can easily be adapted to a smaller-size machine, or revised for special classes of work. It will carry a drill up to 1 in. in diameter. It has four changes of speed, ranging from 84 to 666 revolutions per minute.

The main support is a 3-in. extra-heavy pipe. The height from the floor to the center of the spindle arm is 4 ft. 4 in.; from the floor to the center of the upper arm is 5 ft. 10 in.; from the center of the main support to the center of the spindle is 15 in. The arm which carries the table is adjustable on the pipe support, the latter being turned to a good finish. The tee, which slides on the post, is bored out to fit the latter, and is clamped by means of a threaded handle. The bottom of the main post is split, spread, and bolted to an iron plate. This is imbedded in the concrete base, as shown in the side view.

This Substantial Drill Press was Made by Boys in a School Shop, Pipes and Fittings Being the Chief Materials Used. It has Withstood Hard Wear

The tee under the drive pulley at the upper end of the spindle shaft has a bearing made from a piece of 1¼-in. gas pipe. This is first babbitted, then scraped, and the holes for the set-screws drilled and threaded. The same type of bearing is used in the hangers, four of which are required, two for the upper and two for the lower countershafts. The hangers are forged, as shown in the drawings, from 1½-in. gas pipe.

The gear wheel in the spindle feed is ¾ in. thick and 1¼ in. diameter. The teeth, 12 in number, are made from ¼-in. cold-rolled steel, set into tapped holes. The hollow spindle, which is made from 1½-in. gas pipe, has a row of ⁹⁄₃₂-in. holes drilled in the side, to form a rack for the gear to work in.

is considerable risk of getting the parts mixed, making successful operation of the assembled machine almost

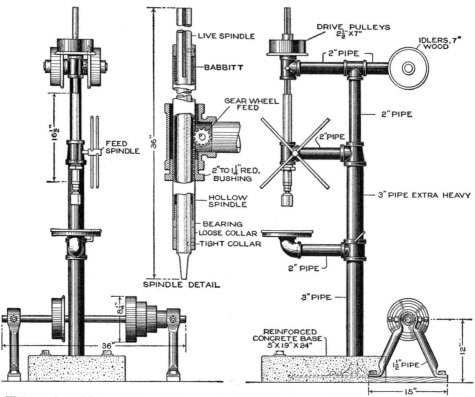

SPINDLE DETAIL

While the Cost of This Drill Press Is Comparatively Slight by Reason of the Use of Pipes and Fittings, the Service It Gives Compares Favorably with Standard Machines of This Type and Size

The chuck should be procured before working up the live spindle, that these parts may be fitted properly.

### Disassembling Rack Keeps Engine Parts in Order

When taking apart an engine, especially one of several cylinders, there

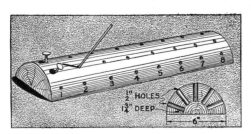

The Engine Parts are Placed Systematically on the Rack When Disassembling, Thus Insuring against Mixing Up the Parts Easily

impossible. A simple method of caring for the parts is to place them on a disassembling rack made of a heavy piece of wood, cut to the shape shown and provided with numerous holes in which pins are inserted for small parts having center openings, and providing also for various kinds of rods. Each cylinder has a separate row on the rack, numbered as indicated.—J. J. Green, Chicago, Ill.

### Simple Method of Soldering Granite Ware

Many persons have the impression that it is almost impossible to repair a leak in a piece of granite ware, but if the following method is tried, the amateur will have perfect success. With a sharp file cut away the porcelain, and buff the exposed metal until it is shiny. Apply soldering acid, and with a hot iron apply half-and-half solder, the same as one does in soldering tin. The solder will repair the leak permanently, for we have pieces of granite ware mended in this way in our kitchen, and they have been in use several months since repairing.—John F. Robinson, North Adams, Mich.

## Slip Gear Minimizes Breakage of Teeth

On many kinds of machinery where inexpensive cast gears are used, as well as in some other cases, a type of gear has been found useful for preventing undue breakage of the teeth. Heavy strain is caused on the gear teeth by sudden stopping, starting, or reversing, and a gear in which the hub is separate from the rim, the two sections being held together by slip rings as shown in the illustration, gives the proper relief to the gear teeth. The slip rings are bolted securely with tension springs. When the strain becomes too great, the outer ring revolves, and the hub re-

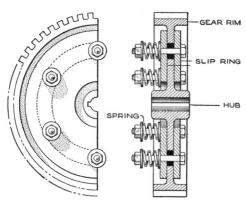

When the Strain on the Gear Teeth Becomes so Great that Breakage may Result, Damage is Prevented by the Slipping of the Rings

mains stationary until normal conditions obtain.—C. Van Den Berg, Jr., Gadsden, Ala.

❦A coating of paraffin oil should be applied to the surface of freshly cleaned iron to protect it from oxidation before the paint is applied.

## Test Box for Electrical Fuse Cartridges

For testing electrical fuses of the cartridge type, to determine whether or not they were serviceable, a small

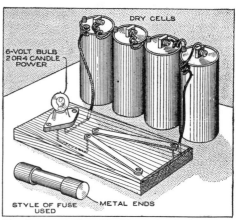

The Fuses are Placed in Circuit by Setting Them across the Brass Strips, and the Bulb Lights as the Current Passes through a Serviceable Fuse

outfit was rigged up as shown. Brass strips were mounted on a board with screws so that fuses of various lengths could be tested by setting them across the strips with the metal ends of the fuse in contact with the brass. If the fuse is good, the small electric bulb is lighted when in circuit with the dry cells.—A. E. Rounds, Milwaukee, Wis.

## Portable Tool Rack for Mill Room Aids in Checking Up Tools

It was customary in a certain plant to "clean up" the mill room every Saturday afternoon. Upon the arrival of the mill hands on Monday morning it was discovered that various tools, such as squares, rules, straightedges, etc., were missing, and it was only after lengthy search that the tools were found in obscure corners or drawers. To overcome this, an A-shaped tool rack was constructed, 5 ft. long and 2½ ft. high, and provided with casters. On "clean-up" day various tools are placed on hooks on the rack, which is pushed around the shop, and finally taken to the tool room.—Joseph Plogmann, Cincinnati, Ohio.

# A Long Island Scooter
## Driven by a Motor Aero-Propeller

By L. B. ROBBINS

A craft that affords much sport for the ice speed enthusiast is the "Long Island Scooter," which gets its name from the fact that it has long been popular on the waters of Long Island Sound. It is something of an amphibious boat-sled, and can sail on the ice, on ice-covered land, or on broken ice with stretches of open water. The original scooter is a sailing craft, rigged in various ways, like an ice sailboat. With the power from a gasoline motor of about 4 hp. applied to an aero-propeller of 3-ft. sweep, the scooter has a much wider range, and is practically independent of wind and weather during its season. It is controlled from the driver's seat at the steering wheel, like an automobile or speed motorboat, as shown in Figs. 3 and 6. The installation for the motor and control mechanism is arranged convenient to the steering post, within easy reach. The engine is set well forward in the cockpit, and the steering wheel on the port side, leaving room for a passenger, or cargo, on the starboard side.

The strong iron runners make the scooter ride easily, and also stiffen the hull. The iron prow aids in climbing over rough areas, and prevents the bow from crawling under ice ledges, when leaving open water. The engine may be of various types, and that indicated is a double-cylinder motor of about 4 hp., air-cooled, developing 500 to 700 r. p. m. on the main drive shaft, and 1,500 to 1,800 r. p. m. on the propeller shaft. The driving mechanism is suggestive only, since many mechanics prefer to devise these features to suit the materials and facilities at hand. This installation may also be left to a professional gasoline-motor mechanic, only the hull and minor fittings being homemade.

Begin the construction by making the framework, shown in Fig. 1. The sides are of ⅞-in. pine, cut 12 in. wide at the middle, 8 in. at the stern, as shown in Fig. 3, and 2 in. at the junction with the wagon-wheel rim, at the bow. The use of a wagon-wheel rim, of oak, which can be obtained of a wheelwright, makes it unnecessary to do the tedious work of steaming and bending this heavy material. The rim is bolted to the sides. The ribs are of hard pine, ⅞ by 2 in. in section. The stern transom, as detailed, is fastened into place with galvanized-iron screws, which are to be used throughout, instead of plain iron screws, as they withstand the water better. The keel, of pine, 1 by 8 in. in section, is laid on the ribs and fastened with screws.

Place the frame, bottom side up, on sawhorses, and plank the bottom with ½-in. pine, or cypress, boards. Set the nail heads and clinch the nails well on the inside. Plane the bottom off smooth and apply a coat of priming paint to the hull. Next cut the deck beams, as detailed, for the various stations. These beams may be steam-bent or cut, 2 in. wide, from a good quality of ⅞-in. stock. Nail the beams into place, as indicated in Fig. 2. Beams Nos. 5 and 6 are set 5 ft. apart, to make a frame for the cockpit, with the beams at the side coaming set 6 in. from the sides. Plank the deck with ⅜-in. cypress, or pine, and cover it with canvas, if desired. Boards for the floor, of ½-in. stock, may be fitted into place, but should not be nailed down until the

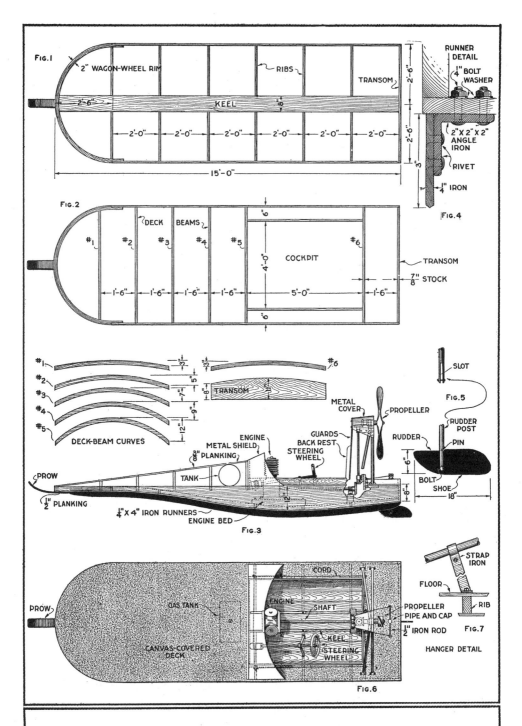

FIG. 1 — 2" WAGON-WHEEL RIM — RIBS — TRANSOM — 2'-6" — KEEL — 2'-0" 2'-0" 2'-0" 2'-0" 2'-0" 2'-0" — 15'-0" — 2'-6" 2'-6" 3"

RUNNER DETAIL — 1/4" BOLT WASHER — 2" X 2" X 2" ANGLE IRON — RIVET — 1/4" IRON — FIG. 4

FIG. 2 — DECK BEAMS — #1 #2 #3 #4 #5 #6 — COCKPIT — TRANSOM — 7/8" STOCK — 1'-6" 1'-6" 1'-6" 1'-6" 5'-0" 1'-6" — 4'-0"

#1 #2 #3 #4 #5 — DECK-BEAM CURVES — #6 — TRANSOM — 3" 5" 7" 8" 9" 12"

FIG. 5 — SLOT — RUDDER POST — PIN — BOLT — RUDDER — SHOE — 6" 8" 18"

PROW — 1/2" PLANKING — 3/8" PLANKING — 1/4" X 4" IRON RUNNERS — ENGINE BED — TANK — ENGINE — METAL SHIELD — GUARDS — BACK REST — STEERING WHEEL — METAL COVER — PROPELLER — FIG. 3

PROW — GAS TANK — CANVAS-COVERED DECK — CORD — ENGINE — SHAFT — KEEL — STEERING WHEEL — PROPELLER — PIPE AND CAP — 1/2" IRON ROD — FIG. 6

STRAP IRON — FLOOR — RIB — FIG. 7 — HANGER DETAIL

The Scooter Is an Interesting Mechanical Construction for the Winter Speed Enthusiast. The Craft may be Made and Installed Complete by the Builder, or He may Make Only the Hull and Its Fittings Other Than the Power Plant and Driving Mechanism. Fig. 1 Shows the Hull-Framing Plan; Fig. 2, the Deck-Framing Plan; Fig. 3, a Side Sectional Elevation; Fig. 6, an Assembly Plan, and the Other Figures, Details of Construction

other interior fittings have been placed finally. Fit the supports under the after deck, for fastening the machinery fittings, and set blocks for strengthening the hull at the rudder post, as de-

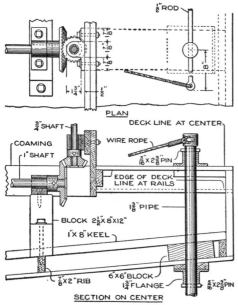

½"ROD

PLAN

¾" SHAFT

DECK LINE AT CENTER

COAMING

WIRE ROPE

1" SHAFT

$\frac{5}{16}$"x2$\frac{3}{8}$"PIN

EDGE OF DECK
LINE AT RAILS

1$\frac{3}{8}$"PIPE

BLOCK 2½"x8"x12"

1"x8"KEEL

$\frac{7}{8}$"x2"RIB

6"x6"BLOCK

1$\frac{3}{8}$"FLANGE

$\frac{5}{16}$"x2$\frac{3}{8}$"PIN

SECTION ON CENTER

FIG. 8

Details of Construction at the Stern: The Section on the Center Shows the Fitting of the Gears and Connections of the Main Drive Shaft and the Vertical Shaft, and the Fitting of the Rudder Post. The Plan Shows a View from Above

tailed in Fig. 8. Fasten the coaming around the cockpit, and build a suitable base for the engine. The metal shield, in front of the engine, can be fitted handily before the machinery is installed, and laid aside until finally needed.

The metal fittings of the hull, apart from the power-plant installation, may be considered next. The runners are shaped, as indicated in Fig. 3 and in the detail drawing, Fig. 4, from ¼ by 3-in. sheet iron. The stern end is tapered off, and the bow end is tapered and curved in, to match the curve of the rim. The runners are fastened by means of angle irons, as detailed, and bolted through the floor, or the floor and iron straps, hung over the top edges of the ribs, adjoining the inner sides of the hull. A metal prow, $\frac{3}{16}$ by 4½ in. in section and hammered to a slight dished effect crosswise, extends 15 in.

beyond the bow rim, and is bolted to the bottom and keel. The rudder is of sheet iron, as detailed in Fig. 5. The lower edges of the runners and the rudder are sharpened slightly to give a good grip for steering the craft on the ice.

The installation of the steering mechanism is shown in plan in Fig. 6, in a side elevation in Fig. 3, and in detail, as to the steering-post fitting, in Fig. 8. The crossbar of the rudder is fastened to a pliable steel cable, $\frac{3}{16}$ in. in diameter, and this is reeved through suitable pulleys to carry it around the cockpit coaming, as shown in Fig. 6. The cable passes through the coaming at each side near the front end of the cockpit, and is wound about five turns around the 3-in. wooden drum, fixed to the steering post. The steering post is of pipe, 1¼ in. in exterior diameter. Its lower end is set into a metal flange, its upper end is shouldered with a threaded collar, and the steering wheel screwed on and suitably capped. The steering post is braced by a hanger of ¼ by 1¼-in. strap iron, as detailed in Fig. 7.

The details of the rudder post are shown in Fig. 8, which also shows the details of the gearing shafts and bear-

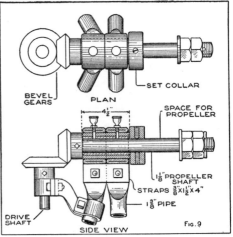

BEVEL
GEARS

PLAN

SET COLLAR

SPACE FOR
PROPELLER

4½"

1$\frac{1}{8}$"PROPELLER
SHAFT

STRAPS $\frac{3}{8}$"x1½"x4"

1$\frac{3}{8}$"PIPE

DRIVE
SHAFT

SIDE VIEW

FIG. 9

Details of Construction at the Propeller Shaft: The Supporting Standards are Forged around the Propeller-Shaft Bearing, and the Vertical Shaft is Held Rigid, at Its Bearing, by a Strap-Iron Bracket

ings at the junction of the main drive shaft and the vertical connecting shaft.

The rudder post is a pipe of 1⅜-in. exterior diameter. It is carried at its ends in pipe flanges bored out to a snug fit. Two round steel pins hold the post in position. A pipe cap at the upper end carries the rudder crossarm, as detailed in the plan. The main drive shaft is carried in a solid bearing, suitably babbitted, or provided with a bronze bushing. The bearing is bolted to a heavy block, as shown. The bevel gears are of machine steel, and are in a ratio of two to one, the smaller gear being of 3-in. pitch diameter. The vertical ¾-in. shaft is carried in a similar smaller bearing, bolted to the reinforced coaming.

The general arrangement of the propeller shaft and its connections and supports is shown in Figs. 3 and 6, and in detail in Fig. 9. A bevel gear of 4½-in. pitch diameter transmits the power from the ¾-in. vertical shaft to the 3-in. bevel gear on the 1⅛-in. propeller shaft. The latter is carried in a bearing made from a seamless steel tube, provided with a suitable bronze bushing and oil cups. A set collar and jam nuts, as well as a keying, or other standard device employed on aero-propellers, hold the propeller in place. The bearing is held solidly in a housing forged into the standards of 1⅜-in. pipe, which support the propeller shaft and connections from the stern deck. The forged pipes are fitted snugly around the bearing, and clamped to it by means of two straps of iron, and bolts, as shown. The vertical shaft is carried in a bearing similar to that used at its connection with the main drive shaft, as indicated in Fig. 8. The bearing is supported rigidly by a brace of 5⁄16 by 1½-in. strap iron, bolted to the forward pipe standards. The lower ends of these standards are split and forged to provide a flange for secure bolting at the reinforced points of fastening on the deck.

The gearing, etc., of the propeller shaft is covered by a sheet-metal hood, as shown in Figs. 3 and 6, as a safety measure, and also as a protection for the machinery. The hood is braced in front by two iron guard rods, as shown in Fig. 3, which support the back rest for the driver and passenger. This rest is also essential in guarding the occupants from the machinery, and the main drive shaft should also be guarded. The driving mechanism, and especially the gearing connections and sizes, are suggestive only. They must be worked out according to the requirements of the power plant used. The propeller may be made or purchased complete.

## Devices for Gripping Stock Accurately in a Vise

When gripping work which is rough in a vise, a frequent source of trouble is that the vise grips on one corner only. In milling or planing, the work is likely to be torn from the vise. To overcome this, the vise can be equipped with a simple jaw which equalizes the grip on the work. A jaw adapted to gripping rough stock is shown in Fig. 1. A is the fixed jaw and B the movable jaw. Attached to the movable jaw is the piece C, held in position by two screws D. This movable piece butts against the movable jaw, at E, and as the jaw is tightened by the screw F, the movable piece pivots at E, adapting itself to the work.

Another method of gripping the work is shown in Fig. 2. The purpose of the pin is to insure against the jaws

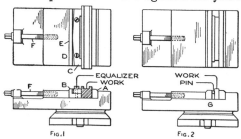

Fig.1    Fig.2

These Simple Methods of Gripping Work in Vises Are of Wide Use

pinching on the lower edge of the work G, causing chattering. These methods are good when gripping finished work that is not parallel.—H. M. Frank, New York, N. Y.

## Novel Method of Strapping Money Satchel to Messenger

A paymaster, who carries a small satchel for his money and accounts, has devised a novel method of strapping  the satchel around his shoulders, as shown in the sketch. A strong strap is fastened to the handle of the satchel and passes up his sleeve, around the right shoulder, and back to the sleeve across the chest. This gives him the free use of both arms in his work, as well as in defense against attack in an emergency.

## Blacksmith's Tongs Made of Iron Strips Bent Cold

When a pair of heavy tongs are needed for an occasional job of forging,  and blacksmith tongs of the usual pattern are not at hand, a substitute can be made quickly of two iron strips bent to the form shown in the sketch. No forging is necessary, as the metal can be drilled for a bolt and then bent cold making proper allowance in the size of work to be handled.—J. A. Ryan, Buffalo, N. Y.

## Polishing Overhead Shafting

In a large factory the brightly polished overhead shafting was quite noticeable. The method used to keep the shafting clean and free from rust was this: A pad covered with emery cloth and fastened to a long pole was held against the revolving shafting. The workman, reaching up with the pole, pressed the emery surface against the shafting, as desired, a fine polish resulting.—F. M. Ball, Kansas City, Missouri.

## Centering Halved Pattern Work in a Lathe

The centering of pieces for halved, or split, patterns in the lathe is often done inaccurately, so that the halves are not equal, and have to be thrown away. A good method is to plane one surface 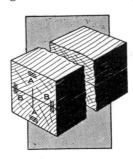 parallel with the parting surfaces, and square up the ends from it. Fasten the pieces together, and, with dividers, scribe lines on both ends, as at A and B. When putting the work in the lathe, center as usual, but do not drive the centers home. Turn down to the outer series of lines, and stop the lathe. The slightest error will be easily detected, as some of the lines will be nearer the cut than others. Tap the wood to center it properly, and set the dead center in slightly. Turn down a small portion, and examine the work, setting it so that it is accurately centered.—D. D. Gurnee, Hempstead, N. Y.

## Collar Setscrews Made from Ordinary Setscrews and Nuts

Fifty collar screws were needed in the shop, and not being able to obtain them locally, we made them as follows: A setscrew of the required size was taken, and a nut screwed very tight up to the head, with a wrench. The screw was then put in a spring collet in a lathe. The corners were broken with a tool, and then smoothed off with a file. This makeshift served the purpose exactly as well as the real article, and could not be noticed by a casual observer. The saving in time was considerable.—S. B. Royal, Baltimore, Md.

# The Selection of Illuminating Units for Home or Office

By K. M. COGGESHALL

The first rule to be remembered in planning artificial lighting is to avoid the use of a very bright spot in a poorly illuminated room. Such a condition prevents concentration, as the eye involuntarily fixes itself on the bright light. There should be a general illumination with additional lamps for local use, if necessary. It is best that only reflected light reach the eye; the source of illumination should be so placed that the direct rays are thrown on the work, and not in the eye. Precautions should also be taken to hang the light unit above the working plane in such a position that distracting shadows are not cast by the furniture or office fixtures, as indicated in one of the sketches, at A and B, as compared with C and D. The higher lights provide better light for both desks, No. 1 and 2, without shadows.

The illumination of a home is perhaps of first importance. If the rating used by manufacturers in classifying standard tungsten lamps is employed, the reception room, library, or living room should have an intensity of .9 watt per square foot of floor space. For instance, if the library is 12 by 16 ft. the floor area is 192 sq. ft. At .9 watt per square foot, about 173 watts are necessary for proper illumination. This value is approximated by using three 60-watt tungsten lamps.

The dining room should have a general illumination of about .4 watt, while the den should have at least .85 to .95 watt per square foot. It is necessary that the latter room be well lighted, as it is generally used for reading, writing, or playing games. Hallways, pantries, and closets should have an illumination of .2 watt. For the sake of sanitation, the illumination of the kitchen should be at least 1.3 watts per square foot. The lamps should be grouped under a cheap, yet efficient, 12-in. white-porcelain reflector near the ceiling. For the bedrooms .3 watt per square foot is satisfactory.

For the average office, an illumination of 1.3 watts per square foot of floor space is sufficient, except in instances where a great deal of stenographic or copy work is done, when

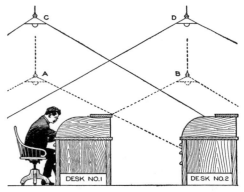

The Higher Lights Provide Better Light for Both Desks, and without Troublesome Shadows

the factor is 1.45 to 1.7 watts. For drafting work the range is 2.45 to 2.75 watts. The subject of spacing of the units is important. It presents a problem which cannot be entirely solved by mathematics; the answer is influenced by individual judgment and the cost of installation. The room should be laid out in sections of equal area, as shown in the other sketch. After the total watts per room have been determined, each section should be allotted its share. Standard lamps should then be installed in the center of each section. For the office, these lamps should be hung 12 to 14 ft. from the floor, while in drafting rooms, mountings as high as 16 ft. are sometimes desirable. Where

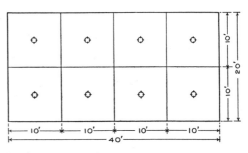

The Room is Laid Out in Squares and Each Section Allotted Units for Proper Illumination

the ceiling is low, limiting the available mounting height, it is desirable to use smaller spacing, and more lamps of smaller candlepower each.

---

## Drainage Pump Improvised on the Job

On an excavation job where water was struck, and had to be removed quickly, a drainage pump was made in short order, and did the work. First a square box for the barrel of the

This Crude Form of Plunger Pump was Rigged Up on the Job When Water was to be Removed from an Excavation Quickly

pump was made, and a valve block with a leather-and-wood valve cap, as shown, was fitted into the pump near the lower end. A spout was fixed near the upper end. The plunger was made of a square pole, at the lower end of which a water lift was rigged, as indicated. Two sections of wood were hinged to the central piece and braced by straps. When the pump plunger is lifting a load, the wooden hinge pieces are weighted down and form a close contact against the sides of the pump barrel. When the plunger is lowered into the water these pieces fold back against the center piece. The parts must be fitted closely to give good results. A spring pole was attached to the upper end of the plunger, and fastened at one end by means of logs.

## Pencil Held to Teeth Detects Knocks in Inclosed Machine

When part of an inclosed machine, for example a blade in a centrifugal pump, is pounding slightly, the affected locality needing adjustment can often be found without removing the casing. The operator touches the casing with a hard pencil point, the butt of the pencil being against his front teeth. The vibrations due to the pounding will attract his attention to the place to be adjusted without removing the casing to locate it.—R. Z. Kirkpatrick, Washington, D. C.

---

## Moving Hand Draws Attention to Window Display

Moving objects in window displays are good means of advertising, as they command attention. A printer having a sample case built directly underneath his show window, had a large hand painted on tin, on which was inscribed "Look at These Samples." He then fastened a wheel to the pointing finger, and connected it to the arm of a printing press near by, by means of a series of grooved pulleys and a string. It was adjusted so that at each revolution the hand would be raised pointing to the samples in the case. As the press

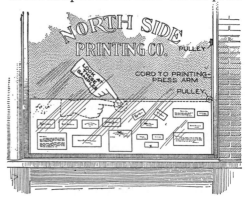

The Hand is Connected to a Near-By Printing Press by a Cord and Pulleys, so That It is Raised and Lowered by the Revolution of the Press Shaft

reaches dead center, the hand remains stationary for a moment, and then disappears from view.—M. J. F. Schramm, Brooklyn, N. Y.

## Special Sliding Caliper Useful on Many Jobs

The usefulness of a sliding caliper can be extended by making the legs pointed and providing the end leg with a vertical adjustment, as shown. A typical example is in scaling the distance between two points not in the same plane, as the points A and B. The body C of the caliper is made of machine steel. The legs D and E are made of the same material and shaped as indicated. The slides on the legs are made by riveting two strips of sheet metal, F, and a third, G, to the leg, as detailed. A thumbscrew through G clamps the leg. The leg E is constructed as shown, a small strip being riveted on the front. The legs may also be machined from solid pieces, the slots being drilled and filed. The leg D may

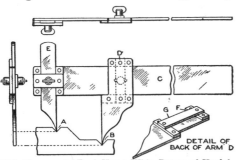

This Homemade Tool Has a Wide Range of Usefulness on Work Not Practicable with an Ordinary Caliper

also be made with a vertical as well as a lateral adjustment.—William A. Robinson, Waynesboro, Pa.

## Knee Lever Actuates Shift Key on Typewriter

An unskilled typist, of the "two-finger" school, found that time was lost in striking the shift key, as this operation took one of the two fingers. In order to save this lost motion, he bored a small hole through his desk directly below the machine, and ran a cord through it, the upper end of which was hooked over the shift key of the typewriter, as indicated. A knee pedal was arranged as shown. The upper end of the pedal was connected with the

string, which passed through an eye, to give a straight pull on the key. To strike a capital, the knee is pressed

Greater Speed can be Attained on the Typewriter if One or More of the Shift Keys are Controlled by Pedals

against the pedal, giving the operator greater speed. This arrangement is practical even for a skilled typist.—John D. Gilbert, Eugene, Ore.

## Lamps for Stock Room Shifted along Horizontal Wires

Below long rows of shelves or racks in stock rooms, it is sometimes necessary to install an electric-lighting system. The method generally used is to have an incandescent lamp on a long cord, the latter dragging on the floor, as the lamp is moved from one portion of the room to another. A better plan is to stretch a steel wire down the center of the aisle, high enough above the

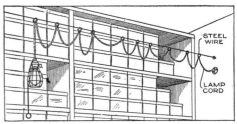

The Light is Moved Along the Wire, and the Cord does Not Drag on the Floor

floor to be over the heads of the clerks. At points 2 ft. apart, rings are fastened, as shown. The lamp cord will be out of the way, and protected from injury. —B. E. Waller, Omaha, Neb.

## Brake Band Repaired with Spring-Steel Strap

The point at which the brake band of an automobile usually breaks is opposite the opening, as shown in the sketch. I found that, by making a repair at this place with a strap of spring steel riveted into place as detailed, the brake band was stronger than when originally fitted. The

spring steel at the break gives the band elasticity, and its strength is equal to, if not greater than, that of the metal where the break usually occurs. When I bought two new brake bands, I had them sawed in half at the point where the break usually occurred and joined by this method.—C. H. Thomas, Kennett Square, Pa.

## Rubber-Covered Instrument Knobs Made from Sink Stoppers

The furnishing of suitable knobs for rotating shafts on small instruments,

and similar constructions, is often a problem to experimenters. Many forms of cheap and attractive insulated handles, or knobs, can be made by fitting rubber sink stoppers, or even chair-leg tips, to common wooden, or other, knobs. The addition of these soft-rubber coverings is desirable where a firm grip for turning a shaft is necessary. —R. U. Clark, III, Newton, Mass.

## Small Floor Pit Convenient for Sheet-Metal Work

In a shop where much cutting was done with large hand shears, it was found that the most convenient way to do this work was to provide a pit in the floor, about 30 in. deep and 4 ft.

square, in which the workman stands. This gives him a large working area on the floor around the pit. The work is brought to a good level for convenience in cutting, and where long strips are to be cut, the large floor area is desirable. The tiresome stooping to the floor is avoided, a feature which appeals to the man on the job.—Lee M. Delzell, Maroa, Ill.

## Inserting Bushings in Motorcycle Connecting Rods

An easy method of inserting bushings in connecting rods of motorcycle engines is to pass

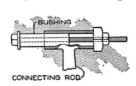

a machine bolt of sufficient size and length through the bushing and connecting rod, as shown. Run the thread up to within 1 in. of the head. Place a ⅜-in. washer on the bolt next to the head. Put the bolt through the bushing and connecting rod. Then put a large washer next to the connecting rod. Put a nut on the bolt and draw it up, until it pulls the bearing into place, and without marring the bearing surfaces.—Walter B. Raynor, Patchogue, N. Y.

## Pipe Wrench Made from Rope and Wooden Strip

When a pipe wrench is needed for turning or holding pipe, and none is at

hand, a substitute can be made of a wooden strip and a piece of rope. Lay the strip across the pipe as shown, and wind the rope around the pipe and over the strip, so that the latter acts as a lever. The rope should, of course, be fastened so that the pull is in the desired direction.—C. M. Hall, St. Louis, Missouri.

## Bronze Disk Takes Up Thrust Wear in Pump

The oil pump of a gasoline engine revealed a gradual drop in pumping capacity and an examination showed that the driven spur gear was subjected to a great longitudinal thrust due to the action of the driving worm. This thrust resulted in the inner wall of the pump case becoming worn, allowing the oil to leak past the gear teeth so that the pump lost a great amount of its pumping force.

A repair was necessary and it was accomplished in the following manner: The pump was dismantled and found to be worn out in the casing wall to a depth of $\frac{1}{16}$ in. A hole equal in diameter to the outside diameter of the gear and $\frac{1}{4}$ in. deep, was bored in the casing on the side subjected to the thrust, and a bronze disk inserted in the hole. This was held in position by two $\frac{1}{4}$-in. headless machine screws.

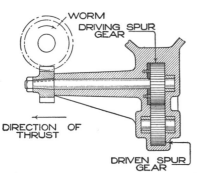

The Cavity Worn in the Casing was Filled by a Bronze Bearing Plate

The disk acted as a sort of thrust plate and instantly brought the pump up to its normal pumping capacity. A new disk replaced the worn one from time to time, so that the least bit of wear was quickly counteracted.

## House Moved over Snow with Makeshift Capstan

On a house-moving job here recently, the movers rigged out a capstan that did the work in first-rate shape, and as will be seen from the photographs it was quite crude as compared with the usual capstan for this purpose. A fork of a tree was strongly braced to a heavy timber foundation, and a vertical drum for the capstan was mounted in it. This made a more convenient arrange-

The Building was Moved Nearly One-Half Mile over Rough Ground by the Use of This Makeshift Capstan Built of a Large Tree Fork

ment than the usual support of two or four upright pieces braced together. The building was moved nearly one-half mile in 40 hours, over very rough and hilly ground, by two men with the aid of one team.—W. E. Covert, Grande Prairie, Alta., Canada.

## Runway over Oil Tanks Saves Lifting of Barrels

Shops using several grades of oil will find it convenient to build a runway or track above their oil-storage tanks, as shown in the photograph. When it is necessary to renew the storage supply,

The Barrels or Drums are Rolled into Position and the Contents Transferred

the barrels, or drums, in which the oil is shipped, are rolled up an incline to the track, and thence along the track to the tank to be filled. A saving of many hours of labor resulted from the adoption of this plan in a large shop, as compared with the pump or dipping method of filling the tanks.—K. M. C., Webster Groves, Mo.

## Square Wrench Seat Fitted on Tank Filler Cap

The filler cap on the gasoline tank of an automobile was of circular shape, and was extremely hard to remove

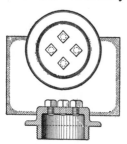

when it was necessary to refill the tank. I decided to improve it in some manner so that a wrench could be used. I took four square-headed machine screws and set them in the top of the cap, as shown in the illustration. The wrench could then be applied with ease, and the cap was quickly removed.—Adolph Klein, New York, N. Y.

## Wooden Expansion Plugs for Screws Easily Made

A wooden expansion plug for holding a screw or bolt in a concrete wall may be made quickly, as shown in the

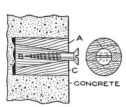

sketch. A round wooden 1-in. plug is sawed diagonally, so that the cross section will show three parts, A, B, and C. The plug is placed in the drilled hole in the wall, and the screw started in the wedge end of B, expanding it tightly against the other sections. The wedge tends to press A and C more tightly against the walls of the hole under an outward pressure. The plugs are best uniformly machine cut.

## Old Paintbrushes Provide Small Tool Handles

When paintbrushes become worn out they are usually thrown away or burned. By saving the handles of these brushes, especially those of the heavier round type, the home mechanic can keep his tool box well stocked with extra handles for small files and other tools. The brush handle can be quickly trimmed to shape with a jackknife, and the end cut for a ferrule, flattened to an oval if necessary.—Frank Jablecnik, Chicago, Ill.

## Printing-Press Gauge Pins Made of Paper

Printers, when doing work with narrow margins, often find that the gauge pins they commonly use are in the

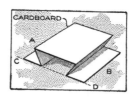

way of the grippers. Instead of using a regular-style gauge pin, a homemade substitute, which is perhaps better since it can be flattened out by the tympan clamps with each impression without doing it any harm, can be used. It is made from a piece of light cardboard, or stiff paper. The paper is folded, as shown, and the ends A and B are pasted at C and D, along the line where the paper will be fed.—Joseph Thalheimer, Jr., Venice, Calif.

## Auto Used as Power Plant without Altering Car

An automobile may be utilized to furnish power for operating small machinery without altering the car in any way, by the use of the driving rigging shown. All that is necessary is to back the automobile up the slight incline, and leave the gears in mesh with the engine running. The tires transmit the power to the 6-in. rollers, and they, in turn, to a belted drive pulley. The wooden rollers are 6 ft. long. Each end is fitted with an axle, 1 ft. long, sufficiently heavy to bear the weight of the automobile used. Two wooden bearing boxes are built of 3-ft. pieces of 2 by 4-in. hard pine, bolted together and bored through the middle, for bearings, where the two faces come together. Small holes are also bored down through the top piece for lubrication. The rollers are assembled with ring washers against their ends, and the bearing boxes are bolted together with two braces. The pulley on the projecting end of the driving axle is set with a setscrew.

A slanting platform, as shown, makes it easy to back up the car on the rollers. The distance between the rollers depends on the diameter of the wheel of the car being used, but for general purposes a space of 18 in. between the two sets of bearings will give ample

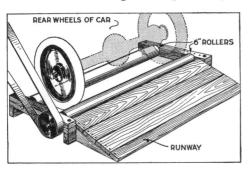

The Rear Wheels of the Automobile are Run onto the Rollers, and Transmit Power to the Drive Pulley

room for the average auto wheel to come well down between the rollers and insure good traction.

### Revolving Check Holder for Lunch Rooms

Instead of having a person at the door to hand out checks during the busy hours, a lunch room uses several holders of a type shown in the sketch. They are filled by the cashier during the part of the day when the patronage is light. As the patrons enter they pick their own checks from the holder, the arrow indicating which end the check should be taken from. The cardboard box in the center, on which the directions are marked, is lifted off, and

the rack for the ticket replaced as required. The rack is pivoted on the

The Patrons Take Their Checks from the Holder Which is Provided with a Filled Rack as New Checks are Needed

center of the wooden base with a bolt. —L. E. Turner, Brighton, Mass.

### Racks for Pipes and Cigars Aid "No Smoking" Enforcement

Considerable trouble was experienced in a large factory where smoking was forbidden in certain of the departments, because lighted cigars, pipes, and cigarettes were carried by persons entering the room to remain only a short time. As a result, racks made of sheet metal, as shown, were provided at the doors, and a suitable sign placed over them. The rule against carrying

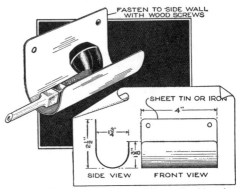

Before Entering the Room Where Smoking is Forbidden, the "Smoke" is Placed on a Rack at the Door

lighted tobacco in various forms was rigidly enforced and hearty coöperation of the men was gained.

## Stove-Lid Lifting Lug
## Repaired with Wire

A neat repair was made when the cast lug on a stove lid broke, by setting a piece of wire across the lifter

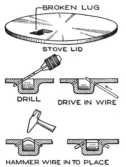

BROKEN LUG

STOVE LID

DRILL　　　DRIVE IN WIRE

HAMMER WIRE INTO PLACE

socket, by the method shown in the illustration. The hole was chipped clear, and holes for the wire were drilled through the sides, at a slight angle, as indicated. The wire was driven through from below, cut off to the proper length, and hammered into place. The bend which the wire must be given to fit into the holes, can be determined easily by a test, the wire being bent with the aid of pliers.—Edwin J. Bachman, Jr., Fullerton, Pa.

## A Pulling Hook with Safety
## Finger Hold

Where hooks of the ordinary design are used on the end of a chain, or line, for pulling objects around by power,

on cranes, etc., accidents occur frequently. The man whose work it is to engage the tackle may try to place the hook in the hole, or fitting, "on the fly," and smashed fingers may result. The safety-first hook shown has a finger hole whereby it may be held without danger. The proportions of such a hook will vary in accordance with the work to be handled. The size of the finger opening should be about 1½ by 4 in. Where the service is not too severe, these hooks may be cut and forged from sheet-steel plate.—E. D. Clifford, Chicago, Ill.

## Handy One-Man Method
## of Using Tapeline

If proper care is taken, measurements can be made with a tapeline by one man with as much accuracy as if an assistant were setting the end of the line. A 6-in. brad awl is set carefully at the mark from which the measurements are made, the point passing through the end loop of the tapeline. While the device is especially useful on wooden structures, it can also be used handily on brickwork, by making the measurements from wooden trimmings, and deducting the lengths which are not to be included in the measurements.

## Leather Cap Remedies Loose Auto-
## Engine Valve

When the valve guide and valve stem became worn on an automobile engine,

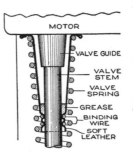

MOTOR

VALVE GUIDE

VALVE STEM

VALVE SPRING

GREASE

BINDING WIRE

SOFT LEATHER

an extra amount of air was sucked in, weakening the mixture coming through the carburetor, thereby causing much trouble. To eliminate this, I shaped a piece of soft leather to fit on the inside of the valve spring. I put a piece of wire around the top to stiffen it and attached the cap to the valve stem at its lowest point of motion. Grease was added, as shown, acting as a lubricant and aiding in keeping out the air. The device is held in place by the pressure of the valve spring, and the leather, being soft, allows for the movement of the valve.—A. Elting, New York, N. Y.

◖When drilling holes in small pieces of metal, especially where a brace or breast drill is used, and no vise is at hand, hold the piece with a monkey wrench, so as not to harm the hands, or weight the wrench, if both hands are needed for drilling.

# Shop Notes

## Homemade Stump-Boring Machine an Aid to Settlers

### By E. R. McIntyre

This Stump-Boring Machine of the "Day" Type Is Very Efficient for Preparing Stumps for Blasting in Clearing Land

AN inexpensive, homemade stump-boring machine is being used extensively by settlers in getting the tough, deep-rooted, long-leaf pine stumps of Mississippi in shape for blasting, in the process of land clearing. Those who have fair mechanical experience build the machine themselves, buying only the necessary metal parts, and local blacksmiths build the outfits at a cost of not over $30. The inventor gave the machine to the settlers for use in de-

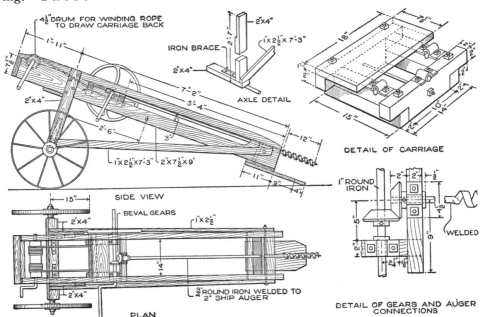

The Construction Is Comparatively Simple: a Local Blacksmith can Easily Provide the Metal Fittings, and the Wooden Parts can be Made in the Farm Workshop

velopment work. This method of boring stumps for blasting is practical for use in many other sections of the country. In a recent test at the Mississippi Agricultural Experiment Station, one man in five hours bored through 27 stumps, averaging 18 in. at the top and 22 in. diagonally, as bored, in diameter.

The construction of the machine, as detailed in the working drawings, is comparatively simple. The large wheels make it easy to transport the outfit, which is set up, when in use, as shown in the photograph. The holes are bored by a 2-in. ship auger, which is welded to a ¾-in. round-iron rod. The power is transmitted to this rod from a crankshaft, geared to the auger rod. The crankshaft and the beveled gear at the upper end of the auger rod are mounted in a carriage, shown in detail. This carriage slides in ways cut into the sidepieces of the frame. The carriage is drawn up, in removing the auger from a bored hole, by means of the drum and ropes at the upper end of the frame. The connections of the auger rod and its driving arrangement are shown in detail. The crankshaft is made of 1-in. round iron bent at one end to form a handle. A flywheel is set on the other end.

The upper end of the main frame is about 5 ft. from the ground. The elevation of the frame, in this manner, braces it against the stump in boring, and brings the crankshaft to a height at which it can be easily turned. It also causes a slight pressure against the auger, which aids in boring steadily at a diagonal, yet does not hinder withdrawal of the auger.

---

### Heating a Small Workshop
### by Means of Blowtorch

A method of warming the small shop on wintry days that is novel and practical makes use of a blowtorch and sections of stovepipe. An elbow and a lengtl. of stovepipe are used as a flue through

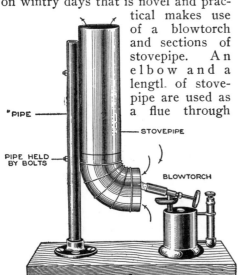

PIPE

STOVEPIPE

PIPE HELD
BY BOLTS

BLOWTORCH

This Arrangement was Successfully Used to Warm a Small Shop When the Thermometer Outside Stood below Zero

which the hot air from the flame of the blowtorch passes. As the heated air rises in the pipe, cold air is drawn in at the opening around the flame, as indicated. The supporting standard is fastened to a base of suitable size, and the pipe is fastened with bolts. The torch should be placed so that the end of the flame just enters the end of the pipe.—Kenneth M. Bard, Manawa, Wisconsin.

---

### Methodical Oiling of Automobile
### Proves Economical

Proper lubrication is one of the most important factors in the preservation of the life of an automobile. The best way to oil the machine is to do it methodically. A procedure that is thoroughly satisfactory, and which does not require a chart of the type in quite common use, is to "map out the oiling campaign" on the car itself. Give every oil hole and every place to be oiled a number, running serially from 1 up. Starting with oil hole No. 1, stamp it with a small die-stamping outfit. At hole No. 10, stamp that number, and stamp each tenth hole thereafter. Then, in oiling, proceed from the first hole, keeping a mental count. If the count agrees with the stamped figures, probably no points have been overlooked.—G. N. Near, New York, N. Y.

## Device Aids in Filling
## Storage Batteries

Storage batteries of the sealed type are difficult to fill, and when a number of cells require filling at one time, it is tedious to watch the height of the solution. The device shown in the sketch audibly indicates when the battery is properly filled. It consists of a length of iron or brass pipe, provided with a stopcock as shown. A short length of lead pipe is fitted into the elbow. The lead pipe should be of such a length that when the longer pipe is laid flat on the top of the cell, the lead pipe is within 3/4 in. of the plates. A small buzzer is mounted on the pipe, one terminal being connected thereto. To the other terminal of the buzzer connect a length of stranded lamp cord, attaching the latter to a steel point fitted into a short stick.

The filling tube is connected to the

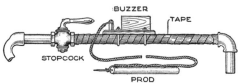
The Buzzer Indicates When the Battery has been
Filled to the Proper Height

water supply by means of a rubber hose. In use, the short pipe is inserted into the vent in the cells; the steel point is then forced into the terminal on the battery, spanning at least one cell. When the electrolyte has reached the proper height, the circuit is closed, and the buzzer announces the fact.—Thomas W. Benson, Philadelphia, Pa.

## Wheel Arrangement for Drying
## Blueprints

A handy arrangement for drying blueprints, and insuring that they will be reasonably flat, can be made by mounting an old buggy, or light wagon, wheel on a pipe standard, as shown in the illustration. Every other spoke is cut out. Two stiff wires are suspended from each spoke, the blueprints being stretched between the wires and held by spring clips, or clothespins. The wooden base is set in a suitable trough,

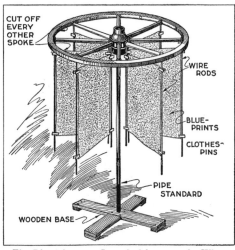
The Blueprints are Stretched between the Wires
Suspended from the Spokes of the
Pivoted Buggy Wheel

into which the water from the prints drips. If they are given a slight preliminary drying, the arrangement may be used on a wooden floor.—Joseph Thalheimer, Jr., Phoenix, Ariz.

## A Post Extractor Mounted
## on Wheels

A type of post extractor, which has long been in use by circus men and tent gangs, can easily be adapted for use by farmers, or others who find it necessary to repair or remove fence posts. An old pair of wheels and an axle from a worn-out farm machine, or

The Post is Quickly Withdrawn with Slight Effort,
by Bearing Down on the End of the Lever

wagon, provide a suitable truck. A heavy piece of hard wood is bolted to the axle, as shown, and an old wagon pole, or even a timber cut from a small tree, can be used for the lever. The wheels may also be made solid, of wood spiked together in cross layers. The operation of the outfit is simple: A chain is formed into a sling around the base of the post and hooked over the short end of the lever. By bearing down on the other end of the lever, the post is withdrawn. Usually, several holds must be taken with the chain to pull out the post completely.—C. L. Moore, Cleveland, Ohio.

## Removing and Replacing Automobile Bushings

Worn bushings in an automobile cause lost motion in the connected parts, as well as undue vibration and

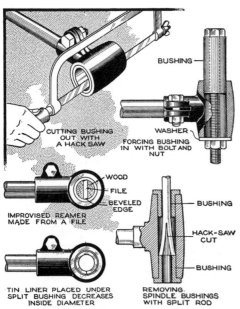

CUTTING BUSHING OUT WITH A HACK SAW

BUSHING

WASHER

FORCING BUSHING IN WITH BOLT AND NUT

WOOD

FILE

BEVELED EDGE

IMPROVISED REAMER MADE FROM A FILE

BUSHING

HACK-SAW CUT

BUSHING

TIN LINER PLACED UNDER SPLIT BUSHING DECREASES INSIDE DIAMETER

REMOVING SPINDLE BUSHINGS WITH SPLIT ROD

The Old Bushings are Removed by Suitable Methods, and New Ones Inserted, as Indicated

noise. The bushings in the steering connections and spring shackles are readily replaced, with the least dismantling of the parts, by the use of a hacksaw and a bolt, with a nut to fit. The blade of the saw is disconnected at one end and placed inside the bushing, as shown. The saw slot cut permits the bushing to be easily removed. To force the new bushing into place, it is filed slightly at one end to start it into the hole. Place the bolt through, and slip a washer over, to make the nut turn easily. A wrench at each end will force the bushing into place. After the bushing is in place, the pivot pin or bolt will probably be too large to enter. For increasing the inside diameter of the bushing, a discarded file makes an excellent reamer, when ground as shown.

Sometimes new bushings are not at hand, in which instance a liner of tin, if fitted around the outside of the split bushing, will reduce the inside diameter sufficiently to be of further service, as shown. Another bushing remover, which is useful for removing the end bushings in the wheel spindles, is made by using a metal rod as shown. Splitting one end of this with a hacksaw and bending the ends apart, makes it ready for use. The ends are sprung together and placed through the upper bushing, after which they will spring open. A hammer is used to drive out the bushings. Coating the exterior surface with grease or graphite grease helps to reduce the labor of replacing the bushings.—G. A. Luers, Washington, D. C.

## Cutting Drafting Sheets Quickly from Roll of Paper

In cutting sheets from a roll of paper considerable stock is often wasted by carelessness in tearing or cutting the paper. A good plan is to unroll the roll to the size of sheet desired, and then to use the edge of the roll as a pencil guide in marking a cutting line. When a number of sheets of the same size are to be cut, and they do not extend the full width of the roll, a section of paper may be cut off and rolled up; the width of the sheets is then marked along the length of the roll, and the roll cut through at one stroke. The resulting strips are then cut to length. —F. B. Mallory, Flemington, N. J.

## Sandpaper Finger Tips an Aid in Feeding Press

In feeding a printing press rapidly, the bare fingers smear the ink when the sheet is pulled off. Instead of winding a strip of sandpaper around the finger, cut round disks of coarse sandpaper a little smaller than a dime, and glue disks on the tips of the first and second fingers. This method enables the feeder to get the printed sheet every time, and does not smear the work.— H. S. Hart, Shreveport, La.

## Concrete Borders on Walks Protect Grassplots

Careless pedestrians often ruin lawns along the edges of walks, even though the walks are of sufficient width. A good method of overcoming this temptation to make a path on the grass bordering the walks is to set a row of low

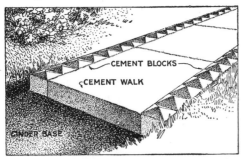

CEMENT BLOCKS
CEMENT WALK
CINDER BASE

The Pyramid Borders Keep Pedestrians on the Walk and Protect the Adjoining Grassplots

concrete pyramids along the edge of the walk, as shown. They may be cast in blocks, or built in a continuous strip with the walk.

## Revolving Nail Holder Made from Cheese Box

A shop contrivance that saves much time and is a help in keeping the shop in order was made from an old cheese box, and provides for nails and other small hardware. Compartments were fitted in the box radially, like the sections of a pie, and openings cut into the sides of the box, as shown. The box

was then mounted on an iron pipe, set in a wooden base. An iron flange

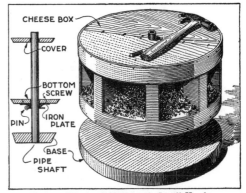

CHEESE BOX
COVER
BOTTOM SCREW
PIN
IRON PLATE
BASE
PIPE SHAFT

The Various Kinds of Nails and Small Hardware are Placed in the Compartments, and Conveniently Removed by Revolving the Cheese Box

plate was fastened to the bottom of the box, and provides a good bearing for a large cotter pin set through the pipe as a support for the box.—F. E. Brimmer, Dalton, N. Y.

## A Strong Table Frame Quickly Made

A common practice in making cheap tables is to end-butt the sides into the legs, connecting the sides by a bridge piece and fastening the latter with screws. The screws need frequent tightening, because of shrinkage and vibration. The method shown is stronger and quicker: Saw out the triangular portion at the top of the leg, and surface the cut with a sharp chisel and block plane. Miter the ends of the two sides against the surface, as shown, and fasten the joints with glue and screws. Reverse the portion cut out

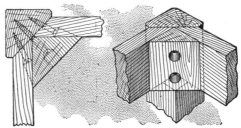

This Table-Frame Joint is Quickly Made and Very Strong

from the leg, and fasten it into the corner.—Henry Simon, Laguna Beach, California.

## Combination Tool Chest and Trestle Folds Compactly

The mechanic who has small repair jobs to do in various places, making it

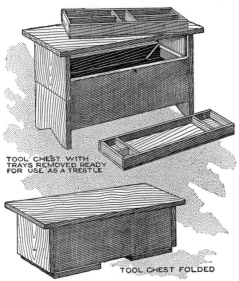

TOOL CHEST WITH TRAYS REMOVED READY FOR USE AS A TRESTLE

TOOL CHEST FOLDED

The Combined Tool Chest and Trestle Folds Compactly for Convenience in Carrying, and, When Opened, Provides a Substantial Support

necessary to carry tools and saw-horses, as well as the home mechanic

who has use for a compact jobbing outfit, will appreciate this combination tool chest and trestle. When folded, as shown, the chest is compact, and affords a good handhold at each end of the top for convenience in carrying. On the job, the lower ends of the legs are folded from under the tool chest, the sides of the latter sliding down to the position shown in the upper sketch. The trays fit inside of the raised sides and can be removed easily. The top of the trestle gives ample space for work, and as a rest for sawing.

The construction is detailed in the working drawings. The end supports are hinged across the middle, their inner edges are grooved, and the two sides of the tool compartment slide in the grooves, as detailed in the plan. The lower tray rests on strips at each end, and the upper one slides on the lower. When the outfit is closed, the lower ends of the support are folded under the tool compartment, the sides being raised in their grooves to their position under the top. The folding ends are locked, at A, by a spring device, shown in detail. A small metal plate, B, is fitted over a part of a shallow mortise in the inner side of the leg, at B, in the side view. Two angles of metal, C, are mounted on a rod, and held apart by a coiled spring, D. When the legs are folded into place, the angles C are pressed together between the thumb and first finger, and their sliding ends permitted to catch under the small plates B. The spring D holds the angles in this locked position. The other details of construction

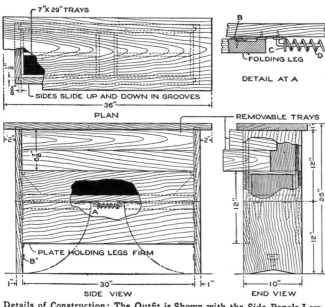

7"X 29" TRAYS

SIDES SLIDE UP AND DOWN IN GROOVES
36"
PLAN

B
FOLDING LEG
DETAIL AT A

REMOVABLE TRAYS

PLATE HOLDING LEGS FIRM
B'
SIDE VIEW
30"

25"
12"
12"
12"
END VIEW
10"

Details of Construction: The Outfit is Shown with the Side Panels Lowered in Their Grooves, and the Trays Partly Removed. The Lower Ends of the Supports Fold under the Bottom, as Indicated in the Side View, and are Locked by the Mechanism Shown in the Detail at A

are simple, and are shown in the dimensioned working drawings and sketches. — George H. Jackson, Toronto, Ont., Canada.

## Overhead Controls for Garage Auto-Washing Hose

In a large auto garage where water was used through a meter, it was found that ordinary shut-off nozzles on the ends of the hose used for washing automobiles were not desirable because of the danger of scratching the finish. A large waste of water resulted by the use of a hose without a means of shutting off the water close at hand. As a result the overhead-control system shown in the sketch was installed, and worked satisfactorily. By this means the operator can shut off the flow of water from his position at any one of the four corners of the machine, by pulling on the nearest control handle.

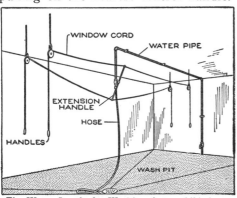

The Water Supply for Washing Automobiles in a Garage was Controlled Conveniently by This Overhead Arrangement

A valve was set at the end of the water pipe near the ceiling, and its stem was fitted with a lever, as shown, to which the four control cords were attached and run through pulleys.—Robert L. Cook. Madisonville, Ky.

## Repair for Broken Cross Hairs in Surveyor's Level

A sudden jar or fall of a surveyor's instrument sometimes causes the hairs to break from the cross-hair ring in the level, and usually the instrument is sent back to the factory for repairs.

When an emergency repair was necessary, a method was devised which proved of permanent value. The instrument was disassembled and the cross-hair ring removed. The grooves

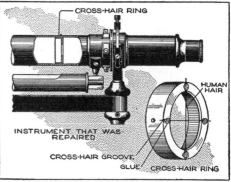

Human Hairs were Glued into the Cross-Hair Ring of the Surveyor's Level and Provided a Satisfactory Substitute for the Broken Cross Hairs

for the hairs were cleaned, and two human hairs were glued into place, as shown. The glue was applied hot, and the hairs were drawn taut across the notches. In a similar repair, carbon filaments from an electric-light bulb were used and proved serviceable, but were harder to put into place because of their brittleness.—A. P. Midland, New York, N. Y.

## Muffler for Injecting Steam into Water Tank

The sketch shows a muffler, which I am using in a feed-water tank, or hot well, as the marine engineer calls it, for stopping the noise created when steam is used for heating water. It consists of a 1½-in. pipe, 1 ft. long, perforated by ¼-in. holes, all around. I filled the pipe with light coil springs from pumps, and reduced the bottom end to ¾ in. and the top to ½ in. and fitted the pipe on, as indicated, with a control valve.—Richard Alte, Baltimore, Md.

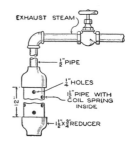

## Holder for Marking Punches Strapped to Workman's Belt

Especially in the machine industries, it is a common practice to mark various parts before assembling them, and

the workman who does this must go from place to place with his set of steel marking punches. It is unhandy to carry these in the box usually provided, and a wide-awake mechanic rigged out a harness - and - belt arrangement, as shown, which proved to be very convenient. He made a curved piece of wood to fit the body at the waistline and attached the straps to it. The punches are carried in holes in the wooden piece, and are handy to get at. —C. C. Spreen, Flint, Mich.

## Babbitting Drill in Drill-Press Spindle Avoids Heavy Work

Some castings were to be drilled, and the only means at hand were a hand breast drill and a heavy radial drilling machine. The chuck of the machine was 4 in. too low, in its upper

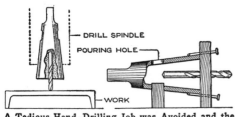

A Tedious Hand-Drilling Job was Avoided and the Work Turned Out in Short Order on a Drill Press by the Method Shown

position, to permit the castings to fit under it. The job was accomplished by babbitting a drill in one of the sock-

ets used to reduce the size of the spindle hole for small taper-shank drills. To hold the drill in place while pouring the babbitt around it, the rigging shown in the sketch was used. The drill was set into the center of a wooden block, held in place as indicated. The socket was suitably plugged, and the metal poured in. The chuck was taken out of the spindle, and the socket became practically a chuck, saving enough height on the spindle to make room for the job.

## Tin and Celluloid Cover Protects Shop Tally Cards

Inspectors in manufacturing plants, and checkers who use tally cards to

check up the work turned out, find difficulty in keeping their records clean and neat. A large automobile plant has provided, for inspectors, holders made of tin as shown. Three of the edges are turned over to form a groove for the card, and transparent celluloid covers the card and also slides in the grooves. The tin provides a base for the card, and it is necessary to withdraw the celluloid only sufficiently to expose the card as desired.—J. S. Hagans, Toledo, Ohio.

## Liquid Shoe Polish Used as Auto Radiator Paint

Because of the difficulty of getting into the spaces in an automobile radiator to clean or paint them, this part of a car is often neglected. The appearance can be improved by painting the webbing with black, liquid shoe polish, diluted to the proper consistency. A convenient method of applying the paint is to use the dauber which usually is attached to the cork of the bottle. —G. A. L., Washington, D. C.

## Paraffin Repairs Small Holes in Cold-Water Tank

When a copper-lined, or porcelain, tank for cold water leaks from small holes, dry off the surface thoroughly with a rag. Then locate the leak, and pour hot paraffin on it. In an emergency, drops of wax from a candle will also do the work. This will often give years of life to such a tank.—Joseph J. Jiannotto, Brooklyn, N. Y.

## Substantial and Economical Concrete Base for Poles

In setting telephone poles, and poles for similar service, in loose sand or gravel, the method shown was used with excellent results. The cup-shaped hollow below the heavy line was first concreted around the pole and then the refill, noted above, was put in

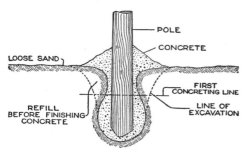

This Type of Base for Poles Is Strong, and Economical of Concrete

place and the concreting finished. The refill is advantageous both because of the narrow girth it gives to the concrete around the bottom of the pole, thus being harder to pull out of the ground, and also because of the saving in cement.—Roy H. Poston, Flat River, Missouri.

## Method of Straightening Freight-Car Frames

The drawing shows my design used on many cars for straightening center sills, end sills, body bolsters, and braces by pulling out the stoved-in ends of cars with powerful jacks. A link, shown in detail, is fitted to the couplers, and the jacks are placed against the end sills, pressure being applied by means of levers. The dotted lines

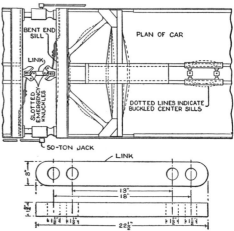

The Car Frames are Straightened by the Use of Powerful Jacks

indicate the buckled portions to be straightened.—John W. Shank, Renovo, Pa.

## A Tickler for Priming Carburetor

A kink that the autoist will appreciate is for priming the carburetor without the necessity of lifting the hood. Two small strips of steel, A, are soldered to the top of the float cover. With the aid of a steel pin, a hinge is formed for the crank B. This is also made from strip steel. A steel wire runs from the crank, through and to the outside of the radiator. A pull

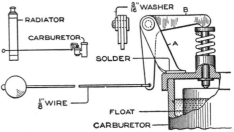

By Drawing on the Wire at the Radiator, the Carburetor is Primed without Raising the Engine Hood

on the wire pushes down the plunger of the tickler, causing the float to drop, and in this manner the carburetor is primed.

## A Strong Gate Built
## of Iron Pipe

A neat and substantial iron gate can be made in the home or farm workshop with iron pipe and fittings. A practical design is shown in the illustration. The gate is made as follows: Prepare

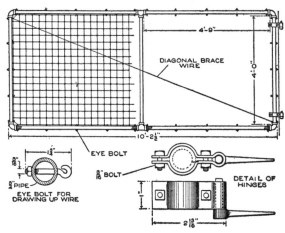

DIAGONAL BRACE WIRE

4'-9"

4'-0"

10'-2½"

EYE BOLT

EYE BOLT FOR DRAWING UP WIRE

½"PIPE

1½"

⅜" BOLT

DETAIL OF HINGES

2 13/16"

This Substantial Iron Gate can be Made in Various Sizes from Pipes and Fittings

four pieces of ¾-in. galvanized-iron pipe, 5 ft. long and threaded at both ends. Cut three pieces 4 ft. long. Four elbows and two tees are also needed. Fit the gate up, as shown, leaving out the two bottom pieces at first. These two pieces are made as shown, one end of each being threaded twice as far as the other end. Screw the long threaded end into the elbow as far as possible, then fit the other end to the tee and screw it into place. The long thread at the ell will become partly unscrewed as the short end enters the tee. Fit both pieces in this manner. The gate frame is now complete, and should be covered with woven-wire fencing. The detail shows the small eyebolts that support the wire and serve to draw it tightly in place. A diagonal wire brace is then put into place, and drawn tightly by twisting it or inserting a turnbuckle. The hinges are made from a piece of ⅛ by 1-in. strap iron, bent to fit around the pipe of the gate and clamped with a bolt, as detailed.—B. Francis Dashiell, Dunkirk, Md.

---

## Electric Auto Spotlight Arranged
## for Easy Focusing

To secure a focusing arrangement that may be readily adjusted to suit various road conditions, I refitted the electric spotlight on my automobile as shown in the diagram. By turning the adjusting handle, the globe is forced in or out, as indicated by the dotted lines, causing the light to spread or be confined in a long, narrow beam, as desired. I sawed off the old handle of the lamp and fitted a bronze bushing into the end of the reflector extension. Into a disk, which forms the adjusting handle, I fitted a bronze screw, the head of which was ground to the shape of a nail head, as shown. This screw is set firmly in the handle, and is adjusted in the threaded bronze bushing. The end of the screw makes contact with the central electrode of the lamp.

The lamp is carried in an insulation bushing and is fitted with a coiled spring, which forces it back into contact with the adjusting screw. The

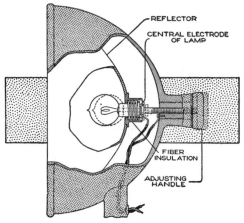

REFLECTOR

CENTRAL ELECTRODE OF LAMP

FIBER INSULATION

ADJUSTING HANDLE

A Simple Method of Adjusting an Auto Spotlight was Provided by Fitting the Reflector with These Special Parts

wiring is connected up as shown, one of the wires being set in the bronze bushing by means of a screw, and the other fixed to the shell of the light-globe plug.—John E. Hogg, Alhambra, California.

## An Alining Tool for Shafting and Machinery

A handy tool, worthy of a place in any mechanic's tool chest, is an alining device, for determining parallelism of machinery shafts and fittings. The hook A is of 1-in. sheet steel, shaped as shown, and snaps over the first shaft. A flat-link brass chain, B, fastened at one end, is drawn through the head C to the approximate distance, and clamped to the stud D by means of the thumbscrew E. Final adjustment is obtained by moving the pointer F along the slot in which it is set, and clamping the thumbscrew G. In opera-

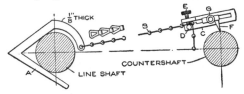

Shafting and Other Parallel Machine Parts are Lined Up Accurately with This Handy Tool

tion, the approximate adjustment is made at one end of two shafts to be lined up, and then the final adjustment is made. The distance is then scaled at several points on the shafting to insure accuracy.—J. B. Murphy, Plainfield, N. J.

## Winding Small Magnet Coils with a Hand Drill

In the winding of a considerable number of small magnet coils, no lathe being available, the rigging shown was adopted. It operated very satisfactorily, and was reserved for future use. A small hand drill, clamped in a vise, was used in turning the spool upon which the coil was to be wound. The spool, as it was wound, was held on a bolt from which the head had been cut, and the bolt was clamped

in the chuck of the hand drill. The spool of new wire was mounted on a bolt set in a suitable support, clamped to the bench top. To prevent the

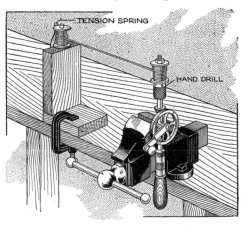

An Ordinary Hand Drill Mounted in a Vise Provides a Practical and Rapid Means of Winding Small Coils

spool from unwinding too rapidly and to provide a tension on the wire, a brass spring was arranged to bear against one of the flanges of the spool. In operation, the crank of the hand drill is turned with the right hand, while the wire is guided onto the spool. After a couple of spools have been wound, the winder can be operated very rapidly and produces a neat coil.—C. A. Foster, Cincinnati, Ohio.

## Preventing Rodents from Entering Drain or Sewer Outlets

A simple and effective device for preventing rodents from entering an outside drainpipe opening is made as follows: Construct a sleeve to fit over the open end of the drainpipe. The end of the sleeve is cut off at an angle, as shown. Hinge a heavy sheet-iron flap over the end of the sleeve. The weight of the flap keeps it closed and prevents the ro-

dents from entering. The force of the outflowing water opens the door and holds it open until the waste has passed. The current prevents the rodents from passing up when the door is opened. The device should be painted thoroughly, and the hinge kept oiled.—B. F. D., Baltimore, Md.

## Wrench Template Saves Draftsman's Time

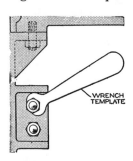

When designing machinery fastenings for close quarters, a convenient method of determining whether there is sufficient room for turning a wrench is to use a template cut from cardboard, as shown in the sketch. A set of these templates for common nut sizes can be kept on hand, in full or half size. A hasty layout of the doubtful corner is made, and the template gives the information required.—J. A. Ryan, Chicago, Ill.

## Hollow Drill for Boring Bamboo and Sheet Fiber

Holes cannot be bored in bamboo easily with ordinary drills, because of the ready splitting of this material. Having occasion to make several hun-

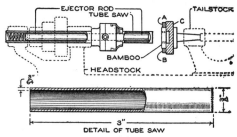

The Tube Saw Cuts Round Holes in Thin Material without Splitting It Easily

dred ⅜-in. holes in narrow strips of bamboo, I made the tube saw shown. A ⅜-in. steel tubing, 3 in. long, with

walls ³⁄₆₄ in. thick, was used. Saw teeth were filed in the trued edge of the tube, so as to lead the points toward the direction of rotation. The tube was held in the chuck of a lathe. A rod extended through the spindle of the lathe and inside of the tube, and was held in position by a spring. The rod automatically pushed out the centers as bored. A wooden pad, C, mounted on a taper stem at the tailstock, centered the strips of bamboo between blocks A and B. The tube saw is also handy for use on thin ivory, bone, fiber, hard rubber, and similar materials.—L. M. Drake, Daytona, Fla.

## A Wire-Skinning Tool of Handy Size

To make a tool for removing the insulation from electric wires, and which is small enough to be carried in a tool kit, it is only necessary to have a short piece of ¾-in. iron bar, a portion of a hacksaw blade, and a setscrew. A slit is first cut in one end of the bar, and a shallow notch filed

as shown. The saw blade is sharpened on the back edge, and inserted in the slit so that the cutting edge is out. A setscrew holds the blade in place. To skin the insulation from a wire, pass the latter through the notch. The knife edge will slit the insulation neatly, so that it can be easily pulled aside.

## Substitute for Pipe Vise

Not having a pipe vise at hand when it was necessary to thread a small piece of pipe, I improvised one from a pipe plier and an ordinary vise. The pipe was held in the plier and the plier handles clamped in the vise firmly. This method worked very well, especially with small pipe.—Abel Greenstein, New York, N. Y.

# Building Up Low-Voltage Generators

## Overcomes Inexpensively the Failure to Retain a Proper Residual Magnetism

By L. N. ROBINSON

THE low-voltage, compound-wound, direct-current generators, employed on electromagnetically operated pipe organs, refused to build up to normal voltage with a permanent setting of the shunt-field rheostat. The solution of the trouble is outlined in this article for application to similar difficulties. The trouble was observed particularly after the machines had been in service a few years. When a machine had been standing idle for a few days, it was quite often, though not invariably, impossible to obtain normal voltage without varying the setting of the field rheostat, or making other adjustments of the machine. The operators employed a rather questionable method in building the voltage up under such circumstances; namely, short-circuiting the line terminals and thus magnetizing the machine by the current in the series field.

A machine was run intermittently for observation. It was rated 300 watts, at 10 volts, 600 revolutions per minute. The organ, to which the generator was normally applied, would operate satisfactorily within a voltage range of 8 to 12 volts. The generator was located in the basement, and the organ on an upper floor of the building. The organist could not be expected to go downstairs and tinker with the generator if it did not build up before he was ready to play. For the same reason, it was essential that the shunt-field rheostat be set to give the desired voltage, and that no adjustment of the rheostat be required in starting.

Ordinarily, sufficient residual magnetism was retained so that the generator produced .3 volt without excitation. The machine would build up satisfactorily with the ordinary setting of the field rheostat when the shunt-field circuit was closed with this .3-volt residual armature voltage. At normal voltage, the shunt field required approximately five amperes' exciting current.

Sometimes, after the generator had been standing idle a few days, there was sufficient residual magnetism to induce only .1 volt in the armature. When the shunt-field circuit was closed

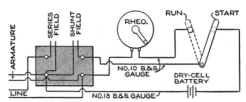

The Diagram Shows the Wiring and Connections for the Building-Up Arrangement

with this .1 volt impressed through the ordinary setting of the field rheostat, there was not sufficient field current to start the machine building up. This loss of residual magnetism was undoubtedly due to the iron being too soft, or of inferior quality. Obviously, it would be quite expensive to take the machine apart and to replace, or harden, the iron. Also, it would incur a considerable loss to ship the machine to the factory and to trade it in for a new and supposedly better one.

The question then was to make it operate as it should at small additional expense and with as few added complications as possible, because of the inexperience of the person who was regularly called upon to operate it. It was seen from the saturation curve that separate excitation of two amperes' field current would produce a generator terminal voltage of aproximately five volts, which was too small to operate the organ, but sufficient to magnetize the iron. Then, if the connections were immediately changed to give shunt excitation, magnetism sufficient to start the building up of the generator would be retained.

This was accomplished by the use of a dry-cell battery and a little additional wire, by locating a single-pole, double-throw switch, as shown in the diagram, at the keyboard, so that the organist, by operating the switch before beginning to play, could throw the battery in temporarily and then change over to the shunt excitation. The arrangement is very simple and does not require any particular experience to operate. The battery used in this case was located near the generator in the basement. With the lengths and sizes of wires shown in the diagram, only one cell was required in the battery. More than one cell would be undesirable in this case, because the battery would give excitation enough to build up sufficient voltage to operate the organ. The organist might discover this and operate the organ with the switch in the starting position. This, of course, would consume the battery very rapidly and give frequent cases when the battery would be in such condition that it would not serve its purpose.

The battery must be renewed occasionally, probably once a year. Thus it is seen that the initial cost of the remedy is small, the maintenance cost merely nominal, and that the system gives the desired results.

## Coat Button Takes Up Slack in Plumb Line

A handy little kink that will save much time in adjusting the length of

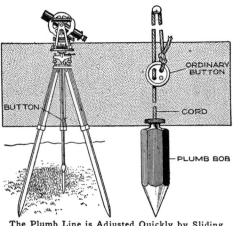

The Plumb Line is Adjusted Quickly by Sliding the Button along It

line attached to a plumb bob is to provide the line with a button adjuster. An ordinary strong coat button, having four holes, is used. The end of the cord is tied in one of the holes, and the other end is then passed through the supporting eye, or over any other supporting point, and through two of the other holes in the button. The adjustment is made by lifting the plumb bob and sliding the button along the cord.

## Garage Patrons Indicate Service Desired by Cards

In a garage where a large number of trucks and pleasure cars were stored, patrons frequently found that their cars were not given certain attention, such as washing, filling of the gasoline tanks, and the making of minor repairs. This work was to be done overnight, and as many of the customers were transients, a loss resulted to the garage owner. He, therefore, made up a set of metal signs, painted in black and white, and indicating the kind of service desired. These signs were kept near the garage door in a rack. The patrons placed the signs on their machines, and the attendants gave the service desired without further orders. The patrons, employes, and the owner were all better satisfied.—L. E. Turner, Brighton, Massachusetts.

## Soldering Joints in Heavy Wire

In soldering large-gauge wire joints, trouble is often experienced in that the solder does not take hold. The flux is usually blamed. By proceeding as follows, good results will usually be obtained: Clean the wire to the required length, and put on the soldering paste. Then dip the ends into the soldering pot slowly, giving them a good tinning. After the wire has cooled off, make the joint in the usual way, and then put a little paste on and solder the joint by holding the ladle as near as possible, pouring the solder over it slowly.—A. Gemmell, Ansonia, Conn.

❈In lacing belts, never cross the laces on the side which is to be placed against the pulley, as they will be cut quickly.

## Magnifying Eyeglass Fitted into Spectacles

A watchmaker's magnifying glass can be used to advantage for many purposes other than watchmaking, but most persons cannot hold the glass over the eye with convenience. The photograph shows a holder which is used like a pair of spectacles. To make it, the lenses were removed from a cheap pair of spectacles, by crushing the glass with a hammer. The rims then were made circular, to approximately the same diameter as the rim of the eyeglass. A strip of tin, $\frac{5}{16}$ in.

wide, was cut into small sections and bent at right angles $\frac{1}{16}$ in. from one end of each. These angles were soldered to the rim of the spectacles, as shown. The eyeglass was then fastened on the rim by bending the tin strips over the edge. The tin was painted black to match the eyeglass.—Alpha C. Johnson, Washington, D. C.

---

## Valve Frees Steam Radiator of Air Quickly

Having steam radiators of the one-pipe system, I found difficulty, after opening up the valve, to rid the radiator of cold air without taking off the cap and screw of the air vent. By the method shown, I not only do away with this trouble,

but also save coal, as I can close the stove damper sooner. The device was made as follows: Take a gas cock from an old gas stove; drill a small hole down through the center, as indicated. Remove the radiator air vent and connect the gas cock. When the handle is horizontal, the air vent is working, and when it is up, the air can escape through the drill hole.—James G. Evans, Richmond Hill, N. Y.

## Small Groove Plane Made from Steel Strip

I recently had occasion to plane some grooves, $\frac{1}{16}$ in. wide, in a board, and accomplished the work easily by the use of a specially made plane. A piece of cold-rolled steel, $\frac{1}{16}$ by 1 by 6 in. long, was rounded at the corners

slightly, and then a hole, $\frac{5}{16}$ in. in diameter, was drilled $\frac{1}{4}$ in. from the edge and near the middle, as shown. A slot was cut to the hole on an angle of 45°. By driving a cold chisel into the slot, the sharp corner was bent out $\frac{1}{32}$ in. This edge was sharpened to form a cutting edge. If the tool is to be used for much work, this edge can be case-hardened.—U. G. L., Chicago, Ill.

---

## Sheave Made from Iron Washers in Emergency

To keep from shutting down on a job where 1-in. rope was to be run over sheaves, it was necessary to make

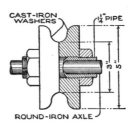

a substitute for these fittings of the usual type, because they could not be obtained within reasonable time. Iron washers, 5 in. in diameter, were used for the purpose, and when fitted together on a bearing, as shown, did the work satisfactorily. The washers were set firmly between nuts on a short section of iron pipe. The bearing axle was fitted inside the pipe and suitably mounted. The sheave gave good service for a long time.—Herman F. Zimmermann, Los Angeles, Calif.

---

❑Soapy water, applied with a brush over joints in gas or pressure pipes, is convenient in locating leaks.

## Stock of Spark Plugs Kept Safely in Racks

Spark plugs are easily injured, especially by the chipping or cracking of the porcelain, when kept loose in a

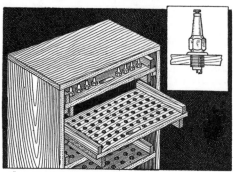

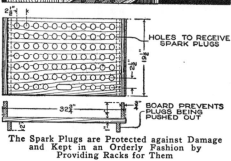

The Spark Plugs are Protected against Damage and Kept in an Orderly Fashion by Providing Racks for Them

drawer with other material. In the home garage, as well as in the commercial garage or repair shop, racks for the spark plugs will be found useful and economical. Where only a few spark plugs are to be accommodated, a small shelf, or rack, provided with suitable holes to receive the spark plugs, may be used. To care for a larger and more varied stock, a case with special racks, like that shown, is best. The racks are fitted with strips on the upper and lower sides, at the ends, which protect the spark plugs when the racks are set on the bench, or stacked one upon the other.

## Two Handles Used on Small File

In doing some filing with a small rat-tail file, I found it difficult to hold the front end of the file. The job to be filed was in such a position that short strokes were necessary. By fitting another small handle over the front end of the file, I found I could hold it securely and file more accurately. This method is handy in many other forms of filing, even where there is plenty of room.—Lee M. Delzell, Maroa, Ill.

## Wire Tools for Laboratory and Workshop Homemade

If a little inventive skill is applied, the worker in the laboratory or small shop can save much time, and expense for the purchase of small equipment, by having on hand a supply of stiff wire and tools for bending it to meet special needs. The several examples of useful tools and implements shown herewith were quickly devised in the laboratory as needed, and will suggest many others. The pinch cock was made of two pieces of wire, A and B, twisted to give a spring pressure on the jaws. The uses of most of the tools are evident. The hook stand can be used in suspending thermometers and other instruments. The tongs with the cork jaws are especially handy for holding hot test tubes. The Bunsen

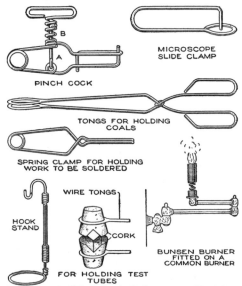

These Practical Tools for the Laboratory or Workshop were Quickly Made as Needed from Stiff Wire

burner, twisted from a piece of wire, is quickly made and practical.—George L. Yaste, Lonaconing, Md.

# A Resawing Device for the Band Saw

### By CHARLES A. KING

IN woodworking shops, equipped with light machinery, there are times when heavier machinery can be used to good advantage; a job of resawing, for instance, makes heavy demands upon a light band saw, but there is so little of such work to be done that it would not be wise to provide expensive equipment for it. The usual method then is to resaw boards up to 8 in. wide on a circular-saw table, by making a cut from each edge of the board, and for boards wider than this the saw cut is made from each edge, and the band saw run through the cuts to finish the job, as at A. This method is often unsatisfactory, as indicated at B and C. These troubles may be overcome by making a simple guide, as shown in Fig. 3, for light work, or as detailed in Figs. 1 and 2, for heavier work.

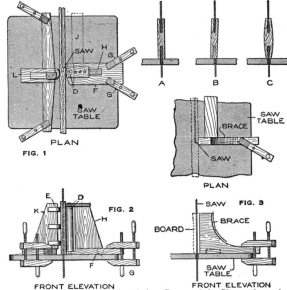

FIG. 1 PLAN

FIG. 2 — FRONT ELEVATION

FIG. 3 PLAN — FRONT ELEVATION

The Guide for the Lumber being Resawed is Clamped to the Saw Table, as Shown in Figs. 1 and 2, and the Boards are Fed between the Roller D and the Springs E

In this device, the operator can control any ordinary deviation of the saw by swinging the board to the right or left, and can regulate the speed of the feed. The essential elements of the device are the roll D, and the springs E, Figs. 1 and 2. The face of the board being resawed should run against the roll, contact being maintained by pressure from springs E. The roll is supported by a frame. The base F is of hard wood, 1¾ in. thick and 6 in. wide, and long enough to permit the hand screws G to hold it firmly at the edge of the table. The brace H is placed well to the back edge of F, as shown, to permit the front hand screw greater leverage. The roll is of hard wood, 2 in. in diameter. The piece J, indicated by dotted lines, may be fastened to the table by a hand screw, and prevents F from pushing back. The brace H is fastened to the base by screws through the latter.

The spring block K is of hard wood. The springs E are made of an old band saw, and are fastened by screws. Piece L is halved and screwed into the bottom piece, which is 1¾ by 4 in. at the middle.

In adjusting the device, care must be used that the bearing of the roll against the side of the board is at the cutting edge of the saw, as seen in Fig. 1. The springs bear ¼ in. or less ahead of the roll. The roll is adjusted to suit the thickness of the stock, by moving the entire frame. Slight changes in the relative positions of the roll, the springs, and the saw may be made by either tilting the table, adjusting the upper or lower guide laterally, shimming with paper or pasteboard, or by adjusting the saw wheels.

---

### Attachment Keeps T-Square Rigid on Board

Many draftsmen prefer the common type of T-square because of its wide range of use and the ease with which it can be removed from the board and used as a straightedge. A simple attachment that does not lessen these advantages of the T-square, and adds even more convenience to its use, is shown in the sketch. A small pulley, as detailed, is fastened to the lower

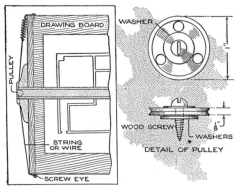

The Spring-and-Cord Arrangement Holds the Head of the T-Square against the Guiding Edge of the Drawing Board

side of the head. A strong cord is fixed to the end of the board, as indicated, and held taut against the pulley by a coiled spring. Thus the head of the square is held firmly against the guiding edge.—J. E. Cahill, Jr., New York City.

## Bins Built in Sections Provide for Increase in Capacity

A bin that may be increased or decreased in capacity has advantages over the fixed-volume type generally found in shops and factories. It is

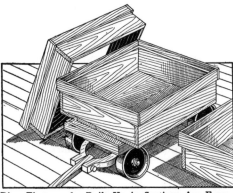

Bins That can be Built Up in Sections Are Especially Useful for Shop Trucks

especially advantageous for hand-truck factory transportation, since the trucker may add or remove sections as

the load to be carried demands. The first-section, or foundation, bin has a bottom; the others are without bottom. A ledge, formed by nailing on a border of strips so that their edges project above the top of the bin, is put on each section, as shown. The lower part of the added section may be fitted into the top of the section below, thus building up the bin to the height desired.

## Guard for Emery-Wheel Dresser

In truing up emery wheels, as is frequently necessary in large shops, considerable danger may be occasioned during this operation if the emery-wheel dresser is not properly guarded. The small sparks and chips may injure the workman's eyes. A good safety

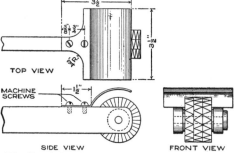

The Guard does Not Interfere with the Work and Protects the Workman

measure is to fit the dresser with a guard made of sheet metal and fastened as shown in the illustration.—K. L. J., Pittsburgh, Pa.

## Carburetor Improved by Air-Check Valve Repair

Many carburetors contain an air check, in the shape of a mushroom, which slides on a spindle. With use the hole in the mushroom part becomes enlarged, and the resulting crooked travel of the valve, with consequent air leakage around the hole, makes the mixture imperfect. If the carburetor is adjusted for high speed and heavy loads, the engine runs irregularly when throttled down. Providing a bushing for this valve, or replacing it, usually makes the engine run more smoothly.

## A Homemade Mechanical Drafting Machine

The draftsman who is also a fair mechanic will find it worth while to make a drafting machine like that shown, as it is inexpensive and takes the place of most of the common measuring and ruling tools. It is clamped on the edge of the drafting board and hinged so that it can be raised out of the way handily, or removed from the board completely. The details of construction, as indicated, are simple. The parts should be made carefully, however, to insure precise work with this instrument.

The clamping arrangement is formed of a piece of sheet metal into which two thumbscrews are set. A door hinge is riveted to one end of the clamp, as shown, and an adjusting screw is set in the center hole of the hinge. The parallel arms are made of strap iron, fitted together at the cross as detailed. The radial-gauge fixture requires careful work. Make the protractor of sheet metal, as shown, and file the degree indications into it with a three-cornered file. Make the pointer

of a strip of sheet-spring brass, and rivet it to a light-weight steel, or other suitable, square. File the pointer to a V-edge, and set it to make a firm contact. Fit the pivot of the radial gauge with a wooden knob and wing nut for adjustment, as shown.—P. P. Avery, Garfield, N. J.

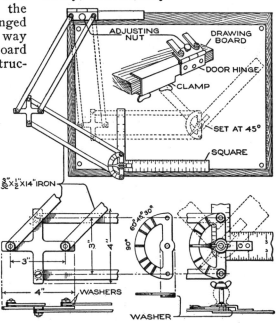

If Carefully Made and Polished, This Drafting Machine will Give Good Service and Save Much Time

## Tap and Reamer Wrench Quickly Made

A wrench that is useful, especially with taps and reamers, was made quickly of two bolts, fitted with nuts, and two ½ by ½ by 2½-in. pieces of steel. The square stock was drilled for the

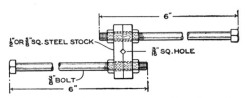

While This Wrench Is So Simple That It can be Quickly Made for Emergency Use, It Is Also Practical as a Regular Tool

bolts and filed to fit the square shank of the tap, or reamer. The bolts serve

as handles, and the jaws can be adjusted to various sizes of small, square shanks. If desired, both handles can be set on one side for convenient use in close quarters.

## Vise for Filing Hand and Circular Saws

It will pay the mechanic who has saws to file now and then to provide himself with a vise suitable for this purpose, and which can be made easily in the small workshop. The vise also has many other uses where thin wood or metal is to be handled. For ordinary handsaws the vise is shaped as shown in the assembly view, and for use with circular saws, a good plan is to round off and bevel the top edge of the front jaw, as shown in detail, at A. A bolt is passed through the jaws for the center hole of the circular saw.

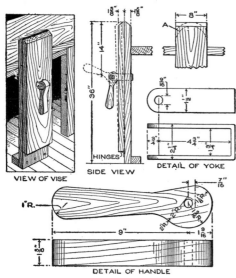

VIEW OF VISE  SIDE VIEW  DETAIL OF YOKE

DETAIL OF HANDLE

**The Saw is Clamped Firmly between the Jaws of the Vise, Which can be Released Quickly by Means of the Cam Handle**

The details of construction, as indicated, require a yoke of strap iron. The handle, one end of which is a cam by which the front jaw is clamped firmly at the yoke, should be made carefully to the measurements given. Hard wood is preferable, especially for the handle.

## Jig for Drilling Holes in Pipe

This jig was designed for drilling holes in small pipes and tubes. The specific job required that the first hole be a certain distance from the end,

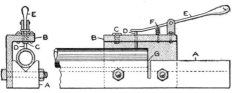

**The Pipe is Set in the Jig and the Holes Spaced by Means of the Lever Device**

and the other holes spaced uniformly in a straight line. The main part, A, of the jig has a V-groove along its

length in which the pipe rests. On the upright B are mounted the drill bushing C and the locating device. This consists of the plunger D, actuated by the lever E and the spring F. A slot is milled across the body, at G. In using the jig, a snug-fitting strip of metal is placed in this slot as a stop for the first hole. Then the strip is removed. When the first drilled hole comes under the plunger D, the spring forces the plunger into the hole, locating the pipe for the next hole. The lever E is then pushed down, raising the plunger, and the pipe is moved until the plunger drops into the hole just drilled, this process being repeated for each hole.

## Mask for Small Negatives Printed on Post Cards

In printing photographic negatives, $1\frac{5}{8}$ by $2\frac{1}{2}$ in. in size, on post cards, I find that a special type of mask saves much time and trouble. Instead of trying to print several of the negatives at once, I fit them singly into the corner of a mask, which is rectangular in shape and as large as four of the small negatives, one-fourth of the rectangle being cut away. The mask is shifted to expose the four negatives in turn, one at a time. A desirable feature is that the light and dense negatives may be timed properly.—Fred Kuhlmann, Peru, Neb.

## Casters on Water Barrels Promote Fire Protection

Large barrels, kept filled with water, are often placed at various points in shops or factories for fire protection. If a fire breaks out some distance from the barrel, it is necessary to carry the water in buckets, and much valuable time is lost. It is a good plan to put four large casters on a wooden frame fastened to the bottom of the barrel. In case of an emergency the several barrels of water in the shop may then be pushed to the fire without trouble or delay.—K. M. Coggeshall, Webster Groves, Mo.

# Shop Notes

## Air Scouting over Battle Fields in a Display Window

### By LLOYD WORSWICK

AN air scout on a perilous flight in search of the enemy's concealed batteries is seen braving death as he skims above the trenches in the show window of an enterprising merchant. The interest of the passer-by is gained, and he becomes curious to know how the effect is produced. The landscape, apparently moving by under the airplane, is a painted strip of muslin, a yard or more wide and about twice the length of the surface exposed as landscape. Oil colors or wax crayons can be used in making the picture, on the full length of the screen, which is set up as a continuous band moving around on the spools at the ends. The spools are wooden rods or cardboard tubes, fitted with end pivots and set up in suitable supports, the lower ends resting on tin bearings, and the upper ends mounted similarly, from the ceiling or other support.

The construction of the spools is shown in the detail sketch. Rubber bands are placed at intervals around the spools, and grip the muslin band, causing it to move around the spools like a belt. A grooved pulley is fas-

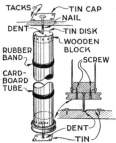

The Airplane in Flight over Ever-Changing Battle Fields Attracts the Passers-By and They Stop to Learn the Secret of the Effect

tened to the lower end of the spool and this is belted to a small motor. The airplane is made to appear as if in flight by means of a draft directed in front of it from a fan suitably supported, as shown. The plane is supported by silk threads.

The construction of the airplane is simple and interesting, as detailed in the sketch. It may be made in various sizes, 16 in. long being suitable. The pilot is a doll, preferably of some light material, and covered with brown paper or cloth. The plane is painted a "war gray," and is fastened together securely, as shown. The propeller is made of wood and is set in place on a bead-head pin. The wheels are wooden buttons, supported on wires. The electric fan is placed directly in a line

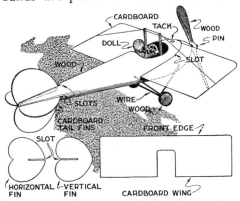

The Model War Plane Is an Interesting Construction, and Easily Built, Largely of Wood and Cardboard

with the airplane so that the current of air will revolve the propeller, without blowing the machine to one side.

## Weatherproof Gooseneck Light Fixture Cheaply Made

Practical and inexpensive light fixtures were required along the outside

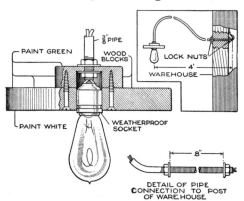

Inexpensive Weatherproof Light Fixtures Were Homemade as Detailed

of a warehouse, and as no roof protection was afforded, the sockets and fittings had to be made weatherproof. Conduits of the gooseneck type were used to support the light, as shown. The straight end of the gooseneck was threaded and fitted with nuts and washers, by means of which the fixture was fastened to the supporting posts of the wall. The wires were carried in the conduit, and the fixture end of the latter was arranged as detailed, providing a weatherproof covering for the socket. Nuts with washers clamp the upper block, as shown, and the lower reflector is fastened with screws. The reflecting surface is painted white and the other parts green. The wires above the socket were taped carefully. —S. Frank Bill, Berkley, Va.

## Ink Preliminary Sketches Prove Economical and Convenient

In making preliminary sketches, most of which were traced directly by a tracer or draftsman, it was found economical of time, and convenient as well, to make the sketches with ordinary writing ink instead of pencil. The writing ink was preferred also over India, or special drawing, ink because, by using a German-silver ruling pen, the designer was able to lay aside the filled pen now and then, instead of wiping it immediately, as is desirable with the usual pen and drafting ink. The time of the tracer was saved, and errors minimized by furnishing him with clean-cut sketches.

## Motor-Driven Grinder for Rail Joints

The arrangement shown was devised for leveling joints in railway tracks, and is useful, also, for other forms of grinding. The power is taken from the trolley wire. The universal joints permit shifting of the motor without blocking it up to a level. The sleeve and extension shaft, joined with a feather key, permit the setting of the motor within a wider range. This feature is also desirable for grinding a wide area without moving the motor. After the rig is set up, the workman bears down on the handle, raising the emery wheel. The current is then turned on, and he lets the wheel rest on the rail. When a car is passing, one workman throws out the switch on the motor and takes the trolley from the wire, while another

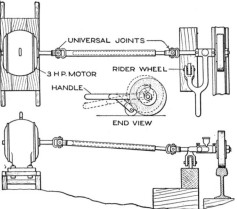

The Universal Joints and the Feather-Key Extension Shaft Permit Satisfactory Operation under Varying Conditions

runs the emery wheel out of the way on the rider wheel.—Bert W. Brintnall, Seattle, Wash.

## Soap Used in Bag Improves Auto Washing

A local garage owner cut down his soap bills considerably by a simple method. Instead of throwing the soap loosely into a bucket when washing cars, the washer puts the soap into a small flour bag, ties the top tightly and then places the bag of soap in the bucket of water. Soap left in the bag is used on another job. The old method never left any soap. A barrel of soap lasts one-third longer now than it did before using the bags, and the work is better, for when the water gets soapy enough the bag is taken out of the water.—L. E. Turner, Brighton, Mass.

## Celluloid Fillet Indicator Handy for Draftsmen

Draftsmen who have had occasion to work on drawings requiring a large amount of corner filleting realize what a job it is to place the fillets accurately. To obviate a great deal of this, I cut a circular piece of thin celluloid, about 2½ in. in diameter, and sandpapered it on one side to a dull finish with a very fine grade of sandpaper. I then made a small hole in the center, and, on the dull side, scribed a number of concentric circles varying ¹⁄₁₆ in. in radius.

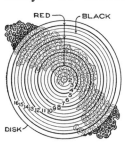

The circles of radii of ¼ in., ½ in., ¾ in., etc., were drawn in red to facilitate reading; the rest, in black India ink. The radii of all circles in sixteenths of inches were placed on the celluloid. In use, the circle of the given radius is placed tangent to the two lines where the fillet is required; the center is marked with the point of the compass, and the celluloid removed. Using this center, the fillet is drawn accurately.—Kenneth E. Ernst, New York, N. Y.

## Ladder with Wheelbarrow Fixture for Repair Work

In making repairs on buildings and other structures, where many tools and, perhaps, a sawhorse must be transported to the job, a handy combination is a ladder-wheelbarrow, as shown. A wheel

The Ladder-Wheelbarrow Appeals to the Workman Who must Transport Tools and Materials

and axle from an old wheelbarrow are fitted to the upper end of a ladder used for repair work and painting. The tools and materials are packed on the ladder, which is wheeled in the usual manner.—A. M. Fairfield, St. Marys, Kansas.

## Special Outlet on Gasoline Tank Provides Reserve Supply

By installing a fitting into the gasoline tank on my automobile I avoid the unpleasantness of suddenly finding myself on the road without a sufficient supply of gasoline to make the supply station, at least. A spe-

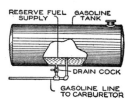

cial outlet was fitted into the tank so that ordinarily the gasoline is not drained to the bottom of the tank, leaving a reserve supply. In an emergency the tank is drained completely by the use of the extra valve at the bottom.—John Edwin Hogg, Alhambra, Calif.

## Makeshift Method of Lifting Auto Truck Out of Rut

A heavy auto truck became mired in a deep rut on a country road, and the

Wheel of Auto Truck Lifted Out of Deep Rut with This Makeshift Rigging

driver, without assistance and with only the auto jack available, was forced to devise some means of getting his machine again under way. The method employed was so simple and effective that it may be of interest to most motorists. Two saplings were set across slabs of wood, laid on either side of the truck wheel, as shown. The tailboard chain was rigged between the saplings just inside of the wheel. A tourniquet of rope was made with a small stick, and fastened to the free ends of the saplings. The jack was set under the rim of the wheel, and, as the latter was lifted, the tourniquet and the tailboard chains were drawn up to bring the saplings close against the wheel. By this means the wheel was gradually lifted out of the rut, and extra slabs placed under it so that the truck was then easily driven to solid ground. Slabs were also piled under the axle as a precaution, in case the wheel should slip back into the rut. —Edwin L. Purkess, Quincy, Mass.

## Making Porous Battery Cups

Certain fluid batteries of the Bunsen or Daniell types require porous cups to separate the solutions used in making them. A good porous cup for this purpose can be made at small expense as follows: From heavy wrapping paper make a roll, the interior diameter of which is the outside diameter of the desired cup, and hold the roll in shape with string. Brush the inside of the roll with melted paraffin. Next mix plaster of Paris and water to a thick paste, set the roll up on a flat paraffined board, and pour sufficient plaster in to form the bottom of the cup, about ⅜ in. thick. While this is drying, cut a round piece of wood the size of the inside of the cup. When the bottom has dried, set the wooden piece inside the roll, and pour in the plaster. When set, remove the wooden piece and the outer roll. Cups of various sizes and shapes may be made by this method.—Thomas W. Benson, Philadelphia, Pa.

## Nut Wedged on Stripped Bolt in Emergency

The threads of several stud bolts in the crank case of a stationary gasoline engine were stripped accidentally.

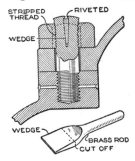

Similar bolts could not easily be procured, and the following method was used to retain the nuts in place, as a quick repair: With a hacksaw, the ends of the bolts were split lengthwise to a depth of the thickness of the nuts. Wedges were made by hammering out the ends of a round brass rod. The nuts were placed over the bolts, and the wedges driven into the slotted bolt ends, expanding them when the nuts were forced up tight, as shown. The nuts were alternately screwed up and wedges driven in, until a snug fit was obtained. With the nuts finally in place, the ends of the bolts were riveted over the wedges to prevent them from loosening. To remove the nuts, it was necessary to drive out the wedges from the side.— G. A. Luers, Washington, D. C.

# A Turntable for the Small Garage

By JOHN E. CAHILL, Jr.

THE advantages of a turntable, especially for the small garage where space is quite limited, are apparent to many automobile owners, but the expense of installing one is usually considered prohibitive. Under these circumstances, the turntable shown in the illustration was designed, and proved comparatively easy to build and thoroughly satisfactory. The turntable was designed to be housed in the garage, and was built in a pit provided in the concrete floor. It may also be built in the open, or protected by a roof. Such a turntable in the garage is very convenient in washing the car, in making repairs, and in taking down the various parts, especially if used in connection with suitable overhead rigging for differential, or other heavy-duty pulleys and tackle.

The details of construction are shown in the plan and elevation views.

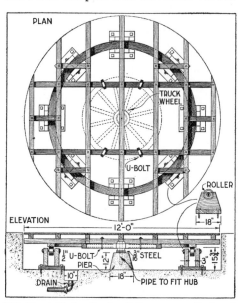

This Turntable for the Small Garage was Designed to be Built at a Minimum Cost, and Yet Provide a Substantial Construction

The general arrangement of the parts is shown in the sectional perspective view. The floor pit is built of concrete, 2 ft. deep and 12 ft. in diameter. It is fitted with a drainage pipe and

outlet. A heavy truck wheel provides a center bearing, and is mounted over a pipe, imbedded in a concrete base.

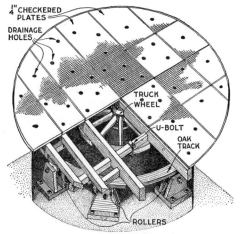

The Framework is Built of Heavy Timber and the Turntable is Carried on Rollers, Bearing against a Wooden Track

Steel washers, $\frac{3}{16}$ in. thick, are set between the foundation and wheel, as bearings. The framework supported on the truck wheel is built up largely of 4 by 4-in. timber, with three 4 by 8-in. pieces, arranged as shown in the plan and bolted at the joints. U-bolts of $\frac{1}{2}$-in. round iron, with clamping plates, fasten the main frame to the truck wheel. An oak track of $1\frac{1}{2}$ by 6-in. timber extends around the lower edge of the framework. The curve for this track is struck with a radius of 4 ft. 6 in. for the inner edge, and the segments are one-eighth of the circumference in length, approximately 4 ft. 8 in., allowing for trimming. This track bears on eight roller bearings, mounted on supports, as shown in the sketch, and detailed in the elevation. The rollers are 3 in. thick and 6 in. in diameter, of cast iron, and mounted on steel shafts, $\frac{11}{16}$ in. in diameter, with cotter pins at the ends. The wooden supports are of 3-in. stock, and carry $\frac{3}{4}$-in. pipe for bushings. The supports are bolted into the concrete.

The framework of the turntable, as originally designed and built, was covered with $\frac{1}{4}$-in. checkered-surface plates of sheet iron, drilled with drainage holes. The plates were set to match on the 4-in. timbers, and fastened at opposite corners with screws, for easy removal in getting at the inner parts of the turntable. The floor may be made also of wood, arranged to be lifted in sections, when desired.

## Tip Boxes Measure Concrete Materials Economically

In the mixing of concrete, the materials should be measured accurately if

STRAP IRON

IRON PIPE

2"X4"   4"X4"

2"X 4"

The Measuring Boxes are Used in Batteries to Make Up a Properly Proportioned Batch at a Time

the best results are to be obtained. Sometimes the wheelbarrow, in which the materials are carried to the mixer, is used for a measure. To insure accuracy in measuring the materials and also a minimum of wasted time, the tip measuring boxes shown in the sketch were made. The boxes are made with the desired cubic capacity, and hung, above the center, on a 1½-in. iron-pipe axle. The boxes should be hung high enough to permit a wheelbarrow to be pushed under the bottom without interference. The supports are made of 2 by 4 and 4 by 4-in. pieces, strongly braced. The outfit may be dismantled quickly, and reassembled at another location, and the parts are of handy size for loading on a vehicle. In use, the shovelers fill the boxes, and the barrow men wheel their barrows under the boxes, which are promptly

dumped. They are then filled again, ready for the return of the barrows.

Several boxes are usually desirable. For example, if a concrete of one part cement, two sand, and four stone is to be mixed, and each batch comprises 10½ cu. ft. of dry material, there should be six tip boxes: one 1½-cu. ft. box for cement, two 1½-cu-ft. boxes for sand, and three 2-cu.-ft. boxes for stone.

For each batch, the routine procedure of filling the battery of boxes, dumping their contents, and wheeling the material to the mixing trough is so simple that mistakes in proportioning the materials are not likely to occur.— Richard L. Nourse, Duluth, Minn.

## A Novel Adjustable Wrench

A type of homemade wrench, which has a wide range of adjustment by means of screws set in a ring, as shown, was made as a novelty, and proved quite useful. Three of the screws can be used at a time for handling one size of hexagonal nut, and the others adjusted for another size. Two opposite screws will grip a square nut, and an octagonal nut can also be held tightly. The screws are loose enough so that they can be turned with the fingers, and are set when necessary

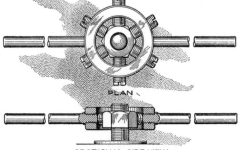

PLAN

SECTIONAL SIDE VIEW
This Wrench, Made as a Novelty, Proved Quite Useful

with a screwdriver. In this way the wrench can be clamped to the nut.—J. Prophet, Pittsfield, Mass.

❡Sheet brass should be inclosed in a large wrought-iron pipe, closed at one end, when being annealed.

## Keyway Cut in Bearing with Massed Hack Saws

It is often a hard job to cut a keyway through a hollow bearing, even with the necessary tools at hand. Such a problem, and with few tools available, confronted a launch owner when the propeller loosened from its seat on the shaft, making it necessary to cut a new keyway and to reseat the propeller at once.

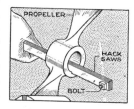

The work was accomplished satisfactorily. Several hack saws were fastened together, with the teeth all extending the same way, and held firmly by means of small bolts through the holes in the ends. Enough blades were assembled to make their thickness a trifle less than the width of the key. The propeller was then held in a vise, and the blades passed through the bearing, as shown, one end of the bunch being grasped in each hand. A new keyway was sawed, and the bottom smoothed out with the edge of a thin file.—Robert L. Binns, Denver, Colorado.

## One-Piece Pipe Bracket of Strap Iron

A pipe bracket, for supporting pipe along the sides of buildings, walls, etc., can be made quickly from a single piece of strap iron, as shown in the sketch. It requires no bolts or rivets to make it retain its shape, and may

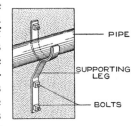

usually be bent cold. Care should be taken to see that the supporting leg is directly under the pipe. The fastening through the supporting structure can be made with bolts or screws.—Roy H. Poston, Flat River, Mo.

## Spring Clip Locks Rolled Measuring Tape

The folding handle of a measuring tape had a tendency to unfold when other articles in the tool box came in contact with it, especially after it had been long in use. This caused the tape to unroll and to be in danger of damage

when extending from the case. As a remedy, a small spring, shaped as shown, was fastened to the case. The handle is kept unfolded under the clip, which acts as a stop both when the tape is in use on the job, and when it is in the tool box. The clip folds against the case closely, and does not interfere with the winding of the tape by means of the handle.—Elmer O. Tetzlaff, DePere, Wis.

## Riveted Stop Collar for Pipe Connection to Flue

Poor draft in the boiler or furnace is often due to a defective flue connection at the smokepipe. The stovepipe is sometimes set into the flue opening without a metal collar being secured to the end of it. The result is that the pipe jams into the flue and cuts off enough of the flue area to

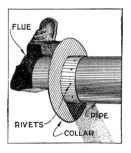

choke the draft. If the sheet-metal collar is riveted in place, as shown, it will prevent this slipping of the pipe. The connection to the flue should, of course, be kept down as far below the ceiling joists as practicable, but if it must be made close to them, the pipe should be covered with a suitable insulation.—Harold V. Walsh, Yonkers, New York.

# An Electric Operation Recorder with Remote Control

By C. H. HOWARD

THERE are many applications for which an operation, or revolution, recorder, which may be actuated

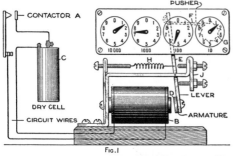

Fig. 1

General Arrangement of the Working Parts: The Recording Action on the Dials is Induced by the Completion of the Electrical Circuit, at Each Motion to be Counted

from a distant location, is desirable. The electric recorder, the arrangement of which is shown in Fig. 1, can be built to satisfy most ordinary requirements of this character, and is also simple in construction and operation. One of these recorders can be made easily, assuming that a movement, or gear train, like that shown, from a discarded watt-hour meter is available. Such a recorder may be adapted to count the number of revolutions made by a distant printing press or other similar mechanism; the number of times a door is opened or closed or the number of times a certain machine performs its functions. It may also be adapted so that it will count the number of turns of wire being wound on a spool or magnet.

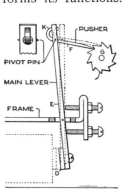

Fig. 2

The contactor A, shown in Fig. 1, is mounted on the device, the operation of which it is desired to record. The counter, with the magnet B and its frame, may be installed at any location within a reasonable distance from A. The circuit wires connect to the contactor

and recorder, as shown. Whenever the contactor A is closed, current is circulated by the battery C around through the now closed circuit, thereby energizing the electromagnet B. The magnet draws over the armature D, which then, by means of the lever E and the pusher F, detailed in Fig. 2, thrusts the ratchet wheel G ahead one notch, thus indicating one operation.

The fine wire spring H, the tension of which may be adjusted at the supporting screw, pulls lever E back to its normal position when B is deënergized. Adjusting screws are provided to limit the movement of the lever E. All the parts of the device, with the exception of the magnet core, the

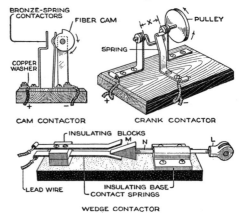

Fig. 3

Details of Three Contactors for Use in Making the Electrical Contacts in Recording Various Kinds of Operations

armature D, and the frame J, which are of iron, should preferably be of brass. As shown in the detail, in Fig. 2, one end of the pusher F is bent around at K. This bent end forms a stop which prevents F from dropping down if its wedge end happens to be pulled back out of engagement with G.

Contactors of various types may be designed for different services and locations. Some simple, effective designs are shown in Fig. 3. The cam contactor is mounted on the end of a shaft. Each time the shaft rotates, the fiber cam forces one phosphor-bronze spring into contact with the other, completing the circuit.

In the crank contactor, detailed in Fig. 3, each time the shaft makes a revolution, it wipes against the leaf contactor spring, and thereby completes the circuit of the recorder. The crank is turned by means of a pulley, which may be driven with a small belt from another shaft. The length of the crank between sides, at X, should be just a trifle less than the distance between the washers soldered on the bearing posts. Thus the longitudinal movement of the shaft will be limited, and no collars on it will be required. The washers soldered to the bearing post prevent the corners of the crank,

as it turns, from striking the post. When an oscillating, or reciprocating, motion is to be recorded, a wedge contactor, as shown, may be utilized. The oscillating motion is communicated to the device by a connecting rod pivoting in the head L.

Each time the rod thrusts forward, the metal wedge M makes a wiping contact between the springs mounted above and below it. Insulation is provided by the fiber rod N. Where the service is severe, it is better to use a metal rod for N, with a connecting rod of insulating material, or a metal connecting rod with an insulating joint.

## Letters on Machinery Chalked White
## for Photographing

In photographing machinery for the making of illustrations for catalogs and similar uses, it is usually desirable to have the trade-mark or manufacturer's name show plainly. When the name is cast on the machinery, as is usually the case, a simple method is to chalk the letters carefully so as to make them appear white in the photograph.

## Nontipping Footstool Handy
## for Draftsmen

A footstool which proved popular with a large staff of draftsmen is

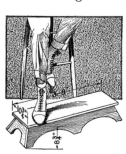

shown in the sketch. It was designed with a wide base so that it is difficult to tip it over with the feet. This also avoids the noise of tipping the stool on edge and then dropping it. The wood used was 7/8-in. pine, and the footstools were stained and shellacked. The dimensions shown were found satisfactory, but may be varied for special needs. In making large drawings, the men find this stool especially convenient.

## Device for Setting Gaskets
## in Pipe Joints

Replacing rubber or other gaskets on flanged pipe joints is often a tire-

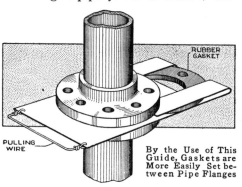

By the Use of This Guide, Gaskets are More Easily Set between Pipe Flanges

some job. To facilitate this work, I made a tool of light-gauge sheet metal, cut to the shape shown in the sketch and bent to hold the rubber gasket at one end. The projecting ends of the piece of metal are folded back over the gasket, and act as guides in sliding the gasket into place. These strips are sprung sidewise after the gasket has been set with a bolt at the open end of the guide. The latter is then drawn out without disturbing the position of the gasket.—A. J. Cohen, Brooklyn, New York.

⟨Glass should not be fitted too closely in a picture frame, to allow for expansion.

## Unusual Boring Job Done on a Lathe

An unusual set-up for a piece of machine work, and an illustration of what may be done on a lathe, is shown in the photograph and the sketch. The job to be made is part of a jig, which required that the hole in each end be bored in line and true to size. The

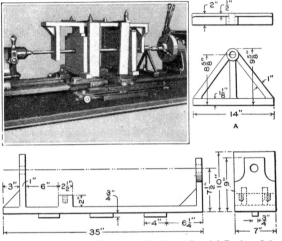

When Only a Lathe Was Available for a Special Boring Job, This Rigging was Set Up, and Accomplished the Work

only machine available for doing the work was a 16-in. lathe. A guide, A, was made for the boring bar. It was not possible to rest the work directly on the saddle, so it was blocked up and clamped down, as indicated. Two cutters were placed in the boring bar, and the work was finished in a short time. A universal joint was used in the center, so that the movement of the bar would not be irregular, even though it might not line up precisely with the centers.—Harvey Mead, Scranton, Pa.

### Conical Fire Buckets Seldom Misused

In a large plant where fire protection is essential, various methods of preventing the use of fire buckets for other than their intended service were tried without success. Finally, pails of about the usual capacity and conical in shape, with a sharp point at the bottom, were installed. These proved satisfactory, as the possibility of their misuse for other purposes is limited.

### Patching Worn Guides in a Wooden Miter Box

A superior method of closing worn-out cuts in a wooden miter box is to cut thin slices of end grain out of the same dimension stuff as the sides of the miter box, and to glue these into the cuts. Cut these slices in the miter box to a thickness which will permit them to slip easily into the cuts they are meant for. With a piece of tin, apply glue to the inner surfaces of the cut, allow it to soak in, and apply more, using plenty. Slip in the filler and allow it to dry. When the glue is set, a new cut is made within 1/8 in. of the old one, or the new cut can be made to run through the old one at an angle. The life of the miter box can in this manner be lengthened considerably, and the new cuts will give good service if carefully made.—Henry Simon, Laguna Beach, Calif.

### Crankshafts Ground to Balance without Weakening Them

In order not to weaken crankshafts by grinding them at certain points so that they balance properly, small rounded knobs, or bosses, were provided on the shaft, as shown in the illustration. The crankshafts could thus be easily balanced by grinding the

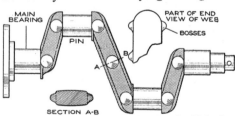

The Small Bosses on the Crankshafts Make It Convenient to Grind Off Excess Metal to Produce the Desired Accurate Balance

bosses at the points where excess weight was to be removed.

## Hacksaws Do Better Work When Properly Selected

Hacksaw blades do smoother work and wear longer if oiled, and especially if a saw of the proper type is selected for the work in hand. Proper hacksaw practice is quite commonly neglected in machine and repair shops where hurry-up jobs are always in order. Considerable time can be saved, and better work turned out, by keeping frames fitted with 14, 18, 24, and 32-tooth blades in the tool room, instead of providing only coarse blades.

## A Painter's Folding Easel Made of Flooring

A painter's and showcard writer's easel, substantial and practical, can be made from tongue-and-groove flooring.

Saw the strips of flooring in halves, lengthwise, and make the large frame of the grooved pieces. If narrow flooring is used, it need not be ripped, the tongue being cut off the strips for the large frame, and the grooves from those for the small one. Make the small frame of the tongue sections, as shown, to fit loosely and slide up and down in the grooves of the large frame. Fasten a screw eye at the top of the large frame, and one in the top of the small frame, and tie a stout cord to the eye in the latter, running it through the eye in the large frame. Nail a strip of wood to the back of the frame, and on this hinge the supporting strip. By pulling on the cord, the small frame is raised and lowered. The canvas, or card, is placed on pegs in the small frame, or a suitable trough may be provided.—E. A. Hoppman, New York, N. Y.

## Device for Grinding Oversize Piston Rings by Hand

The automobile owner who frequently tinkers with small repair jobs, as well as the gasoline-engine mechanic, will find this kink in the grinding of oversize piston rings a handy one. The work should be done very carefully, and the method sometimes employed of rubbing the ring on

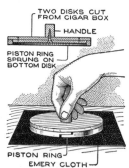

emery cloth, the ring being held with the hand only, is not efficient. The device shown was made of two disks cut from cigar-box wood, and fastened together with a screw set in a small handle. The ring is sprung onto the bottom disk, and is in convenient position for accurate grinding on a sheet of emery cloth laid on a flat, hard surface, preferably a polished metal plate. —G. Brown, Chicago, Ill.

## Shoe Guard for a Shovel

A shoe guard for a shovel which will be appreciated especially by the many women gardeners who are practicing war-time economies, can be

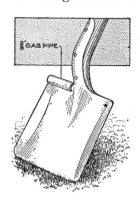

made by fitting a short length of gas pipe tightly over the upper edges of the spade or shovel. The pipe is cut to the proper length as shown, and then sawed open on one side. By spreading it properly and springing it onto the shovel blade, it will stay in place without special fastening.—Marie C. Moore, Seattle, Washington.

## Homemade Water-and-Tube Level Indicator

The homemade instrument shown in the illustration is useful for finding levels at long distances, over obstruc-

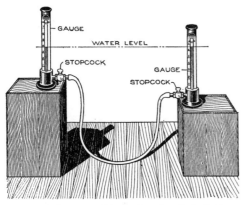

The Glass Gauges are Mounted on Standards Set into Suitable Pipe Flanges and Capped with Metal Fittings

tions or around corners, and for lining up shafting, etc. It indicates that points are out of level, and also shows in inches how much they are out of level. When leveling two points, a gauge is placed on each, as shown. The stopcocks are opened, and when the water comes to rest, closed again. The apparatus may then be lifted up, and carried to the light, if necessary, and the exact position of the water-column height determined on the scales. About 10 per cent of glycerin added to the water before filling the level will ordinarily prevent it from freezing. If accidentally the stop-cocks should be left open, little float valves, located in the cups at the top of the gauges, close the vent holes automatically when the water level rises to them. This avoids the annoyance from overflow of the liquid.

## Enlarging Dials on Machine Produces Closer Work

In handling an exceptionally accurate job of tool making on a milling machine, it was found that the usual dials did not give the accuracy required. Dials, 12 in. in diameter, were made, with the same graduations as the corresponding ones on the machine. These were set over the machine dials very carefully, and used in place of them. Suitable indicating fingers were made to fit the dials where needed, and by this means extreme accuracy was obtained. The dials proved so useful that they were preserved for other jobs. The same method can be applied on a number of other high-class shop machines.—Otto S. Anderson, La Vina, Calif.

## Case at End of Table for Blueprint or Drafting-Paper Rolls

An arrangement which is useful and economical for the drafting or blueprint room is a table with special cases at the ends to contain the rolls of paper and the pieces trimmed off but still useful. The top of the table is marked off in indications for measuring the length of the sheet, which is torn neatly at the iron edge of the box containing the roll of paper. The roll is supported on an iron shaft having a spring

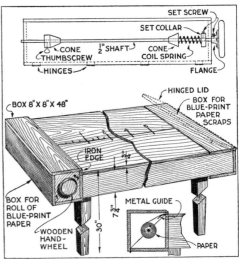

Drafting Papers are Cared For Economically by This Outfit, and the Sheets Cut Neatly and Quickly

and cone device, as detailed, to hold the roll. A metal guide, as shown in the sectional view below, starts the edge of the roll through the slot, when the handwheel is turned to unwind the roll.

## Methods of Testing the Polarity of Line Wires

When installing electrical machinery it is often necessary to locate positive and negative sides of a circuit before a piece of apparatus can be connected. A simple test, for other than high-potential circuits, is shown in Fig. 1, which represents the ends of two wires, one from each side of the circuit, placed about 1 in. apart in a glass of salt water. A suitable resistance, such as one or more lamps, is placed in the circuit. Bubbles arise from each of the terminals. That from which fewer bubbles arise is the positive wire.

The compass test, shown in Fig. 3, is based on the action of the magnetic lines of force, set up around a wire carrying current, upon a magnet placed in the vicinity of the conductor. The conductor is represented perpendicular to the plane of the paper with the current flowing "down," or away from the observer. A compass needle placed in the magnetic field will tend to assume the position shown, its north pole pointing in the direction of the lines of force set up by the current in the conductor.

This test can also be made on a horizontal conductor. Select a part of the wire that is placed, or can be bent, in an approximately north and south direction. Place the compass directly over the conductor, as indicated in Fig. 2. If the current in the conductor is flowing from south to north, the north pole of the compass will be deflected toward the east, and the reverse.

A small reading ammeter in series with a suitable resistance can be used to determine the polarity, as shown in Fig. 4. In order to obtain a proper deflection of the meter needle, the positive ammeter terminal must be connected to the "plus" side of the circuit, and the negative terminal to the "minus" side of the circuit. If the connections are reversed the needle will be deflected in the opposite direction until its further progress is barred by a stop, or by the side of the case.

It is well in this test to use enough resistance in series with the ammeter so that the current through the meter

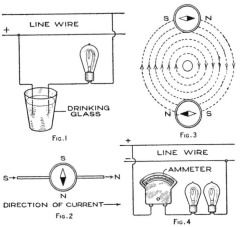

Four Simple Tests to Establish the Polarity of Wires in Electrical Installations

will be small. Permitting a large current to flow through the instrument in the reverse direction may harm it by bending the needle.—Peter J. M. Clute, Schenectady, N. Y.

## Straightening Bent Automobile Axles

A method of straightening bent automobile axles, used by a local repair shop with the best of results, is shown

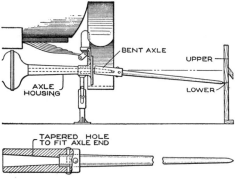

With This Tool, the Work of Straightening the Axle can be Done without Dismantling the Car

in the sketch. The straightening tool is 6 ft. long, drilled with a tapered hole to fit over the axle end. A solid bushing, of the exact size of the roller bearing in which the axle shaft revolves, replaces the roller bearing during the straightening process.

The procedure for straightening is as follows: The axle being jacked up, the straightening bar is slipped over the tapered end of the axle, and held, to prevent it from turning. The axle shaft is revolved by turning the starting crank of the engine with the clutch engaged. An upright board is placed at the extremity of the pointed end of the bar, as shown. The high and low points to which the turning axle moves the pointed end of the bar are marked on the board. The intermediate point of these two positions is measured off, and by pressure on the end of the bar, the axle is sprung back until the pointed end comes to this place. Great care should be taken that the sleeve grips solidly, when the axle is straightened.

## Electric Switch Mounted on Ceiling for Safety

An electric grinder was installed in a 440-volt circuit, and we wanted the switch in a safe place where there

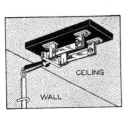

would be no danger of anyone accidentally touching it. The switch was, therefore, rigged on the ceiling and a control device was made for it so that the current could be shut off, or turned on, conveniently at the wall. The lever device shown in the sketch has sufficient play for the switch to open and close, and is operated by sliding the vertical bar up or down.—C. Anderson, Worcester, Mass.

## Makeshift Tool Cuts Round Holes in Sheet Metal

A hole was to be cut in the metal dash of an automobile, and no cutter

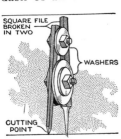

of the usual type was at hand. I devised a substitute tool in a few minutes from an old square file, washers, and two bolts. The file was ground to a sharp point at the tang, and to a cutting point at the other end. It was then broken at

the middle and the parts clamped together, as shown. The device was used like a compass, and cut a clean hole in the metal.—G. I. Mitchell, Ruston, La.

## A Small Blowpipe Torch without Compressed Air

It is often desirable to obtain a higher temperature than the ordinary gas jet or the Bunsen burner will give,

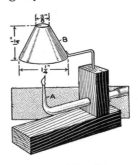

where a source of compressed air is unavailable. A simple burner, arranged as a small blast lamp, is shown in the sketch. By its use, such work as glass-blowing and welding may readily be accomplished. The part A is a portion of a common blowpipe, or may be any similar tube with a tiny outlet in the tip. This blowpipe is connected to the gas supply by rubber tubing, and mounted as shown. A conical hood, suitably supported, is placed above the jet, and acts as a mixer and burner. By adjusting the hood, and thus the draft, the flame may be varied from a small hot point, above B, to a broader tip and an intensely hot region just below the mouth of the mixer. The best adjustment can readily be determined by trial. After the funnel becomes hot, it keeps the heat in and cuts off radiation.—R. D. Rusk, Niles, Ohio.

# An Automatic Warning Gong for Vehicles

By EARL W. DAVIS

A GONG which will sound its alarm, whenever the vehicle on which it is mounted is in motion, is often desirable. Such a gong is detailed in the illustrations. Advantages of this arrangement are its simplicity, and the fact that it is self-contained. Also, the frequency of the gong strokes is proportional to the speed of the vehicle on which the gong is mounted. Thus, when the vehicle carrying the gong is invisible, the listener can judge of the rapidity of its approach. This is of importance in locations which are dimly lighted, in mines, or in dark corridors in industrial plants. Some of the applications for this automatic alarm are on trucks in factories, on monorail telphers, cranes, mine locomotives and cars, and turntables.

As indicated in Fig. 1, the automatic gong is attached to one of the wheels of the vehicle. As the wheel completes a rotation the gong sounds once. At each rotation the steel ball within the tapper cylinder drops against the tapper, making the latter strike the gong. A spring returns the tapper to normal

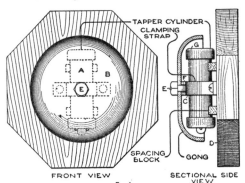

Details of Construction: The Gong is Mounted on a Board and Houses the Operating Mechanism

yoke, clamps the gong in position. A washer, F, is provided between the yoke and the gong so that the gong lies in the correct location to receive the blows from the tapper. Spacing blocks may be inserted to raise the tapper cylinder from the mounting board. This board, with the device on it, is clamped to the vehicle wheel with U-bolts, as shown in Fig. 1. For severe service, mount the gong on a square steel plate, and bolt this to the wheel.

The detailed construction of the tapper cylinder is shown in Fig. 1. A wrought-iron nipple provides the body, which is fitted with malleable-iron pipe caps. One of the caps has a hole drilled through it to accommodate the tapper. Two drive-fit steel-wire pins in the tapper act as stops. The ball is of the usual ball-bearing type. If a bearing ball is not available, a rounded piece of iron will serve. The spring is of No. 14 gauge brass wire, for the average case. The spring returns the tapper after the ball has struck, and holds the tapper in position against the centrifugal action. A cushion for the ball on the rebound is provided by the spiral spring, of No. 18 gauge wire. Experimentation may be necessary to adjust the parts to best advantage for individual installations.

The Automatic Gong is Set on the Vehicle Wheel, and the Sounds Are in Slow or Rapid Succession According to the Speed of Travel

position, for the next stroke. In the assembly view, Fig. 2, the relation of the parts are shown. The assembled tapper cylinder A is mounted within the gong B. A yoke, C, of strap iron, holds the device to the board D, by means of screws. The cap screw E, passing through the hole in the gong and turning into a tapped hole in the

❡Outer corners of machine parts are often rounded slightly because sharp corners become nicked easily.

## Practical Uses for U-Bolts and Rig for Forming Them

Round wrought-iron U-bolts can frequently be employed to excellent advantage as clamps, in piping or in conduit-wiring installations in steel-frame buildings, and for many other

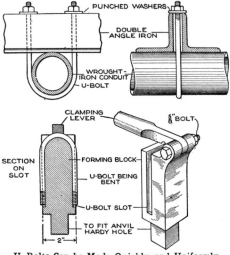

U-Bolts Can be Made Quickly and Uniformly by the Use of This Device

purposes also. A typical method of using a U-bolt for this service is shown in the illustration. The pipe, or conduit, is clamped to a steel member with a U-bolt, between two mild-steel angles. U-bolts for the smaller-sized tubes can be bent cold and formed around a piece of pipe conduit of the correct diameter. The threads should, of course, be cut on the rod before it is bent.

Where U-bolts are required for tubes of larger diameters, it is not practicable to bend them cold. If many U-bolts of the same size are required, particularly in industrial-plant installations, it will pay to construct a bending rig like that shown. This consists of a block of wrought iron in which is cut a groove form. A hinged lever at the top of the block holds the bolt while it is being bent. On the lower end of the block is a square extension, to fit the hardy hole of an anvil.

In using the rig, the wrought-iron rod is heated to a cherry-red, and then held at its middle point in the rig between the lever and the forming block. Pressure on the lever will hold the piece of stock in position. Then, with a wooden, or lead, mallet, the ends of the rod are pounded down to shape.—R. C. Frank, St. Louis, Mo.

## A Rabbeting and Grooving Tool of Wide Use

In getting out a job which required the making of a large number of grooves and rabbets of various sizes, across the grain of the boards, I saved much time by making a simple grooving and rabbeting tool, which was well worth while keeping as a handy device. A piece of hard wood, 2 by 4 by 10 in. long, was shaped as shown in the sketch. The lower edge was curved slightly so that grooves could be cut in somewhat concave surfaces. One side of the block was gained out and fitted with blocks to hold the cutters. These were made of soft steel, filed with teeth as detailed. A strip of wood, fastened with screws, clamps the cutters and cutter blocks into

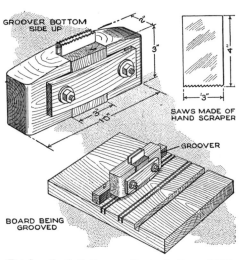

The Saw-Tooth Cutters are Set to the Proper Width and Depth, and a Strip is Used as a Side Guide

place. By providing a set of cutter blocks, the cutters can be set at various standard widths, and, for odd sizes, special blocks can be made quickly. The lower sketch shows the tool in operation, one of the grooves being routed out, and the others having the kerfs as cut by the tool.—Herman F. Zimmerman, Los Angeles, California.

## Oilcan Mounted on Pole for Oiling Overhead Bearings

An ordinary long-spout oilcan, with a spring bottom, was mounted on a pole fitted with a device for pressing the bottom, and proved very useful in a shop where many overhead bearings were to be oiled. The arrangement is, of course, not practical for oiling loose pulleys and similar machine parts, but has a wide range of use otherwise. The supporting rod is shaped as shown, and the can is held in place by a metal

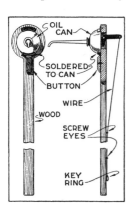

clip at the top, and a button at the lower end. The button engages a small metal angle soldered to the can. This arrangement makes it easy to remove the can for filling. A metal angle is set in a mortise through the pole at the bottom of the can, and this device, controlled by a wire threaded through screw eyes, acts like the thumb in pressing on the bottom of the can in ordinary use.

## Gilding on Bare Wood

For gilding on bare wood, use a size made by mixing a small quantity of white wax, a little white soap, and a few drops of Venice turpentine. Permit this size to remain for about an hour, and lay the gold leaf upon it in the usual manner. It will take a very satisfactory burnish.—A. A. Kelly, Malvern, Pa.

## Strap-Iron Hanger for Fire Buckets

The common type of support for fire water buckets, with the shelf and brackets underneath, is objectionable and often inconvenient. A type of hanger that is easily and inexpensively made is shown in the sketch. It is bent cold, or forged from 1/8 by 1-in. strap iron, or material slightly heavier if the buckets are large. It is fastened to the wall with screws or bolts, and gives proper clearance for the bucket, used only for its proper purpose.

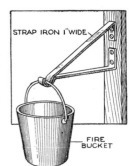

## Foot-Pressure Strap an Aid in Filing

A considerable quantity of castings were made with a "blind" square opening in one side. These openings had to fit a gauge, and, due to defects in molding, they sometimes needed much filing. To file such a part is slow work, and tiring, the filing being done entirely on the point of the file. An ingenious arrangement by which this work

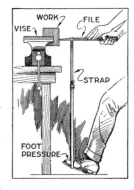

was made easier is shown in the sketch. A leather stirrup for the workman's foot was attached to the file near the point end. As soon as the file is placed in each casting, the workman presses on the stirrup, exerting a pressure on the file greater than could be applied by hand, and at small effort.—D. A. Hampson, Middletown, New York.

## Funnel Device for Lifting Submerged Piles

When submerged piles from piers, foundations, or other structures, are to be removed, the services of a diver are usually necessary. In a job of this kind, where a number of piles broken off by the waves in a fishing ground, were to be raised, an ingenious device was used, and the piles brought to the surface without sending down a diver to adjust the chains. A large sheet-iron funnel was fastened to an iron pipe, as shown. The funnel was set over the pile, with the hauling chain looped over it. The chain was dropped into place, and the funnel withdrawn. The pile was then lifted by means of a powerful hoist.—Henry K. Pasma, Oostburg, Wisconsin.

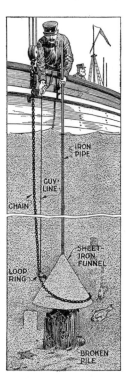

## Special Bobbin for Winding Wire on Rings

Shops in which much electrical work is done will find a special bobbin for holding the wire of great value as a labor and timesaver. For such work as winding wire on small rings, the bobbin should be long and narrow, as shown in the sketch. The wire supply is wound on

the bobbin, and during the process of winding, the latter is passed through the ring, around and through again, until the work is completed. This method avoids twisting and kinking of the wire.

## Convenient Rack for Drying Laboratory Glassware

Space economy and better drying facilities for laboratory glassware are features of a newly designed, home-made rack in use in a dairy chemical laboratory. The frame of the rack is a wall case with open front, of convenient size. The interior rear wall of the case is covered with galvanized sheet iron, and the shelves are made of similar material. They are supported at the ends to slope toward the back. A small space is left between the shelves and the back of the case. The front and rear edges of each shelf are bent at a right angle, to make it rigid. Galvanized wire cloth forms the surface on which the glassware is inverted, after washing. The drip from these dishes runs to the shelf, and thence down the rear lining of the case to a shallow metal tray at the bottom shelf of the case. This tray is inclined toward a drain, as shown. No drip from the dishes on one shelf reaches those on the shelves below.

## Electric-Light Bulbs Painted Black as Substitute for Shades

Switchboard lamps, and other lamps that are in a fixed position for reading instruments such as ammeters, voltmeters, etc., or where a permanent light is desired, may be shaded by painting half of the lamp black with ordinary black paint, or black shellac, instead of using the customary pear-shaped shade and reflector.—P. H. Roy, Kansas City, Mo.

## Breather Cap for an Automobile Engine

The losing of a breather cap on an automobile engine made it necessary to replace the cap quickly. A piece of sheet copper, $\frac{1}{16}$ in. thick, was softened by heating, and permitting it to cool in the air. It was then cut to shape, as shown in the sketch.

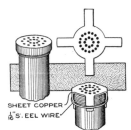

SHEET COPPER
$\frac{1}{16}$" STEEL WIRE

The small holes were drilled, and the four projections bent over the pipe in such a manner that they pressed tightly when the cap was in position. The ends were bent back a trifle to make it pass over the threads easily, and the cap was polished on a buffer. To prevent the cap from coming loose, a lock ring, of $\frac{1}{16}$-in. steel wire, was applied.—Adolph Klein, New York, New York.

## Milling Machine Set Up as Boring Mill

One of the special uses to which a milling machine may be put is as a boring mill. A job came in to our little shop: a pulley too large to swing on our largest lathe. The pulley was to be bored out and a bushing fitted in it. I chucked the pulley up on the milling machine, ran the table out, and placed on it the vise, into which I clamped a boring tool, as shown. I also turned up small chuck work, as well as work between chuck and center, and while it is not quite as handy as a lathe, yet it is a convenience in a "pinch."—Joe V. Romig, Allentown, Pa.

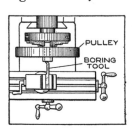

PULLEY
BORING TOOL

## Strong Hand Scoop Made of Drip Pan

When a strong scoop was needed for use in the shop, it was found difficult to shape one with the tools and materials at hand. A large, unused oil drip pan from a shaft bearing was obtained, and easily converted for the purpose. One end was cut out and the sides shaped as shown. A reinforcing plate was riveted into

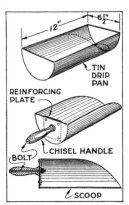

12"  6½"
TIN DRIP PAN
REINFORCING PLATE
BOLT  CHISEL HANDLE
SCOOP

the other end, and an old chisel handle was bolted through the end and the plate.—P. P. Avery, Garfield, N. J.

## Photographic Background with Folding Shelf for Small Objects

Backgrounds for photographic work are often made by stretching white canvas over a wooden frame. These frame backgrounds are light, and when there is much photographic work to be done in a factory, or shop, heavier construction is required. A 4 by 6-ft. white background

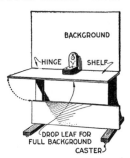

BACKGROUND
HINGE  SHELF
DROP LEAF FOR FULL BACKGROUND
CASTER

used in a large factory is shown in the sketch. The board proper is of 1-in. stock, mounted on standards. The lower section is hinged to the upper section, as shown, and suitably supported. Thus, when machinery is photographed on the floor, the full background is used, and when small objects, such as automobile accessories or electrical devices, are photographed, the shelf is used.—K. M. Coggeshall, Webster Groves, Mo.

## Heavy Stud Bolts Removed
## with Lathe Dog and Lever

Machinists sometimes find stud bolts set so firmly that the ordinary wrenches and devices for removing them are insufficient. Under these conditions, a simple method is to attach a heavy lathe dog to the bolt, as shown, and apply an iron bar as a lever. Tremendous force can be applied in this way, and the bolt easily removed. By reversing the pull, the bolt can be set very firmly.—W. Ichler, Kansas City, Mo.

## Blueprint Holder on Machines Aids
## Efficiency of Machinist

For the convenience of machinists as well as an aid in keeping the work orders or blueprints clean, holders for them were made and placed on each machine and bench in a large shop. A rectangular section of sheet iron, slightly larger than the standard size of drawings employed, was bent to have three of its edges turned over to form a ½-in. border, as shown in the sketch. A strip of iron, ⅛ by ½ in., and of the necessary length, was riveted to the holder, at one end, and the other was fastened to the machine, or to a suitable portable base. The blueprint, placed in the holder, is thus always at hand, and well protected from dirt and the usual wear.—S. A. Groves, Minneapolis, Minn.

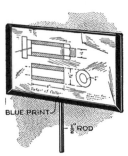

BLUE PRINT
½" ROD

❦ Pure turpentine dropped on a piece of white paper and exposed to the air, will leave no trace of foreign matter.

## Soldering Iron Improved
## for Joining Splices

An improvement which can be made to any soldering iron, and which will prove very convenient, is shown in the sketch. A hole, ¼ in. in diameter and ⅝ in. deep, is drilled in the side of the iron and filled with solder. It is a timesaver for rapidly soldering twisted-wire joints. In this manner splices of the open-end variety may be made with much better results than by using the tip of the iron for soldering. The iron is heated until the solder in the hole melts, and then the splice, covered with soldering paste, or acid, is dipped into it. This makes a well-soldered joint in a remarkably short time.—P. J. M., New York, N. Y.

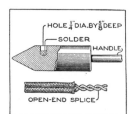

HOLE ¼" DIA. BY ⅝" DEEP
SOLDER
HANDLE
OPEN-END SPLICE

## Adjustable Gauge for Rule
## or Straightedge

A favorite method of gauging, especially in rough work, is to use the end of the ruler, with the hand or fingers as a guide. A similar but better method is to fit the ruler with a homemade gauge, which clamps securely and quickly by means of a bolt and wing nut, as shown. The gauge is bent from two strips of sheet metal, each laid out flat in the shape of a right angle. The short ends are folded up and the longer ends are folded double, and holes for the clamping bolt are bored through the folded parts. The lower ends of the strips, at these folds, grip the edges of the rule, when the wing nut is set.—C. C. Spreen, Flint, Mich.

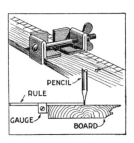

PENCIL
RULE
GAUGE
BOARD

3099

Drafting Room, Electric Drier Used in 2900
Drafting Sheets, Cutting Quickly from
  Roll of Paper ........... 3058
Drafting Table Covered with Heavy
  Paper Has Good Working Surface... 2997
Drafting—Typewriting on Tracing Pa-
  per for Blueprint Reproduction....... 2982
Draftsman's Time, Wrench Template
  Saves ........................... 3066
Draftsmen, Celluloid Fillet Indicator
  Handy for ..................... 3077
Draftsmen, Nontipping Footstool Handy
  for ............................. 3083
Drain or Sewer Outlets, Preventing Ro-
  dents from Entering.............. 3065
Drain Rainwater from Walk with
  Chipped Grooves .................. 3023
Drain Tile, Method of Handling........ 2909
Drainage Pump Improvised on Job..... 3048
Drawer Key, Adjusting to Insure Pri-
  vacy ............................. 2897
Drawers of Drawing File Cabinet, Pro-
  tective Flap for..................... 2898
Drawing File Cabinet, Protective Flap
  for Drawers of..................... 2898
Drawing, Table for Mounting, on Mus-
  lin or Backing..................... 2914
Drawings, Triangle Holder Aids in Ink-
  ing .............................. 2923
Drier, Clothes, Attached to Kitchen
  Boiler ........................... 3015
Drier, Convenient, Corrugated Card-
  board, for Photographic Prints....... 2914
Drier, Electric, Used in Drafting Room 2900
Drift Pin Handle, Handy Wrench with.. 2998
Drill, Babbitting, in Drill Press Spindle
  Avoids Heavy Work................ 3062
Drill, Compressed Air Motor, Operates
  Windlass ......................... 2940
Drill, Hand, Used as Lathe........... 2917
Drill, Hand, Winding Small Magnet
  Coils with........................ 3065
Drill, Hollow, for Boring Bamboo and
  Sheet Fiber ...................... 3066
Drill Press, Power, Substantially Made
  of Pipes and Fittings.............. 3039
Drill Press Spindle, Babbitting Drill in
  Avoids Heavy Work................ 3062
Drill Press Table Supports Tool Tray... 3008
Drill Rod, Extension Solderless........ 2950
Drilling Holes at Ends of Shafting,
  Jig for ........................... 2913
Drilling Holes in Pipe, Jig for......... 3074
Drilling Holes in Small Pieces, Monkey
  Wrench Used for.................. 3054
Drinking Cups, Paper, Containers for
  Wood Finishing Materials.......... 2930
Drinking Fountain, Sanitary, of Con-
  crete ............................ 3003
Drip Pan, Strong, Hand Scoop Made of 3093
Drive, Left Hand, Changing Grinder to 3006
Droplight Gas Fixture, Long, Brace for 2937
Dust, Keeping Down on Concrete Floors 2933

Easel, Artist's Palette Supported by.... 2941
Easel, Folding, Painter's, Made of Floor-
  ing .............................. 3085
Electric Drier Used in Drafting Room.. 2900
Electric Gas Lighter................... 2916
Electric Light Bulbs Painted Black as
  Substitute for Shades.............. 3092
Electric Operation Recorder, with Re-
  mote Control ..................... 3082
Electric Pad Warms Auto Radiators in
  Garage ........................... 2912
Electric Release Weight, Fire or Warn-
  ing Whistle Operated by........... 3008
Electric Spot Welding Machine......... 3027
Electric Stove, Nonwarping Frying Plate
  for .............................. 2937
Electric Switch Controlled by Hinged
  Stair Tread ...................... 2938
Electric Switch Mounted on Ceiling for
  Safety ........................... 3088
Electricity—Methods of Testing Polar-
  ity of Line Wires.................. 3087
Elevator, Freight, Gong Warning Sys-
  tem for........................... 2984
Emergency Lamp, Headlight as, for
  Operating Room ................... 2891
Emergency Pipe Connection, Roofing
  Paper as ......................... 2984
Emergency Sash for Railroad Car Doors 2953

Emery Grinder, Chuck on Used for
  Washing Bottles .................. 2991
Emery Wheel Dresser, Guard for....... 3072
Emery Wheel Dresser Made of Old Em-
  ery Wheel ........................ 3017
Engine, Adhesion and Impulse ........ 2894
Engine and Mower, Small Power Plant
  Tractor Made of................... 2965
Engine, Automobile, Frame for As-
  sembling or Examining............. 2908
Engine Cylinder, Rigging for Reboring
  by Hand .......................... 2978
Engine, Gas, Small, Starting Handle for 3008
Engine, Gas, Transported by Rolling
  It on Flywheel.................... 2998
Engine Nut Recovered with Pill Box on
  Stick ............................ 2971
Engine or Machinery, Device Locates
  Pounding in ...................... 2912
Engine Parts, Disassembling Rack
  Keeps in Order ................... 3040
Envelope Sealer, Pair Scissors Used as 2936
Erasing Shield Adjustable to Various
  Lines ............................ 2936
Excavation Dirt, Hay Carrier Rigged to
  Handle ........................... 2927
Expansion Plugs, Wooden, for Screws,
  Easily Made ...................... 3052
Extension Drill Rod, Solderless........ 2950
Extra Compartment, Folding Table,
  Robe Rack and, in Automobile...... 3015
Extractor, Post, Mounted on Wheels... 3057
Eye Magnet, Making of............... 2939
Eyeglass, Magnifying, Fitted into Spec-
  tacles ........................... 3069
Eyeglass Screws, Device Prevents Loos-
  ening of ......................... 2978
Eyeglasses, Broken, Improvised Frame
  for .............................. 2898
Eyeshade Carried Safely under Shoulder 2967

Faceplate Work, Indicator for Centering 2944
Fans on Machine Shafting Cool Work-
  men ............................. 2948
Farm, Fertilizing and Irrigating with
  Muck from Lake Bed.............. 3019
Farm, Round Storage Cellar for........ 3031
Farm, Traveling Crane for............. 2983
Faucets, Washbasin, Pedal Controls for 3001
Feed and Water Heater, Farm, of Con-
  crete ............................ 3016
Feed Mixer, Revolving................. 2909
Feed Water Pan, Automatic, for Fur-
  naces ............................ 3012
Fence Wire, Device for Tightening..... 2919
Fender, Auto, Loose, Angle Strengthens 2939
Fenders, Auto, Preventing Rapid Rust-
  ing of ........................... 2910
Fertilizing and Irrigating Farm with
  Muck from Lake Bed.............. 3019
Fiber, Bamboo and Sheet, Hollow Drill,
  for Boring ....................... 3066
File Cabinet, Revolving, on Double Desk
  Saves Time ....................... 2973
File, Small, Two Handles Used on...... 3070
Files, Pencil Sharpener with V-Groove
  Made from ....................... 2972
Filing Cabinet for Drawings, Protective
  Flap for Drawers of................ 2898
Filing Cork in Lathe.................. 2957
Filing, Foot Pressure Strap Aid in..... 3091
Fillet Indicator, Celluloid, Handy for
  Draftsmen ....................... 3077
Fillets, Leather Pattern, Set in Shellac 2907
Filter, Water Barrel................... 2908
Finger Hold, Safety, Pulling Hook with 3054
Finger Tips, Sandpaper, Aid in Feeding
  Press ............................ 3059
Finish, Japanese, for Spruce........... 2917
Finish, Wood, Polished Black.......... 2920
Fins, Cylinder Enlarging Aids in Cool-
  ing Engine ....................... 2982
Fire Buckets, Conical, Seldom Misused 3084
Fire Buckets, Strap Iron Hanger for.. 3091
Fire or Warning Whistle Operated by
  Electric Release Weight........... 3008
Fire Plug, Thawing Out Quickly...... 3025
Fire Protection, Casters on Water Bar-
  rels Promote...................... 3074
Fixing Bath, if It has Touched Hands,
  Operator Uses Care in Handling De-
  veloper .......................... 3013

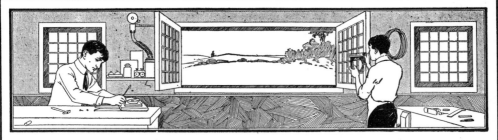

# A Thousand Things
## A Boy Can Make or Do

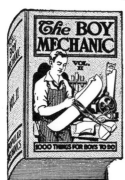

**Bound in cloth, 480 pages, 995 illustrations**

THIS great book contains a world of information. A book every boy wants and should have. Helpful, practical, and instructive. Tells a boy how to make things, both entertaining and useful. It teaches him how to use his hand and his brain. With it and a few tools he can make things which will furnish amusement for himself and others. He can make many useful household articles. It trains his mind along mechanical lines. He experiments. He creates new things, things that really go—things that he can use—things that he can point to with pride and say, "I made that myself." The boy who owns this book never has any time to waste.

# The Boy Mechanic
## Volume II

This is the second volume, and contains new plans, new games, new ideas and new "stunts," which will please every boy. The selection of articles was made from the accomplishments of the mechanical genius of Young America, by mechanical experts who knew what would please the boy of today. Handsomely bound in cloth, contains 480 pages (7x10 inches) and 995 illustrations. The articles contained in this book have been furnished by hundreds of boys who have actually built and experimented with the devices they are now telling other boys how to build. *Price $2 postpaid*

*This book is a sequel to volume one, but contains no duplicate articles*

## Contains Everything a Boy Should
## Know About
Bobsleds—Snow Shoes—Ice Boats—Ice Gliders—Boats—Camps—Fishing Tackle—Houses of Poles—Kites—Aerial Gliders—Motion-Picture Camera—Spot-Light Lantern—Mile-O-View Camera—Photographic Appliances—Indoor Games—Tricks—Cyclemobile—Pushmobile—Flymobile—Roller Coaster—Ferris Wheel—Sunlight Flasher—Reed Furniture—Electrical Devices—Mechanical Contrivances—Art-Craft Work and hundreds of other interesting and useful things.

## Send for It Today

You know some boy who will be glad to get this book. Send it to him without delay. Or, better yet — send him both vols. — entirely different, and help him occupy his leisure hours. Either vol., sent to any address, postpd. $2, or both for $4.

## The Boy Mechanic
### Volume I

Handsomely bound in cloth, 480 pages (7x10 inches), 700 articles, 800 illustrations. Tells about—Many Electrical Appliances—Steam and Gas Engines—Turbines—Motors—Wireless and Morse Telegraph—Self-Propelled Vehicles—Toboggans—Canoes—Paddle Boats—Punts—Camping Outfits—Tents—Magic Lanterns—Search-Lights—Cameras—Telescopes—Gliders—Kites and Balloons—Electric Furnaces—Lathes—Pottery Kilns, etc.

**Price, prepaid to any address, $2**

# Popular Mechanics Book Dept.  6 N. Michigan Ave. CHICAGO, ILL.